Chebyshev Polynomials
in
Numerical Analysis

L. FOX

Professor of Numerical Analysis at the Oxford University Computing Laboratory

and

I. B. PARKER

Research Officer, C.E.G.B.

LONDON
OXFORD UNIVERSITY PRESS
NEW YORK   TORONTO
1968

Oxford University Press, Ely House, London W.1

GLASGOW   NEW YORK   TORONTO   MELBOURNE   WELLINGTON
CAPE TOWN   SALISBURY   IBADAN   NAIROBI   LUSAKA   ADDIS ABABA
BOMBAY   CALCUTTA   MADRAS   KARACHI   LAHORE   DACCA
KUALA LUMPUR   HONG KONG   TOKYO

Printed in Northern Ireland
at The Universities Press, Belfast

Preface

The polynomials whose properties and applications are discussed in this book were 'discovered' almost a century ago by the Russian mathematician Chebyshev (the spelling of which has as many variations as that of Shakespeare). Their importance for practical computation, however, was rediscovered some thirty years ago by C. Lanczos, who must be regarded as the modern 'father' of this field of numerical mathematics. The coming of the digital computer gave further emphasis to this development, and at the present time the research literature of numerical mathematics abounds with papers on applications of Chebyshev polynomials and the theory and practice of Chebyshev approximation. We have effectively tried here to collect into one short book the underlying principles of the Chebyshev theory, and to indicate some of the areas in which much more research is needed.

The first two chapters discuss the ways in which the Chebyshev polynomial and the Chebyshev series, both finite and infinite, occur quite naturally in the approximation of general functions by means of a series of orthogonal polynomials. We include the Chebyshev minimax approximation, the weighted least-squares approximation in both the continuous and discrete cases, and the connexions with Lagrangian interpolation and Gauss-type quadrature formulae. Following a summary in Chapter 3 of facts and formulae about Chebyshev polynomials, we treat in Chapter 4 the Chebyshev approximation of functions defined in various *explicit* forms. Chapters 5 and 6 are mainly concerned with approximation of functions defined *implicitly*, as the solutions of ordinary differential equations, integral equations and partial differential equations. Finally, Chapter 7 indicates the importance of Chebyshev methods in two different areas of numerical linear algebra.

We have borrowed substantially from the books of Hildebrand and Lanczos, and from various published papers, in collecting the material of the first four chapters, and the substance of Chapter 7 is a summary of the relevant work of Varga and, inevitably, Lanczos. Chapter 5, which is by far the longest, contains work which has not previously appeared in print and attempts fairly detailed analysis, comparison, and alleged improvements of methods of solving ordinary differential equations with polynomial coefficients. Chapter 6, the other 'implicit' section, also has some new material but indicates a real lack of present success in the theory and practice of the solution of implicit problems of more than one variable.

The level of treatment is elementary, but we have occasionally indicated where, and briefly how, full rigour can be attained by more advanced mathematical methods. The audience we have in mind includes mathematical undergraduates in their early years, whose interests we hope to stimulate in an important branch of numerical mathematics. The material might also be used in the numerical analysis part of diplomas in computation, and perhaps also by scientists, with a reasonable mathematical training, whose work involves numerical methods and digital computation. We have attempted, in short, both to present some known results and also to indicate the regions in which fruitful research might be attempted.

We are very grateful to the Oxford University Press for their courtesy, skill and despatch, to Professor J. Crank for rescuing us from a feeble first attempt at Chapter 5, to Miss N. K. Nichols for her critical comments on the first two chapters, and above all to Mrs. L. Hayes, who read the complete manuscript, checked and corrected our worked examples, and made sure that the exercises set for students were meaningful in all respects.

L. Fox, Oxford University Computing Laboratory
I. B. Parker
1 May 1967

Contents

1

Approximation. Minimax and Least-squares Theories

Introduction

1.1 One of the most common problems in numerical analysis is the computation of a function $f(x)$ for one or more given values of its argument x. The function may be defined in a variety of ways, either explicitly, as a series, a definite integral or some other computable form; or implicitly, for example as the solution of a differential or integral equation. In the implicit case we may be able to find a *closed* mathematical solution in explicit form. Alternatively we may use a numerical method to produce a mathematical table, consisting of values of $f(x_r)$ calculated to some degree of precision for a set of values of x_r in the range of interest.

The mathematical table has been one of the main aids to computation, and the production of such tables is a skilled and challenging discipline. With the modern digital computer, however, we can hardly spare the space needed for the storage of mathematical tables, nor the time needed for 'scanning' to find the relevant part of the table, and for the computation involved in interpolation for any particular argument. Instead we seek to represent $f(x)$ by an approximation $p(x)$, valid to a certain precision over a large range of x. The approximation should have two desirable features. First, it should be easy to compute. Second, its error in any particular range should satisfy some known criterion, depending on the scientific context of our problem.

1.2 Since a polynomial is probably the easiest form for computation we consider first an approximation to $f(x)$ based on the Taylor expansion

$$f(x) = f(x_0) + (x - x_0)f'(x_0) + \ldots + $$
$$+ \frac{(x - x_0)^n}{n!} f^{(n)}(x_0) + \frac{(x - x_0)^{n+1}}{(n+1)!} f^{(n+1)}(\xi), \quad x_0 \leq \xi \leq x. \quad (1)$$

Here we take $p(x)$ to be the right-hand side of (1) with the omission of the last term. This is a polynomial $p_n(x)$ of degree n, and for the error $e_n(x) = f(x)-p_n(x)$ we have

$$|e_n(x)| = |f(x)-p_n(x)| \le \left| \frac{(x-x_0)^{n+1}}{(n+1)!} f^{(n+1)}(\xi) \right|. \tag{2}$$

If x is within the radius of convergence of the series we take the degree of the polynomial to be large enough to ensure that the *truncation error* satisfies the required criterion.

The Taylor's series, however, has obvious limitations. Its range of convergence may be small, and the number of terms needed to satisfy the accuracy criterion may then depend on the argument x. Near the limit of convergence the necessary degree of $p_n(x)$ could be quite large. For example, the series

$$\ln (1+x) = x-\tfrac{1}{2}x^2+\tfrac{1}{3}x^3-... \tag{3}$$

does not converge for $x > 1$, and for $x = 1$ we should need 10^4 terms to guarantee an error not exceeding 0·000 1. For this precision only three terms are needed at $x = 0·1$.

Even if the range of convergence of the Taylor's series is infinite we may need a very large number of terms. These will often oscillate in sign, and the cancellation of large positive and negative values will then give poor precision in the summation of the series. Examples are functions like $\cos 10x$, with periodic behaviour, or e^{-10x}, with decreasing exponential behaviour. In these circumstances we might prefer expansions in powers of e^{ix} or e^{-x} respectively, so that

$$\left. \begin{aligned} f(x) &= a_0+ \sum_{r=1}^{n} (a_r \cos rx+b_r \sin rx)+E_n(x) \\ f(x) &= a_0+ \sum_{r=1}^{n} a_r e^{-rx}+E_n(x) \end{aligned} \right\}, \tag{4}$$

with much smaller coefficients than those of the Taylor's series. Our accepted approximation, relatively easy to compute, is then the finite part of the expansion which neglects the truncation error $E_n(x)$.

1.3 Finally, we note that expansions in powers of x, e^{ix} or e^{-x} are likely to fail, or will need a very large number of terms, in regions of rapid change in the value of $f(x)$ and especially near poles of $f(x)$, where the function becomes infinite. In such cases we might prefer an expansion of the form

$$f(x) = p(x)/q(x), \tag{5}$$

where $p(x)$ and $q(x)$ are easily computed functions. In particular $p(x)$ and $q(x)$ may be polynomials, in which case $f(x)$ is a *rational function*. Approximations of this type are the subject of much current research (see, for example, Hastings, 1957).

1.4 In any given case the choice of a particular type of approximation is clearly of some importance. In this book we concentrate on approximation by polynomials, and in particular on the part played in theory and in practice by the Chebyshev polynomial. In subsequent chapters we shall discuss various relevant practical properties of this polynomial, and its importance in connexion with the production of approximations for functions defined in a variety of ways, including some of those mentioned in **1.1**. For the rest of this chapter, and also in Chapters 2 and 3, we discuss those theoretical and practical properties of the Chebyshev polynomial which are relevant to its importance in the field of approximation, and the ways in which it occurs in numerical analysis.

The Chebyshev minimax theory

1.5 We consider $p_n(x)$, a polynomial of degree n, as an approximation to a continuous function $f(x)$. For its error $e_n(x) = f(x) - p_n(x)$ we first adopt the *minimax* criterion, that $p_n(x)$ shall be that polynomial of degree n for which the maximum value of $|e_n(x)|$ is a minimum within some specified range, here taken to be $-1 \leq x \leq 1$.

An important case, the starting point of the investigation, is that for which $f(x) \equiv 0$. We are then interested in that polynomial $p_n(x)$ with leading coefficient unity for which $\max |p_n(x)|$ is a minimum in $-1 \leq x \leq 1$. We assert that the required $p_n(x)$ must have alternate maxima and minima, with respective values $+M$ and $-M$, at $n+1$ successive points $-1 < x_1 < x_2 \ldots < x_{n-1} < 1$, including the end points of the interval $(-1, 1)$. For if $q_n(x)$ is another polynomial of degree n with leading coefficient unity, which has smaller extreme values in $-1 \leq x \leq 1$, the difference $p_n(x) - q_n(x)$ has alternate positive and negative values at $n+1$ points, and therefore has n zeros. But $p_n(x) - q_n(x)$ is a polynomial of degree $n-1$ at most, so that this is impossible, and $p_n(x) \equiv q_n(x)$.

The most obvious functions with successively equal and opposite values are the trigonometric functions $\sin \theta$ and $\cos \theta$. Since $\cos n\theta$ is a polynomial of degree n in $\cos \theta$, with equal and opposite values of ± 1 at $n+1$ points in $0 \leq \theta \leq \pi$, including the end points, we deduce that the required unique polynomial is some multiple of the *Chebyshev polynomial*

$$T_n(x) = \cos n\theta, \quad \cos \theta = x, \quad -1 \leq x \leq 1. \tag{6}$$

From the trigonometric identity

$$\cos(n+1)\theta + \cos(n-1)\theta = 2 \cos \theta \cos n\theta, \tag{7}$$

we find the relation

$$T_{n+1}(x) = 2x\, T_n(x) - T_{n-1}(x), \tag{8}$$

and with $T_0(x) = 1$, $T_1(x) = x$, we see that the coefficient of x^n in $T_n(x)$ is 2^{n-1}. Since the maximum absolute value of $T_n(x)$ is unity we conclude that our required minimax polynomial is

$$p_n(x) = 2^{1-n} T_n(x), \tag{9}$$

with maximum modulus $M = 2^{1-n}$ in $-1 \leq x \leq 1$. The maximum values occur at the $n+1$ points

$$x = \cos \frac{r\pi}{n}, \quad r = 0, 1, ..., n, \tag{10}$$

and these separate the zeros at the n points

$$x = \cos(r+\tfrac{1}{2})\frac{\pi}{n}, \quad r = 0, 1, ..., n-1. \tag{11}$$

1.6 We easily extend the results of **1.5**, with similar proof, to produce a more useful theorem of approximation. Given a polynomial $p_n(x)$ of degree n with leading term $a_0 x^n$, the minimax approximation to $p_n(x)$ by a polynomial $q(x)$ of lower degree, at most $n-1$, in the range $(-1, 1)$, is such that $p_n(x) - q(x)$ has the smallest maximum deviation from zero, that is

$$p_n(x) - q(x) = k\, T_n(x), \quad k = a_0\, 2^{1-n}. \tag{12}$$

Suppose, for example, that we seek an approximation of lower degree to the cubic polynomial $x^3 + x^2$. All we have to do is to express x^3+x^2 in the form $k\,T_3(x)+q_2(x)$, where $q_2(x)$ is a polynomial of degree 2 at most, and the required approximation is then just $q_2(x)$. From the recurrence relation (8) we easily find $T_3(x)=4x^3-3x$, so that

$$x^3+x^2 = x^2+\tfrac{3}{4}x+\tfrac{1}{4}T_3(x), \tag{13}$$

and the polynomial $x^2+\tfrac{3}{4}x$ is the best lower-order approximation to x^3+x^2, with maximum error $\pm\tfrac{1}{4}$, in the range $(-1, 1)$.

Applications of minimax theory

1.7 We can try to find a minimax polynomial approximation to a more general continuous function $f(x)$ by using similar ideas. The error, though not now a single Chebyshev polynomial (since in that case $f(x)$ would be a polynomial), should have *Chebyshev-like* behaviour, that is oscillate a sufficient number of times with finite amplitudes $\pm M$. Suppose in particular that there are $n+2$ points at which the error $e_n(x)=f(x)-p_n(x)$ has alternate maximum values of $+M$ and $-M$. Then $p_n(x)$ is the required minimax polynomial of degree n. For if $\bar{p}_n(x)$ were a better approximation with error $\bar{e}_n(x)$, then

$$\bar{p}_n(x)-p_n(x) = \{f(x)-p_n(x)\}-\{f(x)-\bar{p}_n(x)\} = e_n(x)-\bar{e}_n(x). \tag{14}$$

This function has opposite signs at $n+2$ successive points and therefore has at least $n+1$ zeros, and since it is a polynomial of degree n at most it must vanish identically.

We have not here proved that $n+2$ such points can be found, nor given nor even indicated a suitable algorithm for finding them when they do exist, and we defer until Chapter 2 any further discussion of these problems.

1.8 A partial solution, for functions $f(x)$ with bounded derivatives of order $n+1$ in $-1 \leq x \leq 1$, can be obtained by considering the Lagrangian interpolation formula. Here $f(x)$ is expressed as a polynomial of degree n plus a remainder term, the polynomial having the value of $f(x)$ at the $n+1$ points $x_0, x_1,\ldots, x_n$. The formula is

$$\left.\begin{aligned} f(x) &= p_n(x)+\frac{\Pi(x)f^{(n+1)}(\xi)}{(n+1)!} \\ \Pi(x) &= (x-x_0)(x-x_1)\ldots(x-x_n) \end{aligned}\right\}, \tag{15}$$

and we limit our x and x_k, and therefore also ξ, to the range $(-1, 1)$. The classical theory also gives

$$p_n(x) = \sum_{k=0}^{n} l_k(x) f(x_k), \quad l_k(x) = \frac{\Pi'(x)}{\Pi'(x_k)}, \quad (16)$$

where in the second of (16) the primes denote that the terms $x-x_k$ and x_k-x_k are omitted respectively from the products $\Pi(x)$ and $\Pi(x_k)$.

We do not here use the second of (16), but note that $p_n(x)$ has degree n and satisfies our requirement of agreeing with $f(x)$ at the $n+1$ points $x_0, x_1,..., x_n$. Moreover $\Pi(x)$, a polynomial of degree $n+1$ with leading coefficient unity, vanishes at these points. The question is how to choose the points of agreement so that the maximum modulus of the error $f(x)-p_n(x)$ is as small as possible in the range $-1 \leq x \leq 1$. Now the solution of this problem clearly depends on $f(x)$, and no single $p_n(x)$ will suffice for the set of all functions with $n+1$ continuous derivatives in that range. On the other hand, if M_{n+1} is the maximum absolute value of $f^{(n+1)}(\xi)$ we can minimize the quantity

$$\max \left| \frac{e_n(x)}{M_{n+1}} \right| = \frac{\max |\Pi(x)|}{(n+1)!} \quad (17)$$

by choosing $\Pi(x)$ to be the Chebyshev polynomial

$$\Pi(x) = 2^{-n} T_{n+1}(x). \quad (18)$$

The points $x_0,..., x_n$ at which $p_n(x)$ agrees with $f(x)$ are then the zeros

$$x_i = \cos\left(\frac{2i+1}{n+1} \cdot \frac{\pi}{2}\right), \quad i = 0, 1,..., n, \quad (19)$$

of $T_{n+1}(x)$.

We have then ensured that

$$|e_n(x)| \leq \frac{M_{n+1}}{2^n(n+1)!}. \quad (20)$$

Moreover, if M_{n+1} is finite for all n the error $e_n(x) \to 0$ as $n \to \infty$. It follows that for analytic functions $f(x)$ we can approximate as closely as desired, at all points in $-1 \leq x \leq 1$, by choosing polynomials of successively higher degrees which agree with $f(x)$ at the zeros of the relevant Chebyshev polynomials.

This result is particularly interesting, since for other selections of $n+1$ matching points the error may not tend to zero as n increases. For *equal-interval* interpolation, for example, we choose the polynomial which agrees with $f(x)$ at the points $(-1+2r/n)$, $r = 0, 1,..., n$. This choice of matching points fails for the function $(1+25x^2)^{-1}$, the error increasing without bound, at all except the matching points, in the approximate ranges $0.7 \leq |x| \leq 1$ (see, for example, Lanczos, 1957).

Least-squares approximation and orthogonal polynomials

1.9 We turn now to consider another important criterion for the error of our approximation, and some of its consequences. Instead of choosing the approximating polynomial $p_n(x)$ so that its maximum deviation from $f(x)$ is minimized, we now ask that the average error of our approximation should be small, in some reasonable sense, over the whole range $-1 \leq x \leq 1$. The 'whole range' may be considered as a large number $N+1$ of points, or it may consist of the continuous interval $(-1, 1)$. We then try to satisfy the *least-squares* criteria, given respectively by

$$\sum_{i=0}^{N} e_n^2(x_i) = \text{minimum}, \quad \int_{-1}^{1} e_n^2(x)\, dx = \text{minimum}. \tag{21}$$

More generally we may prefer to give different weights to the required precision in different parts of the range, in which case we ask that

$$\sum_{i=0}^{N} w(x_i)e_n^2(x_i) = \text{minimum}, \quad \int_{-1}^{1} w(x)e_n^2(x)\, dx = \text{minimum}. \tag{22}$$

We discuss the discrete case in Chapter 2, and here concentrate on the continuous case, which involves the minimization of the integral in (22).

This criterion will enable us to compute the *coefficients* in our approximating polynomial

$$p_n(x) = a_0+a_1 x+...+a_n x^n, \tag{23}$$

for then from (22) we find

$$S = \int_{-1}^{1} w(x)\{f(x)-(a_0+a_1 x+...+a_n x^n)\}^2\, dx = \text{minimum}. \tag{24}$$

A necessary condition is that $\partial S/\partial a_i = 0$, $i = 0, 1,..., n$, so that

$$\left.\int\limits_{-1}^{1} w(x)x^i\{f(x)-(a_0+a_1 x+...+a_n x^n)\}\,dx = 0 \atop i = 0, 1,..., n\right\} . \qquad (25)$$

This leads to a set of linear simultaneous equations, the *normal equations*, for the coefficients a_i. We write them in the form $\mathbf{Aa} = \mathbf{b}$, where $\mathbf{a}$ is the vector with components $a_0,..., a_n$, and the matrix $\mathbf{A}$ and vector $\mathbf{b}$ have elements typified respectively by

$$a_{ij} = \int\limits_{-1}^{1} w(x)x^{i+j}\,dx, \quad b_i = \int\limits_{-1}^{1} w(x)x^i f(x)\,dx. \qquad (26)$$

We note that the matrix is symmetric and independent of the function $f(x)$.

1.10 The solution of the linear equations is not trivial and would be simplified considerably if the matrix were *diagonal*. Now we do not need to insist on writing our polynomial in the form (23), since we can group together various terms and even parts of such terms to produce the exactly equivalent expression

$$p_n(x) = c_0\,\phi_0(x)+c_1\,\phi_1(x)+...+c_n\,\phi_n(x), \qquad (27)$$

in which $\phi_r(x)$ is a polynomial of degree r but otherwise arbitrary at this stage. Minimization of the expression corresponding to (24) now gives linear equations $\mathbf{Ac} = \mathbf{b}$, with

$$a_{ij} = \int\limits_{-1}^{1} w(x)\phi_i(x)\phi_j(x)\,dx, \quad b_i = \int\limits_{-1}^{1} w(x)\phi_i(x)f(x)\,dx. \qquad (28)$$

If we now choose our polynomials $\phi_i(x)$ to be *mutually orthogonal* with respect to $w(x)$, that is such that

$$\int\limits_{-1}^{1} w(x)\phi_i(x)\phi_j(x)\,dx = 0, \quad i \neq j, \qquad (29)$$

then the matrix is diagonal and we have immediately

$$c_r = \frac{\int\limits_{-1}^{1} w(x)\phi_r(x)f(x)\,dx}{\int\limits_{-1}^{1} w(x)\phi_r^2(x)\,dx}, \qquad (30)$$

in which the denominator is independent of $f(x)$. Assuming that $\phi_r(x)$ does not vanish identically and that $w(x)$ does not change sign in $(-1, 1)$, the c_r are finite and our formula (27) exists. In passing it is easy to prove that the actual value of the resulting $\int_{-1}^{1} w(x)e_n^2(x)\, dx$, with $e_n(x) = f(x) - p_n(x)$ and with $p_n(x)$ defined by (27), is given by

$$\int_{-1}^{1} w(x)\{f(x) - p_n(x)\}^2\, dx = \int_{-1}^{1} w(x)\left\{f^2(x) - \sum_{r=0}^{n} c_r^2\, \phi_r^2(x)\right\} dx. \quad (31)$$

1.11 We have still to determine suitable orthogonal polynomials $\phi_r(x)$. In one method (the *Gram-Schmidt* process), we achieve this by forming appropriate linear combinations of the *linearly independent* polynomials $1, x, x^2, ..., x^n$. Linear independence implies that no linear combination vanishes identically unless every coefficient is zero, that is

$$\alpha_0 + \alpha_1 x + ... + \alpha_n x^n \equiv 0 \quad \text{implies} \quad \alpha_0 = \alpha_1 = ... = \alpha_n = 0. \quad (32)$$

Moreover the *basis* polynomials x^r, $r = 0, 1,..., n$ span the space of polynomials of degree n, that is any such polynomial is some linear combination of the basis polynomials. The first r of the basis polynomials similarly span the space of polynomials of degree r.

Starting with $\phi_0(x) = 1$, we use the basis polynomials to generate orthogonal polynomials by means of the general formula

$$\phi_r(x) = x^r + \sum_{j=0}^{r-1} \lambda_{r,j}\, \phi_j(x), \quad (33)$$

and we choose the $\lambda_{r,j}$ so that $\phi_r(x)$ is orthogonal to $\phi_j(x)$ for $j = 0, 1,..., r-1$. It is not difficult to see that

$$\lambda_{r,j} = -\frac{\int_{-1}^{1} w(x)x^r \phi_j(x)\, dx}{\int_{-1}^{1} w(x)\phi_j^2(x)\, dx}, \quad (34)$$

and this exists since no $\phi_j(x) \equiv 0$ and $w(x)$ is one-signed.

The resulting orthogonal polynomials all have their leading coefficients unity, but this is clearly not essential since if $\phi_r(x)$ is orthogonal to $\phi_s(x)$ then $A_r \phi_r(x)$ is orthogonal to $A_s \phi_s(x)$ for any constants A_r and A_s (excluding zero, since no such polynomial must vanish identically). In fact we can *normalize* the polynomials in any convenient way, and we denote the normalized polynomial of degree r by $\phi_r(x)$ without any subsequent ambiguity. An obvious choice is that for which

$$\int_{-1}^{1} w(x)\phi_r^2(x)\,dx = 1, \tag{35}$$

so that the denominator in (34) is unity. More commonly our normalized $\phi_r(x)$ will have a specified maximum value in the range $-1 \leq x \leq 1$, or a specified value at some particular point in this range. In the sequel we assume that our selected polynomial $\phi_r(x)$ has leading coefficient A_r, and that

$$\int_{-1}^{1} w(x)\phi_r^2(x)\,dx = k_r, \tag{36}$$

the constants A_r and k_r being mutually interdependent.

Properties of orthogonal polynomials

1.12 These orthogonal polynomials have several important properties, one of which will in some cases give a more convenient method for their construction than the Gram-Schmidt process. First, they are clearly linearly independent, since

$$\int_{-1}^{1} w(x)\phi_r(x)\left\{ \sum_{s=0}^{n} \alpha_s \phi_s(x) \right\} dx = \alpha_r k_r, \quad r \leq n, \tag{37}$$

so that $\sum_{s=0}^{n} \alpha_s \phi_s(x) = 0$ implies that $\alpha_0 = \alpha_1 = \ldots = \alpha_n = 0$. From this we conclude that the first n of these orthogonal polynomials span the space of polynomials of degree n.

Second, $\phi_r(x)$ has r real and distinct zeros in $-1 \leq x \leq 1$. To prove this we note first that $\phi_r(x)$ is orthogonal to every polynomial of degree less than r, since every such polynomial is a linear combination of the basis polynomials $\phi_0(x)$, $\phi_1(x),\ldots, \phi_{r-1}(x)$, to each of which $\phi_r(x)$ is orthogonal. Next we see that $\phi_r(x)$ has at least one real zero, since

$$\int_{-1}^{1} w(x)\phi_r(x)\phi_0(x)\,dx = 0. \tag{38}$$

Here $\phi_0(x)$ is a constant, $w(x)$ is of constant sign, and hence $\phi_r(x)$ must have at least one change of sign. Now consider the r zeros $x_k, k = 1, 2,\ldots, r$, of $\phi_r(x)$. Complex zeros will appear in conjugate pairs $\alpha_k \pm i\beta_k$, and of the real zeros some may be equal with even multiplicity and some with odd multiplicity, the distinct roots having multiplicity unity. In the expression $\phi_r(x) = \prod\limits_{k=1}^{r} (x-x_k)$ the factors involving the complex zeros and the equal real zeros of even multiplicity form a function $g(x)$ whose sign does not change in $-1 \leq x \leq 1$. The remaining factor involves the equal real zeros of odd multiplicity, which we denote by $x_1, x_2, ..., x_m$. Clearly $m \leq r$, and if we can show that $m = r$ we have proved that there are r distinct real roots. This follows because, if $m < r$, the orthogonality property ensures that

$$\int_{-1}^{1} w(x)(x-x_1)(x-x_2)...(x-x_m)\phi_r(x)\, dx = 0, \qquad (39)$$

and since $w(x)$ is of one sign the product $(x-x_1)...(x-x_m)\phi_r(x)$ must change sign in $-1 \leq x \leq 1$. But this function is $g(x) \prod\limits_{k=1}^{m} (x-x_k)^2$, which does not change sign, and we have proved our result by this contradiction.

1.13 Finally, we can easily verify that the polynomials satisfy a three-term recurrence relation

$$\phi_{r+1}(x) = (\alpha_r x + \beta_r)\phi_r(x) + \gamma_{r-1}\,\phi_{r-1}(x). \qquad (40)$$

For we can choose α_r so that $\phi_{r+1}(x) - \alpha_r x\, \phi_r(x)$ is a polynomial of degree r, and is therefore expressible as a linear combination of $\phi_i(x), i = 0, 1, ..., r$, which we can write in the form

$$\phi_{r+1}(x) - \alpha_r x\, \phi_r(x) =$$
$$= \beta_r\, \phi_r(x) + \gamma_{r-1}\,\phi_{r-1}(x) + \gamma_{r-2}\,\phi_{r-2}(x) + ... + \gamma_0\,\phi_0(x). \quad (41)$$

Multiplying by $w(x)\phi_i(x)$ and integrating, we find

$$\left.\begin{array}{c} \int_{-1}^{1} w(x)\phi_i(x)\{\phi_{r+1}(x) - \alpha_r x\, \phi_r(x)\}\, dx = \gamma_i k_i \\[1em] i = 0, 1, ..., r-2 \end{array}\right\}, \qquad (42)$$

where k_i is given by (36) and is non-zero. But for $i = 0, 1, ..., r-2$ the left-hand side must vanish, since $\phi_{r+1}(x)$ is orthogonal to $\phi_i(x)$ and $\phi_r(x)$ is orthogonal to $x\, \phi_i(x)$, a polynomial of degree $r-1$ at most. Hence $\gamma_{r-2} = \gamma_{r-3} = ... = \gamma_0 = 0$ in (41).

We can find expressions for the coefficients in the recurrence relation (40) by first observing that, in virtue of the orthogonality of $\phi_r(x)$ with any polynomial of lower degree, equation (36) gives for the relation between k_r and A_r, the coefficient of x^r in $\phi_r(x)$, the simpler form

$$k_r = A_r \int_{-1}^{1} w(x)x^r\phi_r(x)\,dx. \tag{43}$$

The coefficients α_r, β_r and γ_{r-1} in (40) then follow easily. For α_r we observe that $\phi_{r+1}(x) - \alpha_r\, x\, \phi_r(x)$ is a polynomial of degree r, and for β_r and γ_{r-1} we multiply (41) respectively by $w(x)\phi_r(x)$ and $w(x)\phi_{r-1}(x)$ and integrate. We deduce the results

$$\left.\begin{array}{c} \alpha_r = \dfrac{A_{r+1}}{A_r}, \quad \beta_r = \dfrac{-\alpha_r}{k_r} \displaystyle\int_{-1}^{1} w(x)x\,\phi_r^2(x)\,dx \\[2ex] \gamma_{r-1} = -\alpha_r\left(\dfrac{A_{r-1}}{A_r}\right)\left(\dfrac{k_r}{k_{r-1}}\right) \end{array}\right\}, \tag{44}$$

and the apparently uninformative expression for β_r is in fact satisfactory for our present purposes.

1.14 To generate orthogonal polynomials with the use of the recurrence relation (40), with its coefficients given by (44), we clearly need at least some information about the polynomials themselves. Following Hildebrand (1956), we express the $\phi_r(x)$ as solutions of certain differential equations, and this is sufficient for the determination of the coefficients (44).

Since $\phi_r(x)$ is orthogonal to every polynomial $q_{r-1}(x)$ of degree $r-1$ or less, we have

$$\int_{-1}^{1} w(x)\phi_r(x)q_{r-1}(x)\,dx = 0. \tag{45}$$

Integrating r times by parts, using the fact that the rth derivative of $q_{r-1}(x)$ is identically zero, and writing

$$w(x)\phi_r(x) = d^rV_r(x)/dx^r = V_r^{(r)}(x), \tag{46}$$

we deduce that

$$[V_r^{(r-1)}(x)q_{r-1}(x) - V_r^{(r-2)}(x)q'_{r-1}(x) + \ldots + \\ + (-1)^{r-1}V_r(x)q_{r-1}^{(r-1)}(x)]_{-1}^{1} = 0. \tag{47}$$

The fact that $\phi_r^{(r+1)}(x) \equiv 0$ gives from (46) a differential equation for $V_r(x)$. Equation (47), valid for all $q_{r-1}(x)$, provides associated boundary conditions, and the resulting differential system is

$$
\left.
\begin{aligned}
&\frac{d^{r+1}}{dx^{r+1}}\left\{\frac{1}{w(x)}\frac{d^r V_r(x)}{dx^r}\right\} = 0 \\
&V_r(\pm 1) = V_r'(\pm 1) = \ldots = V_r^{(r-1)}(\pm 1) = 0
\end{aligned}
\right\}.
\tag{48}
$$

The function $V_r(x)$ can be used to simplify further the relation (43) between k_r and A_r. For

$$
k_r = A_r \int_{-1}^{1} w(x) x^r \phi_r(x)\, dx = A_r \int_{-1}^{1} x^r V_r^{(r)}(x)\, dx,
\tag{49}
$$

and, integrating r times by parts and using the conditions in (48), we find

$$
k_r = (-1)^r (r!) A_r \int_{-1}^{1} V_r(x)\, dx.
\tag{50}
$$

If we can solve (48) for $V_r(x)$ we can therefore deduce k_r directly.

Legendre and Chebyshev orthogonal polynomials

1.15 We can solve (48) for many cases of interest. For example, if $w(x) \equiv 1$ we find

$$
V_r(x) = C_r(x^2-1)^r, \quad \phi_r(x) = C_r\frac{d^r}{dx^r}\{(x^2-1)^r\}.
\tag{51}
$$

The choice $C_r = 1/2^r(r!)$ gives the standard form of the *Legendre polynomial* $\phi_r(x) = P_r(x)$, with maximum absolute value of unity in $(-1, 1)$ and also with $\phi_r(\pm 1) = 1$. Clearly $P_0(x) = 1$, $P_1(x) = x$, and we can compute higher terms in the sequence from the recurrence relation (40) with the expressions (44) and (50) for its coefficients. We easily find

$$
A_r = \frac{C_r(2r)!}{r!} = \frac{(2r)!}{2^r(r!)^2}, \quad k_r = \frac{2}{2r+1},
\tag{52}
$$

so that
$$
\alpha_r = \frac{2r+1}{r+1}, \quad \gamma_{r-1} = -\frac{r}{r+1},
\tag{53}
$$

and $\beta_r = 0$ since the integrand in (44) is an odd function of x. The recurrence relation is then given by

$$P_{r+1}(x) = \left(\frac{2r+1}{r+1}\right)x\,P_r(x) - \left(\frac{r}{r+1}\right)P_{r-1}(x), \qquad (54)$$

and this is very convenient for the generation of $P_r(x)$ for $r \geq 2$.

Summarizing, we see from (30) that the least-squares polynomial approximation to $f(x)$ in $-1 \leq x \leq 1$ is given by

$$P_n(x) = \sum_{r=0}^{n} c_r P_r(x), \quad c_r = \frac{2r+1}{2}\int_{-1}^{1} P_r(x)f(x)\,dx, \qquad (55)$$

and from (31), (36) and (52) we find that the error in this approximation satisfies

$$\int_{-1}^{1} e_n^2(x)\,dx = \int_{-1}^{1} f^2(x)\,dx - \sum_{r=0}^{n}\left(\frac{2}{2r+1}c_r^2\right). \qquad (56)$$

1.16 As a second special case we consider the weighting factor $w(x) = (1-x^2)^{-\frac{1}{2}}$, designed to make small the errors near the ends of the range. In this case it is easier to start from (45), using the transformation $x = \cos\theta$ and deducing that the required polynomials satisfy the equation

$$\int_{0}^{\pi} \phi_r(\cos\theta)q_{r-1}(\cos\theta)\,d\theta = 0. \qquad (57)$$

Since $q_{r-1}(\cos\theta)$, a polynomial of degree $r-1$ at most in $\cos\theta$, can be written as $\sum_{s=0}^{r-1}\alpha_s\cos s\theta$, and since these trigonometric functions satisfy the orthogonality conditions

$$\int_{0}^{\pi} \cos r\theta\cos s\theta\,d\theta = 0, \quad r \neq s, \qquad (58)$$

we can clearly take $\phi_r(x)$ to be our Chebyshev polynomial

$$\phi_r(x) = T_r(x). \qquad (59)$$

From (36), by changing the variable again from x to θ, we find

$$\left.\begin{aligned}
k_r = \int_{0}^{\pi} \cos^2 r\theta\,d\theta &= \pi, \quad r = 0 \\
&= \frac{\pi}{2}, \quad r \neq 0
\end{aligned}\right\} \qquad (60)$$

The least-squares polynomial for $f(x)$, with weighting factor $(1-x^2)^{-\frac{1}{2}}$, is then

$$
\left.
\begin{aligned}
p_n(x) &= \sum_{r=0}^{n} c_r T_r(x) \\
c_0 = \frac{1}{\pi} \int_{-1}^{1} (1-x^2)^{-\frac{1}{2}} f(x)\, dx, \quad c_r &= \frac{2}{\pi} \int_{-1}^{1} T_r(x)(1-x^2)^{-\frac{1}{2}} f(x)\, dx
\end{aligned}
\right\}, \quad (61)
$$

and the error satisfies

$$
\int_{-1}^{1} (1-x^2)^{-\frac{1}{2}} e_n^2(x)\, dx
$$
$$
= \int_{-1}^{1} (1-x^2)^{-\frac{1}{2}} f^2(x)\, dx - \tfrac{1}{2}\pi(2c_0^2 + c_1^2 + \ldots + c_n^2). \quad (62)
$$

1.17 In passing it is interesting to note a connexion between these least-squares polynomials and an extension of our work on the Lagrangian interpolation formula. In **1.8** we observed that the difference $e_n(x)$ between $f(x)$ and $p_n(x)$ was some multiple of $\Pi(x) = (x-x_0)\ldots(x-x_n)$, where $f(x)$ agrees exactly with $p_n(x)$ at the $n+1$ points $x_0, \ldots, x_n$. To minimize the maximum value of $|\Pi(x)|$ we found that the fitting points $x_0, \ldots, x_n$ should be the zeros of the Chebyshev polynomial $T_{n+1}(x)$, and that $\Pi(x)$ is then $2^{-n} T_{n+1}(x)$.

If instead we proceed in a least-squares sense and minimize the quantity $\int_{-1}^{1} w(x) \Pi^2(x)\, dx$, the conditions for a minimum with respect to the coefficients of the polynomial $\Pi(x)$, of degree $n+1$ with leading coefficient unity, reduce to

$$
\int_{-1}^{1} w(x) \Pi(x) x^r\, dx = 0, \quad r = 0, 1, \ldots, n. \quad (63)
$$

It follows that $\Pi(x)$ is orthogonal with respect to $w(x)$ to all polynomials of degree less than $n+1$. For $w(x) = 1$ the polynomial $\Pi(x)$ must therefore be the Legendre polynomial

$$
\Pi(x) = \frac{2^{n+1}\{(n+1)!\}^2}{(2n+2)!} P_{n+1}(x), \quad (64)
$$

and the matching points are the zeros of $P_{n+1}(x)$. Similarly, for $w(x) = (1-x^2)^{-\frac{1}{2}}$ we have the Chebyshev polynomial

$$
\Pi(x) = 2^{-n} T_{n+1}(x), \quad (65)
$$

the same result as we obtained in the minimax theory for $\Pi(x)$.

Series expansion by orthogonal polynomials

1.18 We consider now expansions of $f(x)$ in infinite series, of which the Taylor's series is one example. Other expansions can be obtained as series of orthogonal polynomials, and indeed we already have *Legendre series* and *Chebyshev series* by letting $n \to \infty$ in (55) and (61) respectively. We can produce similar expansions for a range of other polynomials, called the *ultra-spherical* polynomials, which are orthogonal with respect to $(1-x^2)^{\alpha}$ for various values of α. From (48) and (46) we find

$$V_r(x) = C_r(1-x^2)^{r+\alpha}, \quad \phi_r(x) = C_r(1-x^2)^{-\alpha}\frac{d^r}{dx^r}\{(1-x^2)^{r+\alpha}\}, \quad (66)$$

where C_r is again chosen to satisfy some normalization condition, say that $|\phi_r(x)|$ has a maximum value of unity in $(-1, 1)$.

Now the coefficient c_r in the orthogonal expansion of $f(x)$ is given by (30), which with the use of (36) and (50) can be written in the form

$$(-1)^r(r!)A_r c_r = \frac{\int\limits_{-1}^{1} f(x)V_r^{(r)}(x)\,dx}{\int\limits_{-1}^{1} V_r(x)\,dx}, \quad (67)$$

where $V_r(x)$ is given in (66). Repeated integration by parts of the numerator, and the use of the boundary conditions for the derivatives of $V_r(x)$ given in (48), produce the simplification

$$r!A_r c_r = \frac{\int\limits_{-1}^{1} f^{(r)}(x)V_r(x)\,dx}{\int\limits_{-1}^{1} V_r(x)\,dx}. \quad (68)$$

Since $V_r(x)$ does not change sign in $-1 \leq x \leq 1$ we can invoke the second law of the mean, and write

$$r!A_r c_r = f^{(r)}(\xi), \quad -1 \leq \xi \leq 1. \quad (69)$$

Moreover it is clear, from the nature of the function $V_r(x)$, that for large values of $r+\alpha$ the major contribution to the integrals in (68) comes from the region near $x = 0$, so that to a good approximation we can write finally

$$r!A_r c_r \sim f^{(r)}(0), \quad c_r \sim \frac{f^{(r)}(0)}{r!A_r}. \quad (70)$$

1.19 Following Lanczos (1952), this result will enable us to assess the relative rates of convergence of certain series expansions in terms of ultra-spherical orthogonal polynomials. More specifically, we can find the relative effects of truncating the expansions after the terms $c_n \phi_n(x)$. For if $\phi_r(x)$ is normalized to have a maximum absolute value of unity, the truncation error cannot exceed $\sum_{r=n+1}^{\infty} |c_r|$, so that the relative values of c_r for the various expansions give the information we seek.

Equation (70) shows that c_r is inversely proportional to A_r, and the rates of convergence are therefore proportional to the reciprocals of the coefficients of x^r in $\phi_r(x)$ for sufficiently large r.

Now in (66) the case $\alpha = 0$ corresponds to the Legendre polynomial, and $\alpha = -\frac{1}{2}$ to the Chebyshev polynomial. Moreover, by observing that $\phi_r(x)$ in (66) satisfies the differential equation

$$(1-x^2)\phi_r''(x)-2(\alpha+1)x\,\phi_r'(x)+r(r+2\alpha+1)\phi_r(x) = 0, \quad (71)$$

we deduce, by dividing (71) by α and letting $\alpha \to \infty$, that the Taylor's series, with polynomial $\phi_r(x) = x^r$, corresponds to the limiting ultra-spherical orthogonal expansion as $\alpha \to \infty$.

For the Legendre polynomial the coefficient A_r is given in (52), and for large r this is approximately $2^r/(\pi r)^{\frac{1}{2}}$. For the Chebyshev polynomial this coefficient has the much larger value 2^{r-1}. Indeed the theorem, that of all polynomials of degree r with leading coefficient unity, the polynomial $2^{1-r}T_r(x)$ has the smallest deviation from zero in $-1 \le x \le 1$, can be recast in the form that, of all polynomials of maximum absolute value unity in $-1 \le x \le 1$, the Chebyshev polynomial $T_r(x)$ has the largest possible coefficient 2^{r-1} of x^r. Conversely, for the Taylor's series the 'orthogonal polynomial' has for the coefficient of x^r the smallest possible value unity.

We deduce that, of all expansions in terms of ultra-spherical polynomials, the Chebyshev series will generally have the fastest rate of convergence and the Taylor's series the slowest.

EXERCISES 1

1. Show that the Chebyshev polynomial $2^{1-n}T_n(x)$ is the largest polynomial of degree n, with leading coefficient unity, *outside* the range $(-1, 1)$. That is, if M is the maximum of $|p_n(x)|$ in $(-1, 1)$, show that, for $|\xi| > 1$, $|p_n(\xi)| \le M2^{1-n}|T_n(\xi)|$. (Note that the

definition $T_n(x) = \cosh(n \cosh^{-1} x)$ is the natural definition of the Chebyshev polynomial for $|x| > 1$.)

2. Show that of all polynomials of degree n which take the value unity at $x = k \geq 1$, the polynomial $T_n(x)/T_n(k)$ has the smallest absolute value in $-1 \leq x \leq 1$.

3. Show that the minimax polynomial approximation of degree less than n to the polynomial x^n in the range $(-1, 1)$ is a polynomial of degree $n-2$. Is this also true in the range $(0, 1)$? (Hint: transform the range $(0, 1)$ to $(-1, 1)$ by a linear change of variable, and consider the corresponding change in the argument of the Chebyshev polynomials.)

4. If we use the zeros of $T_{n+1}(x)$ as the data points x_k in the Lagrange interpolation formula $p_n(x) = \sum\limits_{k=0}^{n} l_k(x) f(x_k)$, show that

$$l_k(x) = \frac{(-1)^k (1-x_k^2)^{\frac{1}{2}} T_{n+1}(x)}{(n+1)(x-x_k)}.$$

5. Show that in $(-1, 1)$ the maximum of the absolute value of the second derivative of the function $(1+x^2)^{-1}$ is equal to 2 at the point $x = 0$. Hence show that the Lagrange polynomial which fits $(1+x^2)^{-1}$ at the zeros of $T_2(x)$ is $p_n(x) = \frac{2}{3}$, with a maximum absolute error not exceeding $\frac{1}{2}$. Show that the maximum error of this approximation is in fact $\frac{1}{3}$ at $x = 0$.

Show further that the minimax polynomial of degree less than two is the constant $p_n(x) = \frac{3}{4}$, with a maximum error of $\pm\frac{1}{4}$, at $x = -1, 0, 1$.

6. Prove the result of equation (31).

7. Give a detailed description and proof of the Gram-Schmidt orthogonalization process of **1.11**.

8. Starting with the basis polynomials $1, x, x^2$, use the Gram-Schmidt process to produce corresponding orthogonal polynomials of degrees 0 to 2, relative to the weighting functions $w(x) = 1$, $w(x) = (1-x^2)^{-\frac{1}{2}}$, and in each case choose the normalization of equation (35).

9. Use the results of equation (44) to find the recurrence relation satisfied by $T_r(x)$.

10. It is known that a certain $f(x)$ cannot be approximated conveniently by a polynomial of small degree, but the function

$f(x)/g(x)$ can be approximated satisfactorily in this way. If the approximation is $\sum\limits_{r=0}^{n} c_r \phi_r(x)$, chosen so that

$$\int_{-1}^{1} w(x)\left\{\frac{f(x)}{g(x)} - \sum_{r=0}^{n} c_r \phi_r(x)\right\}^2 dx = \text{minimum},$$

show that this is also obtained by minimizing

$$\int_{-1}^{1} \bar{w}(x)\left\{f(x) - g(x)\sum_{r=0}^{n} c_r \phi_r(x)\right\}^2 dx, \quad \text{where} \quad \bar{w}(x) = w(x)/g^2(x).$$

Hence show that if we want to approximate $f(x)$ by $(1-x^2)^{-\frac{1}{2}}p_n(x)$, in a least-squares sense with weight function $w(x) = (1-x^2)^{\frac{1}{2}}$, we have

$$p_n(x) = \tfrac{1}{2}b_0 + \sum_{r=1}^{n} b_r T_r(x), \quad b_r = \frac{2}{\pi}\int_{-1}^{1} f(x) T_r(x)\, dx.$$

11. Prove that the zeros of the orthogonal polynomial $\phi_r(x)$ in $(-1, 1)$ separate those of $\phi_{r-1}(x)$. (Hint: consider the recurrence relation, and examine the signs of $\phi_r(x)$ near the zeros of $\phi_{r-1}(x)$.)

12. Show that the Legendre polynomial

$$P_r(x) = \frac{1}{2^r(r!)} \cdot \frac{d^r}{dx^r}\{(x^2-1)^r\}$$

has absolute value unity at $x = \pm 1$ and no greater absolute value in $(-1, 1)$.

13. Prove the results of equation (66), for $V_r(x)$ defined in (48). Show also that $\phi_r(x)$ in (66) satisfies the differential equation (71). (Hint: show that

$$y(x) = \frac{d}{dx}\{(1-x^2)^{1+\alpha}q'(x)\}$$

$$= (1-x^2)^\alpha\{(1-x^2)q''(x) - 2x(1+\alpha)q'(x)\}$$

for any function $q(x)$, and that $(1-x^2)^{-\alpha}y(x)$ is orthogonal with respect to $w(x) = (1-x^2)^\alpha$ to any polynomial of degree $r-1$ or less, so that $(1-x^2)^{-\alpha}y(x)$ is a multiple of $\phi_r(x)$ when $q(x) = \phi_r(x)$. There remains only the determination of the factor $r(r+2\alpha+1)$.)

14. Find in $-1 \leq x \leq 1$ the expansions

$$|x| = \tfrac{1}{2} + \sum_{r=1}^{\infty} (-1)^{r+1} \frac{(2r-2)!}{(r-1)!(r+1)!} \cdot \frac{4r+1}{2^{2r}} P_{2r}(x)$$

$$= \frac{2}{\pi} + \frac{4}{\pi} \sum_{r=1}^{\infty} \frac{(-1)^{r+1}}{4r^2 - 1} T_{2r}(x),$$

and show that the ratio of the coefficients of $T_{2r}(x)$ and $P_{2r}(x) \to$ $(1/\pi r)^{\frac{1}{2}}$, a multiple of $2^{-\frac{1}{2}}$ of that estimated in **1.19**. (Hint: use the Stirling approximation $r! \sim e^{-r} r^r (2\pi r)^{\frac{1}{2}}$.)

15. Show that the function $U_r(x) = \sin(r+1)\theta / \sin\theta$ is a polynomial of degree r in $x = \cos\theta$, that it satisfies

$$U_{r+1}(x) = 2x\, U_r(x) - U_{r-1}(x),$$

the recurrence relation of the T_r polynomials, and that it is the least-squares polynomial in $(-1, 1)$ for the weighting function $(1-x^2)^{\frac{1}{2}}$. ($T_r(x)$ is the *Chebyshev polynomial of the first kind*, $U_r(x)$ the *Chebyshev polynomial of the second kind*.)

2

Fourier and Chebyshev Series. Discrete Least-squares Approximation

Introduction

2.1 We have discussed the least-squares theory in terms of poly-nomials orthogonal with respect to particular weighting functions. In theory the *orthogonality* is the important quality, and in practice *polynomials* are valuable mainly because they are easy to compute. Approximations can be found, however, in terms of members of a wider class of orthogonal *functions*. In particular, trigonometric functions are not difficult to compute, and their orthogonal prop-erties in $-\pi \le x \le \pi$ generate the classical Fourier series. This is of particular interest since the Fourier series is intimately connected with the Chebyshev series, and some known convergence properties of the former provide valuable results for the latter.

The Fourier (trigonometric) series

2.2 The system of independent functions $1, \cos x, \cos 2x, \dots, \sin x$, $\sin 2x, \dots$ is orthogonal with respect to the unit weighting function in $-\pi \le x \le \pi$; that is any two different members $f(x)$ and $g(x)$ of this system satisfy the equation

$$\int_{-\pi}^{\pi} f(x)g(x)\,dx = 0. \tag{1}$$

It follows that the 'trigonometric polynomial'

$$p_n(x) = \tfrac{1}{2}a_0 + \sum_{k=1}^{n}(a_k \cos kx + b_k \sin kx), \tag{2}$$

with the (Fourier) coefficients defined by

$$a_k = \frac{1}{\pi} \int\limits_{-\pi}^{\pi} f(x) \cos kx \, dx, \quad b_k = \frac{1}{\pi} \int\limits_{-\pi}^{\pi} f(x) \sin kx \, dx, \quad (3)$$

is a least-squares approximation to $f(x)$, with unit weight function, in $-\pi \leq x \leq \pi$.

2.3 The Fourier series, obtained by letting $n \to \infty$ in (2), is apparently most valuable for the approximation of functions of period 2π. Indeed for certain classes of such functions $f(x)$ the series will converge for most values of x in the complete range $-\infty \leq x \leq +\infty$. Such classes include functions with the following properties:

(i) $f(x)$ is defined arbitrarily in $-\pi \leq x < \pi$, and for all other values of x by the periodicity condition $f(x+2\pi) = f(x)$;

(ii) $f(x)$ is absolutely integrable, that is $\int\limits_{-\pi}^{\pi} |f(x)| \, dx$ exists.

Then at any interior point x of any interval in which $f(x)$ is bounded, and has a finite number of maxima and minima and a finite number of non-coincident discontinuities, the Fourier series converges to $\frac{1}{2}\{f(x_+)+f(x_-)\}$, which reduces to $f(x)$ at a point of continuity.

This class includes most of the functions whose expansions are needed in practical problems. It is interesting to note that continuity alone is not sufficient to guarantee convergence everywhere, since some continuous functions may have intervals containing an infinite number of maxima and minima. In this respect, however, it can be shown that although the Fourier series

$$f(x) \sim \tfrac{1}{2}a_0 + \sum_{k=1}^{\infty}(a_k \cos kx + b_k \sin kx) \quad (4)$$

may or may not converge to $f(x)$ at every point for a continuous and periodic $f(x)$, it is certain that the integrated series

$$\int\limits_{0}^{x} f(t) \, dt = \tfrac{1}{2}a_0 x + \sum_{k=1}^{\infty} \int\limits_{0}^{x} (a_k \cos kt + b_k \sin kt) \, dt \quad (5)$$

does converge for such a function at every point on the real axis.

2.4 Our main concern, however, is with expansions valid over a finite interval, which we can here take as $-\pi \leq x \leq \pi$. The Fourier coefficients are computed from values of $f(x)$ in this interval only, and to this extent periodicity gives no particular advantages. On the other hand, unless $f(x)$ and all its derivatives have the same values at $-\pi$ and $+\pi$ there is a 'terminal discontinuity' of some order at these points. The rate of convergence of the Fourier series, that is the rate of decrease of its coefficients, depends on the degree of smoothness of the function, measured by the order of the derivative which first becomes discontinuous at any point in the closed interval $-\pi \leq x \leq \pi$. Even if $f(x)$ is perfectly smooth it may have terminal discontinuities in relation to the Fourier theory, and this will affect the rate of convergence of its Fourier series.

Consider, for example, the function $f(x)$ defined in $-\pi \leq x \leq \pi$. We can represent $f(x)$ as the sum of the respective even and odd functions $f_1(x) = \frac{1}{2}\{f(x)+f(-x)\}$, $f_2(x) = \frac{1}{2}\{f(x)-f(-x)\}$. For their expansions we need consider only the range $0 \leq x \leq \pi$, and obtain respectively the cosine series

$$f_1(x) = \tfrac{1}{2}a_0 + \sum_{k=1}^{\infty} a_k \cos kx, \quad a_k = \frac{2}{\pi} \int_0^{\pi} f_1(x) \cos kx\, dx, \qquad (6)$$

and the sine series

$$f_2(x) = \sum_{k=1}^{\infty} b_k \sin kx, \quad b_k = \frac{2}{\pi} \int_0^{\pi} f_2(x) \sin kx\, dx. \qquad (7)$$

All terms in the sine series vanish at $x = 0$, where $f_2(x) = 0$, and also at $x = \pi$, where $f_2(x) = \frac{1}{2}\{f(\pi)-f(-\pi)\}$. Unless $f(\pi) = f(-\pi)$ the series will never give the correct answer at π and $-\pi$ and may converge only slowly at intermediate points. The cosine series for $f_1(x)$ can converge correctly to any $f(\pi)$ and $f(-\pi)$, but its first derivative vanishes at the terminal points, and unless $f_1(x)$ also has this property we have a 'discontinuity' in the first derivative at the two end points. This is less serious than a discontinuity in the function value, and we would expect the cosine series to converge faster than the sine series for smooth functions.

Finally, we might be interested in an $f(x)$ defined only in the range $0 \leq x \leq \pi$. In this case we are at liberty to extend its definition to the remainder of the periodic interval $-\pi \leq x \leq 0$ in any way we please. We can regard $f(x)$ as an odd function and find its sine series, but unless $f(0) = f(\pi) = 0$ we have discontinuities at 0 and π. The effect of these can be diminished by fitting the sine series to the function $f(x)-(a+bx)$, the linear term being chosen so that this function vanishes at $x = 0$ and π; in this case we probably have a discontinuity in the second derivative, and this is generally the best possible result for the sine series. If $f(x)$ is defined to be even, the cosine series will probably have a more significant discontinuity in the first derivative.

2.5 To verify these remarks we examine the behaviour of the coefficients in the sine and cosine series. Integration by parts gives

$$\left.\begin{aligned}
\int_0^\pi f(x) \cos kx \, dx &= \frac{1}{k^2}[f'(x) \cos kx]_0^\pi - \frac{1}{k^2} \int_0^\pi f''(x) \cos kx \, dx \\
\int_0^\pi f(x) \sin kx \, dx &= -\frac{1}{k}[f(x) \cos kx]_0^\pi + \frac{1}{k} \int_0^\pi f'(x) \cos kx \, dx
\end{aligned}\right\}. \quad (8)$$

For large k the integrals are likely to be small, being dominated by the oscillations in $\cos kx$. We deduce that the cosine series converges ultimately like k^{-2}, and the sine series like k^{-1}, unless $f(x)$ has special properties. For example if $f(0) = f(\pi) = 0$ we can show by extension of (8) that the sine series converges like k^{-3}, in general the fastest possible rate for any Fourier series.

The Chebyshev series

2.6 The terminal discontinuities of a non-periodic $f(x)$ are avoided with the Chebyshev form of the Fourier series. We consider the range $-1 \le x \le 1$ and make the change of variable $x = \cos \theta$, so that

$$f(x) = f(\cos \theta) = g(\theta), \quad 0 \le \theta \le \pi. \quad (9)$$

The function $g(\theta)$ is even and genuinely periodic, since $g(\theta+2\pi) = g(\theta)$. Moreover if $f(x)$ has a large number of finite derivatives in $-1 \le x \le 1$, then $g(\theta)$ has similar properties in $0 \le \theta \le \pi$. We should then expect the cosine Fourier series

$$g(\theta) = \tfrac{1}{2}a_0 + \sum_{k=1}^\infty a_k \cos k\theta, \quad a_k = \frac{2}{\pi} \int_0^\pi g(\theta) \cos k\theta \, d\theta, \quad (10)$$

to converge quite rapidly.

Interpreting (10) in terms of the original variable x, we produce the *Chebyshev* series

$$f(x) = \tfrac{1}{2}a_0 + \sum_{k=1}^{\infty} a_k T_k(x), \quad a_k = \frac{2}{\pi} \int_{-1}^{1} (1-x^2)^{-\frac{1}{2}} f(x) T_k(x)\, dx. \quad (11)$$

This has the same convergence properties as the Fourier series for $f(x)$, with the advantage that the terminal discontinuities are eliminated.

We found this series in **1.16** by direct appeal to the theory of least squares and orthogonal polynomials, and noted in **1.19** that for sufficiently smooth functions the coefficient a_k has order of magnitude $1/2^{k-1}(k!)$, considerably smaller for large k than the k^{-3} of the best Fourier series.

Discrete least-squares approximation

2.7 We turn now to the discrete case of least-squares approximation, mentioned in **1.9**, in which the integrated mean square error is replaced by a sum over a finite number of points $x_0, x_1, \ldots, x_N$. The function $f(x)$ is approximated by $p(x)$, with error $e(x) = f(x) - p(x)$, and we find the $p(x)$ for which

$$S = \sum_{k=0}^{N} w(x_k) e^2(x_k) = \text{minimum}. \quad (12)$$

With the methods of Chapter 1 we seek an expansion of the form

$$p_n(x) = \sum_{r=0}^{n} c_r\, \psi_r(x). \quad (13)$$

Here the functions $\psi_0(x), \psi_1(x), \ldots, \psi_n(x)$ are at this stage arbitrary members of some particular system, and we do not yet specify that the system should consist of polynomials, or trigonometric functions, etc. Conditions for a minimum with respect to the coefficients c_r produce as before a set of algebraic equations for these quantities, and the matrix is diagonal if the functions $\psi_r(x)$ are now chosen to satisfy the summation orthogonality conditions

$$\sum_{k=0}^{N} w(x_k)\psi_r(x_k)\psi_s(x_k) = 0, \quad r \neq s. \quad (14)$$

The corresponding coefficients c_r are then given by

$$c_r = \frac{\sum\limits_{k=0}^{N} w(x_k) f(x_k) \psi_r(x_k)}{\sum\limits_{k=0}^{N} w(x_k) \psi_r^2(x_k)}, \quad r = 0, 1, \ldots, n, \tag{15}$$

and the value of S in (12) is

$$S_{\min} = \sum_{k=0}^{N} w(x_k) \left\{ f^2(x_k) - \sum_{r=0}^{n} c_r^2 \psi_r^2(x_k) \right\}, \tag{16}$$

in analogy with equations (30) and (31) of Chapter 1 for the continuous case.

2.8 We assume first that the $N+1$ points $x_0, x_1, \ldots, x_N$, and the corresponding weights $w(x_k)$, $k = 0, 1, \ldots, N$, are specified in advance. Then with any particular system of functions $\psi_r(x)$ we are trying, in the language of matrix algebra, to approximate to a vector **f**, with $N+1$ components $f(x_k)$, $k = 0, 1, \ldots, N$, by a linear combination of $n+1$ other vectors $\mathbf{\psi}_0, \mathbf{\psi}_1, \ldots, \mathbf{\psi}_n$, where $\mathbf{\psi}_r$ has the $N+1$ components $\psi_r(x_k)$, $k = 0, 1, \ldots, N$.

In fact we are attempting to solve the algebraic equations

$$\mathbf{Ac} = \mathbf{f}, \tag{17}$$

where **c** is the vector with $n+1$ components $c_0, c_1, \ldots, c_n$, and **A** is the $(N+1) \times (n+1)$ matrix whose columns are the vectors $\mathbf{\psi}_0, \mathbf{\psi}_1, \ldots, \mathbf{\psi}_n$. If $n = N$ and the matrix **A** is not singular, that is if its column vectors are independent, we can solve the equations exactly, so that $e(x_k) = 0$ for all $k = 0, 1, \ldots, N$, and $S = 0$ in (12). If $N > n$ we are seeking the weighted least-squares solution, for which the 'normal' equations are given by

$$\mathbf{A'WAc} = \mathbf{A'Wf}, \tag{18}$$

where the prime denotes matrix transposition and where **W** is the diagonal matrix of order $N+1$ with elements $w(x_k)$, $k = 0, 1, \ldots, N$. The equations (18) are most easily soluble if $\mathbf{A'WA}$ is a diagonal matrix, that is if the vectors $\mathbf{\psi}_r$ satisfy the orthogonality conditions

$$\mathbf{\psi}_r' \mathbf{W} \mathbf{\psi}_s = 0, \quad r \neq s. \tag{19}$$

For any chosen system of functions $\psi_r(x)$ we can generate a suitable orthogonal system in various ways. For example we can apply an obvious generalization of the Gram-Schmidt process introduced in **1.11**. Suitable orthogonal *polynomials*, in particular, can be generated from a recurrence relation analogous to that satisfied by the ultra-spherical polynomials of Chapter 1. We defer until Chapter 4 a discussion of this and allied techniques, in relation to the standard problem of curve fitting.

Fourier and Chebyshev discrete least-squares theories

2.9 At this point it is more interesting to consider various function systems which, for *some* particular choice of data points and weights, obviously satisfy the orthogonality conditions (14), and which are relevant to the Chebyshev theory.

It is convenient first to consider the function $g(\theta)$ in the range $0 \le \theta \le \pi$. In the trigonometric identity

$$\tfrac{1}{2} + \cos\theta + \cos 2\theta + \ldots + \cos(N-1)\theta + \tfrac{1}{2}\cos N\theta = \tfrac{1}{2}\sin N\theta \cot \tfrac{1}{2}\theta,$$
(20)

the right-hand side vanishes if $\theta = k\pi/N$ for any integral value of k. Since

$$2\cos r\theta \cos s\theta = \cos(r+s)\theta + \cos(r-s)\theta, \qquad (21)$$

it follows that the independent functions $\psi_r(\theta) = \cos r\theta$ satisfy the orthogonality conditions

$$\sum_{k=0}^{N}{}'' \psi_r(\theta_k)\psi_s(\theta_k) = 0, \qquad \theta_k = k\pi/N, \quad r \ne s, \qquad (22)$$

where the double prime indicates that both the first and last terms of the sum are taken with factor $\tfrac{1}{2}$. Further, we find from (20) and (21) that the normalization factors for these orthogonal functions are

$$\left.\begin{aligned}\sum_{k=0}^{N}{}'' \psi_r^2(\theta_k) &= \tfrac{1}{2}N, \quad r \ne 0 \\ &= N, \quad r = 0, N\end{aligned}\right\} \qquad (23)$$

For the function $g(\theta)$ a trigonometric least-squares approximation, over the $N+1$ equally-spaced points $\theta_k = k\pi/N, k = 0, 1,\ldots, N$, with weights $\tfrac{1}{2}$ at the first and last points and unity elsewhere, is then given by

$$p_n(\theta) = \sum_{r=0}^{n}{}' c_r \cos r\theta, \quad c_r = \frac{2}{N}\sum_{k=0}^{N}{}'' g(\theta_k)\cos r\theta_k, \quad \theta_k = k\pi/N, \quad (24)$$

the single prime denoting that the first term only is taken with factor $\tfrac{1}{2}$. From the last of (23) we deduce that if $n = N$ we produce the exact fit with the 'interpolation' formula

$$p_N(\theta) = \sum_{r=0}^{N}{}'' c_r \cos r\theta, \quad c_r = \frac{2}{N} \sum_{k=0}^{N}{}'' g(\theta_k) \cos r\theta_k, \quad \theta_k = k\pi/N. \quad (25)$$

2.10 The corresponding Chebyshev least-squares approximation follows immediately from the substitution $x = \cos\theta$, so that $g(\theta) = f(x)$ in $-1 \le x \le 1$, and we find

$$p_n(x) = \sum_{r=0}^{n}{}' c_r T_r(x), \quad c_r = \frac{2}{N} \sum_{k=0}^{N}{}'' f(x_k) T_r(x_k), \quad x_k = \cos\left(\frac{k\pi}{N}\right), \quad (26)$$

with a double prime in the first summation if $n = N$ for the exact fit. Here the data points are not at equal intervals in x, but they are equally spaced in $\theta = \cos^{-1}x$.

The results (24) and (26), of course, relate to rather special problems, with very specific weights and data points. We show in **2.14** below that these expansions are approximations to the Fourier and Chebyshev series which, as we have seen, can be obtained from the continuous least-squares theory with particular weighting functions. In practice the formulae (24) and (26) provide relatively easy methods, avoiding the evaluation of definite integrals, for the approximate computation of the coefficients in the Fourier cosine series and Chebyshev series respectively.

Orthogonal polynomial discrete least-squares theory

2.11 Similar particular solutions can be found using any of the systems of orthogonal polynomials introduced in Chapter 1, and these solutions can also be regarded as good approximations to the corresponding continuous solutions. We found that these polynomials satisfy a three-term recurrence relation

$$\phi_{r+1}(x) = (\alpha_r x + \beta_r)\phi_r(x) + \gamma_{r-1}\phi_{r-1}(x), \quad (27)$$

with coefficients given by

$$\alpha_r = \frac{A_{r+1}}{A_r}, \quad \gamma_{r-1} = -\frac{A_{r+1}}{A_r} \cdot \frac{A_{r-1}}{A_r} \cdot \frac{k_r}{k_{r-1}}, \quad (28)$$

where A_r is the coefficient of x^r in $\phi_r(x)$, and

$$k_r = \int_{-1}^{1} w(x)\phi_r^2(x)\, dx. \quad (29)$$

Following Lanczos (1957), we choose the normalization $k_r = 1$, and write (27) in the form

$$p_{r-1}\,\phi_{r-1}(x) + (q_r - x)\phi_r(x) + p_r\,\phi_{r+1}(x) = 0, \qquad (30)$$

where
$$p_r = A_r/A_{r+1}, \qquad q_r = -\beta_r\,p_r. \qquad (31)$$

If we define $\phi_{-1}(x) = 0$, and choose the $N+1$ data points x_k so that $\phi_{N+1}(x) = 0$, we see that the x_k are the $N+1$ zeros of the orthogonal polynomial $\phi_{N+1}(x)$, and they are also the eigenvalues of the symmetric co-diagonal matrix

$$\mathbf{A} = \begin{bmatrix} q_0 & p_0 & & & & \\ p_0 & q_1 & p_1 & & & \\ & p_1 & q_2 & p_2 & & \\ & & & \ddots & & \\ & & & p_{n-2} & q_{n-1} & p_{n-1} \\ & & & & p_{n-1} & q_n \end{bmatrix}. \qquad (32)$$

The eigenvector corresponding to the eigenvalue x_k has components $\phi_0(x_k)$, $\phi_1(x_k)$,..., $\phi_N(x_k)$, and from the theory of symmetric matrices we know that the set of these vectors, for $k = 0, 1,..., N$, forms an independent orthogonal system. In fact if each vector is normalized to be a unit vector, which we represent by the equation

$$\lambda_k \sum_{r=0}^{N} \phi_r^2(x_k) = 1, \qquad (33)$$

the resulting vectors form the orthogonal matrix

$$\mathbf{X} = \begin{bmatrix} \lambda_0^{\frac{1}{2}}\phi_0(x_0) & \lambda_1^{\frac{1}{2}}\phi_0(x_1) & . & \lambda_N^{\frac{1}{2}}\phi_0(x_N) \\ \lambda_0^{\frac{1}{2}}\phi_1(x_0) & \lambda_1^{\frac{1}{2}}\phi_1(x_1) & . & \lambda_N^{\frac{1}{2}}\phi_1(x_N) \\ . & . & . & . \\ \lambda_0^{\frac{1}{2}}\phi_N(x_0) & \lambda_1^{\frac{1}{2}}\phi_N(x_1) & . & \lambda_N^{\frac{1}{2}}\phi_N(x_N) \end{bmatrix}. \qquad (34)$$

The equations $\mathbf{XX'} = \mathbf{X'X} = \mathbf{I}$ then produce, in addition to (33), the identities

$$\left. \begin{aligned} \sum_{k=0}^{N} \lambda_k\,\phi_r^2(x_k) &= 1, \quad r = 0, 1,..., N \\ \sum_{k=0}^{N} \lambda_k\,\phi_r(x_k)\phi_s(x_k) &= 0, \quad r \neq s \end{aligned} \right\}. \qquad (35)$$

It follows that a solution of the least-squares problem (12), with weights $w(x_k) = \lambda_k$, and with the data points taken at the $N+1$ zeros of $\phi_{N+1}(x)$, is given by

$$p_n(x) = \sum_{r=0}^{n} c_r \phi_r(x), \quad c_r = \sum_{k=0}^{N} \lambda_k f(x_k)\phi_r(x_k). \tag{36}$$

We have an exact fit at these data points with (36) for $n = N$.

2.12 For the Chebyshev case, using the normalization (29) with $k_r = 1$, and weight function $w(x) = (1-x^2)^{-\frac{1}{2}}$, we find

$$\phi_0(x) = \pi^{-\frac{1}{2}}T_0(x), \qquad \phi_r(x) = (\tfrac{1}{2}\pi)^{-\frac{1}{2}}T_r(x), \quad r = 1, 2, \ldots. \tag{37}$$

Then (33) gives

$$\left.\begin{aligned}
\lambda_k^{-1} &= \frac{2}{\pi} \sum_{r=0}^{N}{}' T_r^2(x_k) = \frac{2}{\pi} \sum_{r=0}^{N}{}' \cos^2 r\theta_k \\
\theta_k &= \frac{2k+1}{N+1}\cdot\frac{\pi}{2}, \quad k = 0, 1, \ldots, N
\end{aligned}\right\} \tag{38}$$

and with the trigonometric identity (20) we find for the weights λ_k the simple expression

$$\lambda_k = \pi/(N+1). \tag{39}$$

Finally, we can combine (36), (37) and (39) to produce the least-squares solution

$$\left.\begin{aligned}
p_n(x) &= \sum_{r=0}^{n}{}' b_r T_r(x) \\
b_r &= \frac{2}{N+1} \sum_{k=0}^{N} f(x_k)T_r(x_k), \quad x_k = \cos\left(\frac{2k+1}{N+1}\cdot\frac{\pi}{2}\right)
\end{aligned}\right\} \tag{40}$$

for constant weights and the zeros of $T_{N+1}(x)$ as data points.

With $n = N$ the fit is exact at the data points, and the corresponding $p_n(x)$ must then be the Lagrange interpolation polynomial

$$p_N(x) = \sum_{k=0}^{N} l_k(x)f(x_k), \tag{41}$$

which uses the zeros of $T_{N+1}(x)$ as data points. In **1.8** we illustrated the advantages of this particular choice in relation to the minimax theory, and the results (40) give a satisfactory method of computing the coefficients of this polynomial expressed as a finite Chebyshev series.

We note also that this Chebyshev solution is not identical with that of (26), which we obtained via a finite Fourier series based on the trigonometric identity (20). Both these solutions are good approximations to the continuous Chebyshev series, and this we discuss further in **2.14** below. Finally, it is clear that we can produce a Fourier least-squares fit which is different from (24) by retracing our steps and representing the Chebyshev solution (40) in terms of trigonometric functions.

Summary of Chebyshev expansions

2.13 It is convenient to collect together the various Chebyshev expansions, in $-1 \leq x \leq 1$, which we have studied so far.

(i) *Continuous least-squares fit*

The expansion

$$p_n(x) = \sum_{r=0}^{n}{}' c_r T_r(x), \quad c_r = \frac{2}{\pi} \int_{-1}^{1} (1-x^2)^{-\frac{1}{2}} T_r(x) f(x)\, dx, \quad (42)$$

has the property that the error $e_n(x) = f(x) - p_n(x)$ satisfies the least-squares condition

$$S = \int_{-1}^{1} (1-x^2)^{-\frac{1}{2}} e_n^2(x)\, dx = \text{minimum}. \quad (43)$$

The minimum value is given by

$$S_{\min} = \int_{-1}^{1} (1-x^2)^{-\frac{1}{2}} f^2(x)\, dx - \tfrac{1}{2}\pi(2c_0^2 + c_1^2 + \ldots + c_n^2). \quad (44)$$

As $n \to \infty$ we produce the Chebyshev series, which has the same convergence *properties* as those of the Fourier series, discussed in **2.3**, but generally with a much faster *rate* of convergence.

(ii) *Discrete least-squares fit*

For the expansion

$$\left. \begin{aligned} p_n(x) &= \sum_{r=0}^{n}{}' c_r T_r(x) \\ c_r &= \frac{2}{N} \sum_{k=0}^{N}{}'' f(x_k) T_r(x_k), \quad x_k = \cos\frac{k\pi}{N} \end{aligned} \right\} \quad (45)$$

the error $e_n(x) = f(x) - p_n(x)$ satisfies the discrete least-squares criterion

$$S = \sum_{k=0}^{N}{}'' e_n^2(x_k) = \text{minimum},\tag{46}$$

and

$$S_{\min} = \sum_{k=0}^{N}{}'' \left\{ f^2(x_k) - \sum_{r=0}^{n} c_r^2 T_r^2(x_k) \right\}.\tag{47}$$

For the expansion

$$\left.\begin{aligned} p_n(x) &= \sum_{r=0}^{n}{}' c_r T_r(x) \\ c_r &= \frac{2}{N+1} \sum_{k=0}^{N} f(x_k) T_r(x_k), \quad x_k = \cos\left(\frac{2k+1}{N+1} \cdot \frac{\pi}{2}\right) \end{aligned}\right\},\tag{48}$$

the error satisfies the discrete least-squares criterion

$$S = \sum_{k=0}^{N} e_n^2(x_k) = \text{minimum},\tag{49}$$

and

$$S_{\min} = \sum_{k=0}^{N} \left\{ f^2(x_k) - \sum_{r=0}^{n} c_r^2 T_r^2(x_k) \right\}.\tag{50}$$

(iii) *Interpolation formulae*

The function

$$\left.\begin{aligned} p_N(x) &= \sum_{r=0}^{N}{}'' c_r T_r(x) \\ c_r &= \frac{2}{N} \sum_{k=0}^{N}{}'' f(x_k) T_r(x_k), \quad x_k = \cos\frac{k\pi}{N} \end{aligned}\right\},\tag{51}$$

which is effectively (45) with $n = N$, is the polynomial of degree N which fits $f(x)$ exactly at the data points x_k of (51), with $k = 0, 1, ..., N$.

The function

$$\left.\begin{aligned} p_N(x) &= \sum_{r=0}^{N}{}' c_r T_r(x) \\ c_r &= \frac{2}{N+1} \sum_{k=0}^{N} f(x_k) T_r(x_k), \quad x_k = \cos\left(\frac{2k+1}{N+1} \cdot \frac{\pi}{2}\right) \end{aligned}\right\},\tag{52}$$

which is (48) with $n = N$, is the polynomial of degree N which fits $f(x)$ exactly at the data points x_k of (52), with $k = 0, 1, ..., N$. These data points are the zeros of the Chebyshev polynomial $T_{N+1}(x)$, and over the complete range $-1 \leq x \leq 1$ the error $e_N(x) = f(x) - p_N(x)$

satisfies for sufficiently smooth functions the minimax criterion

$$\max |e_N(x)/f^{(N+1)}(\xi)| = \text{minimum}, \qquad (53)$$

where ξ is some point in $(-1, 1)$. The error also satisfies, for a less restrictive class of functions, the continuous least-squares criterion

$$\int_{-1}^{1} (1-x^2)^{-\frac{1}{2}} \, \Pi^2(x) \, dx = \text{minimum}, \quad \Pi(x) = \prod_{k=0}^{N} (x-x_k). \quad (54)$$

Analogy between continuous and discrete least-squares expansions

2.14 We now demonstrate the analogies between the discrete least-squares solutions (45) and (48), with effectively constant weight functions, and the continuous least-squares solution (42) with weight function $(1-x^2)^{-\frac{1}{2}}$.

The substitution $x = \cos \theta$ in (42) gives for the coefficients of the Chebyshev series the alternative form

$$c_r = \frac{2}{\pi} \int_{0}^{\pi} \cos r\theta \, f(\cos \theta) \, d\theta. \qquad (55)$$

The trapezoidal rule for integration, with interval $h = \delta\theta = \pi/N$, produces the approximation

$$\bar{c}_r = \frac{2}{N} \sum_{k=0}^{N}{}'' \cos r\theta_k \, f(\cos \theta_k), \quad \theta_k = k\pi/N, \qquad (56)$$

which is exactly the corresponding coefficient in the 'discrete' expansion (45). Similarly, the use of the mid-point quadrature formula, in which the abscissae are taken midway between the equidistant points $\theta_k = k\pi/(N+1)$, gives the approximation

$$\bar{\bar{c}}_r = \frac{2}{N+1} \sum_{k=0}^{N} \cos r\theta_k \, f(\cos \theta_k), \quad \theta_k = \frac{2k+1}{N+1} \cdot \frac{\pi}{2}, \qquad (57)$$

which is exactly the corresponding coefficient in the other 'discrete' expansion (48).

The maximum difference between (55) and (56), that is the error term in the trapezoidal rule, can be expressed in the form $M\pi^3/12N^2$, where M is the maximum value, in $0 \leq \theta \leq \pi$, of the second derivative of the integrand $\cos r\theta \, f(\cos \theta)$. The maximum difference between (55) and (57) is about half this amount. It follows, for sufficiently well-behaved functions $f(x)$, that both discrete least-squares solutions converge, as $N \to \infty$, to the continuous least-squares solution, with (48) giving a slightly better approximation than (45) for finite N.

Orthogonal polynomials and Gauss-type quadrature formulae

2.15 There is a remarkable connexion, which we proceed to discuss, between the weights λ_k of the orthogonal polynomial discrete least-squares solutions of **2.11** and the weights of corresponding Gauss-type quadrature formulae.

We note first that we can produce from the Lagrange interpolation formula

$$\left. \begin{aligned} f(x) &= \sum_{k=0}^{N} l_k(x) f(x_k) + \frac{1}{(N+1)!} \, \Pi(x) f^{(N+1)}(\xi) \\ \Pi(x) &= \prod_{k=0}^{N} (x - x_k) \end{aligned} \right\}, \qquad (58)$$

the Lagrange approximate quadrature formula

$$\int_{-1}^{1} w(x) f(x) \, dx \sim \sum_{k=0}^{N} \mu_k \, f(x_k). \qquad (59)$$

Here

$$\mu_k = \int_{-1}^{1} w(x) l_k(x) \, dx, \qquad (60)$$

and $p_N(x) = \sum\limits_{k=0}^{N} l_k(x) f(x_k)$ is the polynomial of degree N which fits $f(x)$ exactly at the $N+1$ zeros of $\Pi(x)$.

The formula (59) is exact if $f(x)$ is a polynomial of degree N or less, but for more general functions it has an error of amount

$$E_N(x) = \frac{1}{(N+1)!} \int_{-1}^{1} w(x) \, \Pi(x) f^{(N+1)}(\xi) \, dx, \qquad (61)$$

obtained by integrating the corresponding term in the interpolation formula (58), in which ξ is an unknown function of x. We would like to choose the data points so that $E_N(x)$ is minimized as well as possible, and for functions $f(x)$ whose $(N+1)$th derivative is bounded an obvious partial solution is to minimize $\int_{-1}^{1} |w(x) \, \Pi(x)| \, dx$. An elementary but lengthy argument (Todd, 1962) shows that for

$w(x) \equiv 1$ the 'minimizing' $\Pi(x)$ is the Chebyshev polynomial of the second kind,

$$\Pi(x) = U_{N+1}(x) = \frac{\sin(N+2)\theta}{\sin \theta}, \quad \cos \theta = x, \qquad (62)$$

and the data points are the zeros $x_k = \cos\{k\pi/(N+2)\}$, $k = 1, 2,...,$ $N+1$, of this polynomial.

2.16 Corresponding to (59), the Gauss quadrature formula has the form

$$\int\limits_{-1}^{1} w(x)f(x)\, dx \sim \sum_{k=0}^{N} \nu_k\, f(x_k), \qquad (63)$$

where the weights ν_k and abscissae x_k are not related to the Lagrangian interpolation formula, but are chosen so that (63) will be exact for polynomials of as high a degree as possible. Since there are $2N+2$ parameters in the formula, we should expect to be able to make (63) exact for polynomials $f(x)$ of degree $\leq 2N+1$.

For this purpose we consider a system of polynomials $\phi_0(x)$, $\phi_1(x),..., \phi_{N+1}(x)$ which satisfy the orthogonality condition

$$\int\limits_{-1}^{1} w(x)\phi_r(x)\phi_s(x)\, dx = 0, \quad r \neq s. \qquad (64)$$

Suppose also that $f(x)$ is a polynomial of degree $2N+1$, and write

$$f(x) = q_N(x)\phi_{N+1}(x) + r_N(x), \qquad (65)$$

where the suffixes indicate the degrees of the polynomials involved. The orthogonality relations show that

$$\int\limits_{-1}^{1} w(x)f(x)\, dx = \int\limits_{-1}^{1} w(x)r_N(x)\, dx, \qquad (66)$$

which by (59) can be expressed exactly by

$$\int\limits_{-1}^{1} w(x)f(x)\, dx = \int\limits_{-1}^{1} w(x)r_N(x)\, dx = \sum_{k=0}^{N} \mu_k\, r_N(x_k), \qquad (67)$$

for specified x_k and corresponding μ_k. If we choose the x_k to be the zeros of $\phi_{N+1}(x)$, it follows from (65) that $r_N(x_k) = f(x_k)$, so that we have formally the required Gauss formula (63), with $\nu_k = \mu_k$.

Now $r_N(x)$, a polynomial of degree N, can be represented exactly by

$$r_N(x) = \sum_{r=0}^{N} c_r \, \phi_r(x), \tag{68}$$

where, with the normalization (29) with $k_r = 1$, the coefficients are given by (36) and (33). Then

$$\int_{-1}^{1} w(x) r_N(x) \, dx = \int_{-1}^{1} w(x) \left(\sum_{r=0}^{N} c_r \, \phi_r(x) \right) dx = c_0 \phi_0 \int_{-1}^{1} w(x) \, dx, \tag{69}$$

using (64) with $r = 0$. Moreover, substituting for c_0 from (36), and invoking (29) with $k_r = 1$, we can write

$$c_0 \phi_0 \int_{-1}^{1} w(x) \, dx = \sum_{k=0}^{N} \lambda_k \, f(x_k) \int_{-1}^{1} w(x) \phi_0^2 \, dx = \sum_{k=0}^{N} \lambda_k \, f(x_k). \tag{70}$$

It follows that the weights ν_k in the Gauss formula (63), which is exact for polynomials $f(x)$ of degree $\leq 2N+1$, are exactly the weights λ_k of the discrete least-squares solution (36), and the x_k are the zeros of the relevant orthogonal polynomial $\phi_{N+1}(x)$. The weights are also the μ_k of (60), where, in the Lagrange formula,

$$l_k(x) = \frac{\Pi'(x)}{\Pi'(x_k)}, \quad \Pi(x) = \prod_{k=0}^{N} (x - x_k), \tag{71}$$

the primes denoting that the terms $x - x_k$ and $x_k - x_k$ are omitted from the respective products.

2.17 For the Gauss-Chebyshev quadrature formula we have from **2.12** the result

$$\int_{-1}^{1} (1 - x^2)^{-\frac{1}{2}} f(x) \, dx \sim \frac{\pi}{N+1} \sum_{k=0}^{N} f(x_k), \quad x_k = \cos\left(\frac{2k+1}{N+1} \cdot \frac{\pi}{2}\right). \tag{72}$$

We note in passing that this formula, with equal weights, gives the minimum mean square arithmetic error arising from *rounding* errors in the computed $f(x_k)$. For with any formula of the kind $\int_{-1}^{1} w(x) f(x) \, dx = \sum_{k=0}^{N} c_k \, f(x_k)$, where $f(x_k)$ can have rounding errors distributed between $\pm \varepsilon$, the root mean square error of the linear combination is proportional to $\varepsilon (\sum c_k^2)^{\frac{1}{2}}$. Since $\sum_{k=0}^{N} c_k$ is constant, the formula being exact for $f(x) \equiv 1$, it can be shown that the root mean square error is minimized if all the c_k are equal.

All the Gauss quadrature formulae are reasonably satisfactory in this respect, since all the weights are at least positive. The weights of the corresponding integrated Lagrange formulae, particularly when the x_k are equally spaced (giving the Newton-Cotes formulae) have no such guarantee, and indeed oscillate increasingly, with constant sum, as N increases.

2.18 More classical expressions for the weights of the Gauss formulae can also be found by extension of the analysis of **2.11**. We write the orthogonal-polynomial recurrence relation (30) in the form

$$x\,\phi_r(x) = q_r\,\phi_r(x) + p_r\,\phi_{r+1}(x) + p_{r-1}\,\phi_{r-1}(x), \qquad (73)$$

and consider the similar formula for any other argument y in the interval $(-1, 1)$. Multiplying (73) by $\phi_r(y)$, the similar formula by $\phi_r(x)$, subtracting and summing the resulting expressions, we find

$$(x-y)\sum_{r=0}^{N}\phi_r(x)\phi_r(y) = p_N\{\phi_{N+1}(x)\phi_N(y) - \phi_N(x)\phi_{N+1}(y)\}. \quad (74)$$

Now letting $y \to x$, taking x to be a zero x_k of $\phi_{N+1}(x)$, and using (33) and (31), we deduce the result

$$\lambda_k^{-1} = \frac{A_N}{A_{N+1}}\phi'_{N+1}(x_k)\phi_N(x_k), \qquad (75)$$

where the prime here denotes the derivative of $\phi_{N+1}(x)$ at $x = x_k$, and A_N is the coefficient of x^N in the $\phi_N(x)$ normalized according to (29) with $k_r = 1$.

In Chapter 1 we used a different normalization, choosing $\phi_r(x)$ to have a specified maximum value in $(-1, 1)$ or a particular value at some point. If, without ambiguity, A_N is now taken to be the coefficient of x^N in this $\phi_N(x)$, and k_N is computed from (29), we easily find from (75) the relevant weight

$$\lambda_k = \frac{A_{N+1}}{A_N}\cdot\frac{k_N}{\phi'_{N+1}(x_k)\phi_N(x_k)}, \qquad (76)$$

the form most often used in the literature.

2.19 Finally we mention the Hermite interpolation formula, which is the classical starting point for the Gauss quadrature formula, and which provides an error term for it. The Hermite polynomial matches both $f(x)$ and its derivative $f'(x)$ at $N+1$ selected points x_k. It is given by

$$f(x) = \sum_{k=0}^{N} h_k(x)f(x_k) + \sum_{k=0}^{N} \bar{h}_k(x)f'(x_k) + \frac{1}{(2N+2)!} f^{(2N+2)}(\xi)\,\Pi^2(x),$$

(77)

where

$$h_k(x) = \{1 - 2l'_k(x_k)(x-x_k)\}\{l_k^2(x)\}, \quad \bar{h}_k(x) = (x-x_k)\{l_k^2(x)\}, \quad (78)$$

$l_k(x)$ is the standard polynomial in the Lagrange formula and defined in (71), and ξ is in the range bounded by the extreme values of x_k and x. Then

$$\int_{-1}^{1} w(x)f(x)\,dx = \sum_{k=0}^{N} H_k\,f(x_k) + \sum_{k=0}^{N} \bar{H}_k\,f'(x_k) + E,$$

(79)

where

$$H_k = \int_{-1}^{1} w(x)h_k(x)\,dx, \quad \bar{H}_k = \int_{-1}^{1} w(x)\bar{h}_k(x)\,dx,$$

(80)

and E is the error term in the approximate quadrature formula.

Now $l_k(x)$ is a polynomial of degree N, and

$$\bar{h}_k(x) = \frac{l_k(x)\,\Pi\,(x)}{\Pi'\,(x_k)},$$

(81)

so that $\bar{H}_k$ will vanish if we choose $\Pi\,(x)$ as a multiple of the orthogonal polynomial $\phi_{N+1}(x)$. Moreover we then have for H_k the expression

$$H_k = \int_{-1}^{1} w(x)l_k^2(x)\,dx.$$

(82)

Since this must be the weight of the Gauss quadrature formula, we have from (60) the interesting result

$$H_k = \int_{-1}^{1} w(x)l_k^2(x)\,dx = \int_{-1}^{1} w(x)l_k(x)\,dx,$$

(83)

and the classical theory then proceeds as in **2.18**.

2.20 For the error of the approximate Gauss formula we find

$$E = \frac{1}{(2N+2)!} \int\limits_{-1}^{1} w(x) f^{(2N+2)}(\xi) \, \Pi^2(x) \, dx. \tag{84}$$

Since $w(x)$ is of constant sign and $\Pi^2(x)$ is positive, and since for our orthogonal polynomials all the x_k and therefore ξ lie in $-1 \leq x \leq 1$, we can invoke the second law of the mean and write

$$E = \frac{1}{(2N+2)!} f^{(2N+2)}(\eta) \int\limits_{-1}^{1} w(x) \, \Pi^2(x) \, dx, \tag{85}$$

where η is in $(-1, 1)$. For the normalization involved in equation (76), with $\Pi(x) = A_{N+1}^{-1} \, \phi_{N+1}(x)$, we can finally express the error in the form

$$E = \frac{1}{(2N+2)!} f^{(2N+2)}(\eta) \frac{k_{N+1}}{A_{N+1}^2}. \tag{86}$$

This theory, again, is more convenient than that of the Lagrange quadrature formula, with error given by (61). Here the term $w(x) \, \Pi \, (x)$ multiplying $f^{(N+1)}(\xi)$ in the integrand is not one-signed, and deeper analysis (Steffenson, 1927) is needed to produce a useful expression for the error.

Additional notes on Chapters 1 and 2

In the theories of minimax and least-squares approximation, developed in Chapters 1 and 2, we have attempted little in the way of rigorous justification of many of the results, and certain matters have been unexplored. For example, we showed in **1.7** that for a function $f(x)$ continuous in $-1 \leq x \leq 1$ the minimax polynomial $p_n(x)$ is that polynomial for which the error $e_n(x) = f(x) - p_n(x)$ has equal and successively opposite values at $n+2$ points in the interval. We did not prove that such a polynomial exists, nor that the error gets successively smaller in absolute value with increasing n.

Similarly we considered least-squares approximations

$$p_n(x) = \sum_{r=0}^{n} c_r \, \phi_r(x),$$

where $\phi_r(x)$ is a member of a system of orthogonal functions, but did not in general consider the nature of convergence of the corresponding expansion $f(x) \sim \sum\limits_{r=0}^{\infty} c_r \, \phi_r(x)$, obtained by letting $n \to \infty$.

Only in the case of the trigonometric Fourier series, and therefore implicitly for the corresponding Chebyshev series, did we state (in **2.3**) sufficient conditions for the point-wise convergence of this series.

Fully rigorous treatment is beyond both our scope and our available space, but we indicate here the lines of approach to a unified theory which is given in detail in more advanced books. The starting point is the definition of vector spaces (see, for example, Birkhoff and MacLane, 1956).

A linear vector space Y consists of elements $\mathbf{y}_r$ with which we can perform the basic operations of addition and scalar multiplication (multiplication by a constant c) to produce other elements of the space. The 'axioms' of vector spaces are summarized by the formulae

$$\mathbf{y}_1 + \mathbf{y}_2 = \mathbf{y}_2 + \mathbf{y}_1, \qquad \mathbf{y}_1 + (\mathbf{y}_2 + \mathbf{y}_3) = (\mathbf{y}_1 + \mathbf{y}_2) + \mathbf{y}_3,$$

$$c_1(c_2)\mathbf{y} = (c_1 c_2)\mathbf{y}, \qquad c(\mathbf{y}_1 + \mathbf{y}_2) = c\mathbf{y}_1 + c\mathbf{y}_2,$$

$$(c_1 + c_2)\mathbf{y} = c_1\mathbf{y} + c_2\mathbf{y}.$$

The space has a zero element $\mathbf{0}$, and to each element $\mathbf{y}$ there is a unique inverse $-\mathbf{y}$, so that

$$\mathbf{y} + \mathbf{0} = \mathbf{y}, \qquad \mathbf{y} + (-\mathbf{y}) = \mathbf{0}.$$

The *linear combination* $\sum_{r=1}^{n} c_r \mathbf{y}_r$ is therefore an element of the space, obtained from certain elements $\mathbf{y}_r$, $r = 1, 2, ..., n$. These particular elements are *linearly dependent*, if there are some constants c_r, not all zero, for which $\sum_{r=1}^{n} c_r \mathbf{y}_r = \mathbf{0}$, the zero element. If $\sum_{r=1}^{n} c_r \mathbf{y}_r = \mathbf{0}$ implies that every $c_r = 0$, then the elements $\mathbf{y}_r$ are *linearly independent*. The space has dimension n if it has only a finite number n of independent elements; otherwise we have an infinite-dimensional space. Any set of elements $\mathbf{y}_1, \mathbf{y}_2, ..., \mathbf{y}_n$ is said to form a *basis* for the space of finite dimension n if these elements are independent, and in this case every member of Y can be expressed as a linear combination of the basis elements. We say that these elements *span* the space Y. The first r of these independent elements will span a *subspace* of Y of dimension r.

An example from linear algebra of a linear space of dimension n is the set of all real vectors with n components. If $\mathbf{y}_r$ is the rth column of the unit matrix $\mathbf{I}_n$, every vector in the space is some linear combination $\sum_{r=1}^{n} c_r \mathbf{y}_r$, and the columns of the unit matrix form n

independent vectors spanning the space. There are, of course, other sets of n independent vectors, notably the orthogonal system consisting of the eigenvectors of any symmetric matrix of order n.

Another space of finite dimension, mentioned in **1.11**, is the set of all polynomials of degree n, spanned by the independent polynomials $1, x, x^2, ..., x^n$. The first r of these polynomials span a subspace, the space of all polynomials of degree r for $r < n$. On the other hand the space of all continuous functions has infinite dimension, and we cannot represent all arbitrary continuous functions exactly by linear combinations of a finite number of certain *basis continuous functions*. Indeed this is the whole point of our approximation attempts; we seek that combination of basis functions which makes small in some sense the error in the approximation.

We can measure the error most easily in terms of a suitable *norm* of the linear vector space. A norm $\|\mathbf{y}\|$ of the vector space Y satisfies the conditions

$$\|\mathbf{y}\| \geq 0,$$

$$\|\mathbf{y}\| = 0 \quad \text{only if } \mathbf{y} \text{ is the zero element,}$$

$$\|c\mathbf{y}\| = |c| \, \|\mathbf{y}\| \quad \text{for any scalar (constant) } c,$$

$$\|\mathbf{y}_1 + \mathbf{y}_2\| \leq \|\mathbf{y}_1\| + \|\mathbf{y}_2\|.$$

There may be several different norms, and all our problems of approximation can be reformulated in terms of the minimization of the error in some particular norm. For example, the minimax problem requires the determination of an approximating function for which the maximum error in a given interval is as small as possible in absolute value. In the case of approximation by polynomials $p_n(x)$ to continuous functions $f(x)$, we can now say that $f(x)$ is an element of the space of functions continuous in $-1 \leq x \leq 1$, the approximation $p_n(x) = \sum_{r=0}^{n} c_r x^r$ is a linear combination of basis elements of a subspace, the error $e_n(x) = f(x) - p_n(x)$ is another element of the space, and the minimax polynomial has those coefficients c_r for which the particular norm $E_n = \max |e_n(x)|$ is minimized. In geometrical terms $p_n(x)$ is the projection of $f(x)$, a member of the infinite-dimensional space, on the subspace of dimension n spanned by the polynomials $1, x, x^2, ..., x^n$.

We digress for a moment to comment, without proof, on the matters unresolved in our minimax theory. For $f(x)$ continuous in $-1 \leq x \leq 1$ it can be shown that for each n there is a polynomial

$p_n(x)$ of degree n which is the best approximation to $f(x)$ in the minimax sense. From this fact can be proved the existence of $n+2$ real abscissae, in $-1 \leq x \leq 1$, at which $e_n(x)$ has equal and opposite values, and hence that the best approximation of degree n is unique. The simple observation that $p_n(x)$ is formed of a particular linear combination of the basis elements $1, x, x^2, \ldots, x^n$ and x^{n+1}, which generate $p_{n+1}(x)$, then shows that $E_1 \geq E_2 \geq \ldots \geq E_n$. Finally, the theorem of Weierstrass, that for a continuous function $f(x)$ in a finite range there is a polynomial $p_n(x)$ of sufficiently high degree such that $|e_n(x)| \leq \varepsilon$ at all points of the range, shows that our minimax polynomials tend uniformly to $f(x)$ as $n \rightarrow \infty$. Details are given by Todd (1962) and Davis (1963).

For the norm relevant to the least-squares theory we consider only those vector spaces which are also *inner product spaces*. For any two elements $\mathbf{y}_1$ and $\mathbf{y}_2$ of such a space there exists a scalar, denoted by $(\mathbf{y}_1, \mathbf{y}_2)$, and called the *inner product*, which satisfies the relations

$$(\mathbf{y}_1, \mathbf{y}_2) = (\mathbf{y}_2, \mathbf{y}_1),$$

$$(\mathbf{y}_1 + \mathbf{y}_2, \mathbf{y}_3) = (\mathbf{y}_1, \mathbf{y}_3) + (\mathbf{y}_2, \mathbf{y}_3),$$

$$(c\mathbf{y}_1, \mathbf{y}_2) = c(\mathbf{y}_1, \mathbf{y}_2).$$

The norm $\|\mathbf{y}\|$ of the element $\mathbf{y}$ is defined as $(\mathbf{y}, \mathbf{y})^{\frac{1}{2}}$.

The space of our particular interest has inner product

$$(f, g) = \int_{-1}^{1} w(x) f(x) g(x) \, dx,$$

for functions $w(x)$ of constant sign, so that the space concerned has as elements all the functions $f(x)$ and $g(x)$ for which the inner product exists. The norm of $f(x)$ in this space is

$$\|f\| = \left\{ \int_{-1}^{1} w(x) f^2(x) \, dx \right\}^{\frac{1}{2}},$$

which satisfies all the conditions for the norm of a vector space.

Our continuous least-squares approach, which produces an approximation $p_n(x)$ to $f(x)$ such that

$$\int_{-1}^{1} w(x) \{ f(x) - p_n(x) \}^2 \, dx = \int_{-1}^{1} w(x) e_n^2(x) \, dx = \text{minimum},$$

is clearly equivalent to the minimization of the norm of $e_n(x)$ in this inner product space.

The concept of orthogonality follows naturally from the identity

$$\|f+g\|^2 = \|f\|^2 + \|g\|^2 + 2(f, g),$$

which reduces to the 'Pythagoras theorem' for 'right-angled triangles' if

$$(f, g) = 0.$$

Functions whose inner product vanishes are called *orthogonal*, and a system of such functions is an orthogonal system. In analogy with the *expression* of an arbitrary vector $\mathbf{y}$ in n-dimensional Euclidean space as a linear combination $\sum_{r=1}^{n} c_r \mathbf{y}_r$ of an orthogonal system of basis vectors, we might here consider the *expansion* of a function $f(x)$ in our infinite-dimensional inner product space in the form

$$f(x) \sim \sum_{r=0}^{\infty} c_r \phi_r(x),$$

where the functions $\phi_r(x)$ are independent members of an orthogonal system in this space.

If we assume the existence of such an expansion, and that the series for $f(x)$ is uniformly convergent, we can find the coefficient c_r (the *Fourier* coefficient) by multiplying this series by $w(x)\phi_r(x)$ and integrating; so that

$$c_r = \frac{\int_{-1}^{1} w(x)f(x)\phi_r(x)\, dx}{\int_{-1}^{1} w(x)\phi_r^2(x)\, dx}$$

$$= k_r^{-1} \int_{-1}^{1} w(x)f(x)\phi_r(x)\, dx.$$

This is the result obtained in Chapter 1 by our least-squares approach applied to the *finite* approximation $\sum_{r=0}^{n} c_r \phi_r(x)$. (It is of course a valuable feature of orthogonal expansions that the addition of extra terms does not change the previous coefficients.)

We can proceed more rigorously by considering the *partial sum*

$$s_n(x) = \sum_{r=0}^{n} c_r \phi_r(x),$$

with c_r as defined above; the partial sum exists, for functions in our inner-product space, independently of the existence of the infinite series for $f(x)$. For any other similar expression

$$t_n(x) = \sum_{r=0}^{n} b_r \, \phi_r(x),$$

with arbitrary coefficients b_r, we find, for the square of the error norm, the result

$$(f-t_n, f-t_n) = (f,f) - 2(t_n, f) + (t_n, t_n)$$

$$= \|f\|^2 + \sum_{r=0}^{n} k_r(b_r^2 - 2b_r c_r)$$

$$= \|f\|^2 + \sum_{r=0}^{n} k_r(b_r - c_r)^2 - \sum_{r=0}^{n} k_r c_r^2.$$

Since $k_r > 0$ it follows that the norm is minimized when $b_r = c_r$, that is $t_n(x) = s_n(x)$, so that of all approximations $\sum_{r=0}^{n} b_r \, \phi_r(x)$ to $f(x)$ the best in the least-squares sense is that for which b_r is the Fourier coefficient c_r.

We also deduce from the last equation, with $b_r = c_r$, that

$$\sum_{r=0}^{n} k_r c_r^2 \leq \int_{-1}^{1} w(x) f^2(x) \, dx,$$

so that $\sum_{r=0}^{\infty} k_r \, c_r^2$ is convergent for functions in our inner product space. Moreover if $(f-s_n, f-s_n) \to 0$ as $n \to \infty$, that is if

$$\lim_{n \to \infty} \int_{-1}^{1} w(x) \Big\{ f(x) - \sum_{r=0}^{n} c_r \, \phi_r(x) \Big\}^2 \, dx \to 0,$$

then

$$\sum_{r=0}^{\infty} k_r \, c_r^2 = \int_{-1}^{1} w(x) f^2(x) \, dx,$$

the *Parseval formula*.

In this case the series $\sum_{r=0}^{\infty} c_r \, \phi_r(x)$ is said to converge to $f(x)$ *in the mean*. The set of orthogonal functions $\phi_0(x), \phi_1(x), \ldots$ is said to be *complete* in the inner product space if the relevant 'Fourier' expansion converges in the mean for every $f(x)$ in that space.

We may be able to show that the orthogonal system is complete in a subspace of the inner product space. For example for the subspace of continuous functions the completeness condition implies that a function is uniquely determined by its Fourier coefficients, so that two functions with the same Fourier coefficients are identical. From the theorem of Weierstrass we can then prove that the functions $1, x, x^2, \ldots$, and therefore the independent orthogonal *polynomials* generated by these functions, are complete for the subspace of continuous functions. It follows that all our expansions in terms of orthogonal polynomials converge in the mean for continuous functions belonging to our inner product space. It is known, moreover, that the system of trigonometric functions $1, \cos x, \cos 2x, \ldots$, $\sin x, \sin 2x, \ldots$, is complete for the space of quadratically integrable functions, that is for functions $f(x)$ for which $\int_{-\pi}^{\pi} |f(x)|^2 \, dx$ exists. Since $\int_{-\pi}^{\pi} f(x)g(x) \, dx$ is the inner product relevant to the Fourier series, we deduce that the latter converges in the mean for all functions in the relevant inner product space.

Convergence in the mean, however, does not imply point-wise convergence, that is $\sum_{r=0}^{\infty} c_r \, \phi_r(x)$ does not necessarily converge correctly to $f(x)$ at every point in the relevant interval. We have given in **2.3** some sufficient conditions for the point-wise convergence of the Fourier series, and hence of the Chebyshev series, but each particular function-system will need separate investigation. Uniform convergence, which may sometimes be verified by standard tests, is in all cases a sufficient condition for point-wise convergence.

EXERCISES 2

1. For the least-squares approximation

$$p_n(x) = \tfrac{1}{2}a_0 + \sum_{k=1}^{n} (a_k \cos kx + b_k \sin kx)$$

to a function $f(x)$ in $-\pi \leq x \leq \pi$, show that

$$\min \int_{-\pi}^{\pi} \{f(x) - p_n(x)\}^2 \, dx = \int_{-\pi}^{\pi} f^2(x) \, dx - \pi \left\{ \tfrac{1}{2}a_0^2 + \sum_{k=1}^{n} (a_k^2 + b_k^2) \right\}.$$

2. Find, in $-\pi \leq x \leq \pi$, the Fourier series

$$|x| = \frac{\pi}{2} - \frac{4}{\pi} \sum_{k=1}^{\infty} \frac{1}{(2k-1)^2} \cos (2k-1)x,$$

noting the convergence like k^{-2}. Find the similar series in the range $-1 \leq x \leq 1$.

3. By finding the Fourier cosine series for $|\cos \theta|$ in $0 \le \theta \le \pi$, and comparing with Exercise 14 of Chapter 1, verify that the Chebyshev series for $f(x)$ is exactly the Fourier series for $f(\cos \theta)$.

4. Prove equation (20). (Hint: note that the series $\sum_{k=0}^{N} e^{ik\theta}$ is geometric.)

5. Prove that the functions $\cos r\theta$, $r = 0, 1,..., N$, are orthogonal under summation over the points

$$\theta_k = \frac{2k+1}{N+1} \cdot \frac{\pi}{2}, \quad k = 0, 1,..., N,$$

and hence find a discrete least-squares Fourier series different from (24).

6. Using the Chebyshev expansions of Exercise 14, Chapter 1, and the relevant Parseval formula, find the rapidly convergent series

$$\frac{\pi^2}{8} = 1 + 2 \sum_{r=1}^{\infty} \frac{1}{(4r^2 - 1)^2}.$$

7. Show that, corresponding to the Chebyshev result (37), the orthogonal polynomials for $w(x) \equiv 1$ are $\phi_r(x) = \sqrt{\left(\frac{2r+1}{2} \right)} P_r(x)$, where $P_r(x)$ is the standard Legendre polynomial. In the notation of **2.11** show, for $N = 2$, that $\lambda_0 = 5/9$, $\lambda_1 = 8/9$, $\lambda_2 = 5/9$, and deduce the Gauss quadrature formula

$$\int_{-1}^{1} f(x)\, dx = \frac{1}{9} \left\{ 5f\left(-\sqrt{\frac{3}{5}}\right) + 8f(0) + 5f\left(\sqrt{\frac{3}{5}}\right) \right\}$$

and its error term.

8. Show that a solution of the discrete least-squares problem, with data points x_k at the zeros of $P_{N+1}(x)$, and with $w(x_k) = \lambda_k$, is given by

$$p_n(x) = \sum_{r=0}^{n} b_r P_r(x), \qquad b_r = \frac{2r+1}{2} \sum_{k=0}^{N} \lambda_k f(x_k) P_r(x_k),$$

$$\lambda_k^{-1} = \sum_{r=0}^{N} \frac{2r+1}{2} P_r^2(x_k).$$

Show also that this is the discrete analogy of the continuous least-squares Legendre expansion, with unit weight function, given in equation (55) of Chapter 1. (Hint: we have to show that for $n = N$ tending to infinity,

$$\lim_{N \to \infty} \sum_{k=0}^{N} \lambda_k f(x_k) P_r(x_k) = \int_{-1}^{1} P_r(x) f(x) \, dx.$$

Use the Gauss quadrature formula for $\int_{-1}^{1} P_r(x) f(x) \, dx$, and assume that the $(2N+2)$th derivative of $P_r(x) f(x)$ is bounded.)

3

Practical Properties of
Chebyshev Polynomials and Series

Introduction

3.1 In this chapter we first develop and list those properties of Chebyshev polynomials which are necessary for practical applications to be discussed later. They include the use of generating functions to produce the explicit polynomial formulae for $T_n(x)$, and the important inversion to produce x^n in terms of $T_r(x)$, $r \leq n$. We note some analytical properties, formulae for derivatives and integrals, some functional equations, and for convenience we discuss both the ranges $-1 \leq x \leq 1$ and $0 \leq x \leq 1$.

Secondly we treat the Chebyshev series, giving methods for its evaluation, with associated error analysis, in both important ranges. We also consider term-by-term integration and differentiation, the results being expressed in similar Chebyshev-series form.

Elementary properties in $-1 \leq x \leq 1$

3.2 We have already seen that the Chebyshev polynomial

$$T_r(x) = \cos r\theta, \quad \cos \theta = x, \quad -1 \leq x \leq 1, \tag{1}$$

can be generated from the recurrence system

$$T_{r+1}(x) = 2x\, T_r(x) - T_{r-1}(x), \quad T_0(x) = 1, \quad T_1(x) = x, \tag{2}$$

and we easily find the first few successive members

$$\left.\begin{aligned}
T_2(x) &= 2x^2 - 1 \\
T_3(x) &= 4x^3 - 3x \\
T_4(x) &= 8x^4 - 8x^2 + 1 \\
T_5(x) &= 16x^5 - 20x^3 + 5x
\end{aligned}\right\}. \tag{3}$$

The polynomials of even order are obviously even functions of x, and the polynomials of odd order are odd functions of x.

We easily see that all $T_r(x)$ have the value unity at $x = 1$, and at $x = -1$ the value is $+1$ for even r and -1 for odd r. The turning points of $T_r(x)$ occur at the zeros of $\sin r\theta / \sin \theta$, that is at the $r-1$ points

$$\theta_i = \frac{i\pi}{r}, \quad x_i = \cos\left(\frac{i\pi}{r}\right), \quad i = 1, 2, ..., r-1, \tag{4}$$

and at these points

$$T_r(x_i) = (-1)^i. \tag{5}$$

The turning points are separated by the r zeros, at

$$\theta_i = (i+\tfrac{1}{2})\frac{\pi}{r}, \quad x_i = \cos(i+\tfrac{1}{2})\frac{\pi}{r}, \quad i = 0, 1, ..., r-1, \tag{6}$$

and both turning points and zeros are symmetrically disposed about the origin $x = 0$. The general shapes of $T_r(x)$, for even and odd r, are typified in Fig. 1 for $r = 4$ and $r = 3$, each $T_r(x)$ having $r+1$ equal maximum and minimum values in $-1 \leq x \leq 1$.

3.3 In many applications it is desirable to express the powers of x in terms of the polynomials $T_r(x)$, and we can easily find the first few such formulae by reversing (3). We find, with the omission of the argument x for simplicity, the results

$$\left.\begin{aligned}
1 &= T_0 \\
x &= T_1 \\
x^2 &= \tfrac{1}{2}(T_0 + T_2) \\
x^3 &= \tfrac{1}{4}(3T_1 + T_3) \\
x^4 &= \tfrac{1}{8}(3T_0 + 4T_2 + T_4) \\
x^5 &= \tfrac{1}{16}(10T_1 + 5T_3 + T_5)
\end{aligned}\right\}, \tag{7}$$

and again we note the separation of the 'even' and 'odd' formulae.

The range $0 \leq x \leq 1$

3.4 Any finite range, $a \leq y \leq b$, can be transformed to the basic range $-1 \leq x \leq 1$ with the change of variable

$$y = \tfrac{1}{2}(b-a)x + \tfrac{1}{2}(b+a), \tag{8}$$

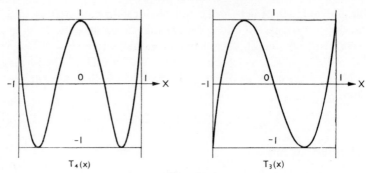

Fig. 1

and for the special range $0 \leq y \leq 1$ we can write

$$y = \tfrac{1}{2}(x+1), \qquad x = 2y-1. \tag{9}$$

It is convenient to have a special notation for this range, and following Lanczos we write

$$T_r^*(x) = T_r(2x-1), \quad 0 \leq x \leq 1. \tag{10}$$

All the properties of $T_r^*(x)$ can be deduced from those of $T_r(2x-1)$ and in particular, corresponding to (3) and (7), we can find formulae of the kind

$$\left.\begin{aligned}
T_0^* &= 1 & 1 &= T_0^* \\
T_1^* &= 2x-1 & x &= \tfrac{1}{2}(T_0^*+T_1^*) \\
T_2^* &= 8x^2-8x+1 & x^2 &= \tfrac{1}{8}(3T_0^*+4T_1^*+T_2^*) \\
T_3^* &= 32x^3-48x^2+18x-1 & x^3 &= \tfrac{1}{32}(10T_0^*+15T_1^*+6T_2^*+T_3^*)
\end{aligned}\right\}. \tag{11}$$

The first batch comes either from the replacement of x by $2x-1$ in (3) or by use of the recurrence relation

$$T_{r+1}^*(x) = 2(2x-1)T_r^*(x)-T_{r-1}^*(x). \tag{12}$$

In (11), of course, both odd and even terms appear in the general formulae.

3.5 For the approximation of a general function $f(x)$ we should expect, with the same number of terms, to get a smaller minimax error with the $T_r^*(x)$ in $0 \leq x \leq 1$ than with the $T_r(x)$ in the larger range $-1 \leq x \leq 1$. For example we saw in **1.6** that the best quadratic approximation to x^3+x^2 in $(-1, 1)$ is $x^2+\frac{3}{4}x$, with a maximum error of modulus $\frac{1}{4}$. For the range $(0, 1)$ we find

$$x^3+x^2 = \tfrac{1}{32}(10T_0^*+15T_1^*+6T_2^*)+x^2+\tfrac{1}{32}T_3^*, \qquad (13)$$

so that the best quadratic approximation is $\frac{1}{32}(1-18x+80x^2)$, with a maximum error of modulus $\frac{1}{32}$.

Generating functions and functional equations

3.6 To find the general expressions of types (3), (7) and (11) we establish a generating function for the series $\sum\limits_{r=0}^{\infty} p^r T_r(x)$. In terms of $\theta = \cos^{-1}x$ this is the real part of $\sum\limits_{r=0}^{\infty} p^r e^{ir\theta}$, and we can write

$$\sum_{r=0}^{\infty} p^r e^{ir\theta} = (1-pe^{i\theta})^{-1} = \{1-p(\cos\theta+i\sin\theta)\}^{-1}$$

$$= \{1-px-ip(1-x^2)^{\frac{1}{2}}\}^{-1} = \frac{1-px+ip(1-x^2)^{\frac{1}{2}}}{(1-px)^2+p^2(1-x^2)}. \qquad (14)$$

Taking the real part we deduce the result

$$1+pT_1(x)+p^2T_2(x) + \ldots = \frac{1-px}{1-2px+p^2}$$

$$= (1-\tfrac{1}{2}p.2x)\{1+p(2x-p)+p^2(2x-p)^2+\ldots\}, \qquad (15)$$

and evaluation of the coefficient of p^r on the right-hand side gives for $r \geq 1$ the required general expression

$$T_r(x) = \frac{1}{2}\left[(2x)^r-\left\{2\binom{r-1}{1}-\binom{r-2}{1}\right\}(2x)^{r-2}+\right.$$

$$\left.+\left\{2\binom{r-2}{2}-\binom{r-3}{2}\right\}(2x)^{r-4}-\ldots\right]. \quad (16)$$

The corresponding result for x^r in terms of $T_r(x)$ comes more easily from the identity

$$x^r = \left(\frac{e^{i\theta}+e^{-i\theta}}{2}\right)^r, \qquad (17)$$

giving

$$x^r = \frac{1}{2^{r-1}}\left\{T_r(x) + \binom{r}{1}T_{r-2}(x) + \binom{r}{2}T_{r-4}(x) + \ldots\right\}, \qquad (18)$$

in which, for even r, we take half the coefficient of $T_0(x)$.

3.7 The corresponding results for the range $0 \leq x \leq 1$ can be obtained by replacing x by $2x-1$ in (16) and (18), but it is simpler to use the functional equation

$$T_s(T_r(x)) = T_r(T_s(x)) = \cos(rs\theta) = T_{rs}(x). \qquad (19)$$

In particular, for $s = 2$ we find

$$T_r(T_2(x)) = T_r(2x^2-1) = T_2(T_r(x)) = 2T_r^2(x)-1 = T_{2r}(x), \qquad (20)$$

and if we replace x^2 by x we find

$$T_r(2x-1) = T_r^*(x) = 2T_r^2(x^{\frac{1}{2}})-1 = T_{2r}(x^{\frac{1}{2}}). \qquad (21)$$

The results corresponding to (16) and (18) then follow easily. From (16) and (21) we deduce

$$T_r^*(x) = \tfrac{1}{2}\left[2^{2r}x^r - \left\{2\binom{2r-1}{1} - \binom{2r-2}{1}\right\}2^{2r-2}x^{r-1} + \ldots\right], \qquad (22)$$

and from (18) and (21) we find

$$x^r = \frac{1}{2^{2r-1}}\left\{T_r^*(x) + \binom{2r}{1}T_{r-1}^*(x) + \ldots\right\}, \qquad (23)$$

with a factor $\tfrac{1}{2}$ associated with the coefficient of $T_0^*(x)$.

3.8 In certain applications we need expressions for products like $T_r(x)T_s(x)$ and $x^rT_s(x)$. The first comes easily from an obvious trigonometric identity, and we find

$$T_s(x)T_r(x) = \tfrac{1}{2}\{T_{s+r}(x) + T_{s-r}(x)\}. \qquad (24)$$

From (24) and the functional equation (21), noting that $T_p(x) = T_{|p|}(x)$, we can then easily obtain

$$T_s^*(x)T_r^*(x) = T_{2s}(x^{\frac{1}{2}})T_{2r}(x^{\frac{1}{2}}) = \tfrac{1}{2}\{T_{2s+2r}(x^{\frac{1}{2}}) + T_{2s-2r}(x^{\frac{1}{2}})\}$$

$$= \tfrac{1}{2}\{T_{s+r}^*(x) + T_{s-r}^*(x)\}, \qquad (25)$$

a formula identical with that for the $T(x)$ functions.

For an expansion for $x^r T_s(x)$ we use (18) and (24) to find

$$x^r T_s(x) = \frac{1}{2^{r-1}}\left\{T_r(x)T_s(x) + \binom{r}{1}T_{r-2}(x)T_s(x) + \ldots\right\}$$

$$= \frac{1}{2^r}\left[T_{s+r}(x) + T_{s-r}(x) + \binom{r}{1}\{T_{s+r-2}(x) + T_{s-r+2}(x)\} + \ldots\right]$$

$$= \frac{1}{2^r}\sum_{i=0}^{r}\binom{r}{i}T_{s-r+2i}(x), \tag{26}$$

with the help of the identity

$$\binom{r}{i} = \binom{r}{r-i}.$$

Again we can use the functional equation (21), together with (26), to find the corresponding expression

$$x^r T_s^*(x) = \frac{1}{2^{2r}}\sum_{i=0}^{2r}\binom{2r}{i}T_{s-r+i}^*(x), \tag{27}$$

with smaller coefficients but with nearly twice as many terms as (26).

Analytical properties

3.9 In **1.18** we noted that the Chebyshev polynomial could be defined by

$$T_r(x) = C_r(1-x^2)^{\frac{1}{2}}\frac{d^r}{dx^r}\{(1-x^2)^{r-\frac{1}{2}}\}, \tag{28}$$

where C_r is a constant to be determined from some normalization criterion, and that this function satisfies the differential equation

$$(1-x^2)y'' - xy' + r^2 y = 0. \tag{29}$$

Similarly the function $U_r(x)$, the Chebyshev polynomial of the second kind (see Exercise 15 of Chapter 1), is defined by

$$U_r(x) = \frac{\sin(r+1)\theta}{\sin\theta}$$
$$= C_r(1-x^2)^{-\frac{1}{2}}\frac{d^r}{dx^r}\{(1-x^2)^{r+\frac{1}{2}}\}, \tag{30}$$

and satisfies the differential equation

$$(1-x^2)y'' - 3xy' + r(r+2)y = 0. \tag{31}$$

Both (29) and (31) can be obtained without consideration of the orthogonal expansion, by writing $x = \cos\theta$, deducing

$$\left.\begin{aligned} \frac{d^2 T_r}{d\theta^2} + r^2 T_r &= 0 \\ \frac{d^2 U_r}{d\theta^2} + \frac{2\cos\theta}{\sin\theta}\frac{dU_r}{d\theta} + (r^2 + 2r)U &= 0 \end{aligned}\right\}, \qquad (32)$$

and reconverting to x as independent variable.

We shall not be very concerned with these differential equations, but they serve to relate the Chebyshev polynomials to the standard functions of mathematical physics. For example the hypergeometric function $F(\alpha, \beta, \gamma; y)$, defined by the series

$$F = 1 + \frac{\alpha.\beta}{\gamma.1}y + \frac{\alpha(\alpha+1)\beta(\beta+1)}{\gamma(\gamma+1)1.2}y^2 + \dots, \qquad (33)$$

satisfies the differential equation

$$y(1-y)\frac{d^2 F}{dy^2} + \{\gamma - (\alpha+\beta+1)y\}\frac{dF}{dy} - \alpha\beta \, F = 0. \qquad (34)$$

The change of variable $x = 2y - 1$ converts (34) to

$$(1-x^2)F'' + \{2\gamma - (\alpha+\beta+1)(1+x)\}F' - \alpha\beta \, F = 0, \qquad (35)$$

and with suitable normalization we find the relations

$$\left.\begin{aligned} T_r(x) &\propto F\left(r, -r, \tfrac{1}{2}; \frac{1+x}{2}\right) \\ U_r(x) &\propto F\left(r+2, -r, \frac{3}{2}; \frac{1+x}{2}\right) \end{aligned}\right\}. \qquad (36)$$

3.10 We are more concerned with integrals and derivatives. For indefinite integration we easily find

$$\int T_r(x)\, dx = -\int \cos r\theta \sin\theta \, d\theta$$

$$= -\tfrac{1}{2}\int \{\sin(r+1)\theta - \sin(r-1)\theta\}\, d\theta$$

$$= \frac{1}{2}\left\{\frac{1}{r+1} T_{r+1}(x) - \frac{1}{r-1} T_{r-1}(x)\right\}. \qquad (37)$$

For the special cases $r = 0$ and $r = 1$ we find

$$\int T_0(x)\,dx = T_1(x), \qquad \int T_1(x)\,dx = \tfrac{1}{4}\{T_0(x)+T_2(x)\}. \quad (38)$$

The first derivatives cannot be expressed directly in terms of similar functions, but going via the variable θ we produce

$$T'_r(x) = r\,U_{r-1}(x), \qquad (1-x^2)U'_r(x) = x\,U_r(x)-(r+1)T_{r+1}(x), \quad (39)$$

and from the first of (39) we have a simple formula for the indefinite integral of $U_r(x)$. A variety of other allied formulae is given by Lanczos (1952), and we include some of them in the exercises.

Evaluation, integration and differentiation of Chebyshev series

3.11 We turn now to an examination of the corresponding properties of the finite Chebyshev series

$$p(x) = \sum_{r=0}^{n}{}' a_r\,T_r(x), \quad (40)$$

where, as usual, the prime denotes that the first term is taken with factor $\tfrac{1}{2}$, and in which $p(x)$ is the truncation of the infinite series $f(x) = \sum_{r=0}^{\infty}{}' a_r\,T_r(x)$.

To evaluate $p(x)$ for a given value of x we may convert (40) to the polynomial form

$$p(x) = \sum_{r=0}^{n} c_r\,x^r, \quad (41)$$

and perform the process of *nested multiplication*, producing $p_n(x)$ from the 'backward' recurrence system

$$q_r(x) = x\,q_{r+1}(x)+c_r, \qquad q_{n+1}(x) = 0, \quad (42)$$

which gives $q_0(x) = p(x)$. Since $|x| \leq 1$ the process is relatively stable, and for some purposes this is a useful method.

But it has two disadvantages. First, it turns out that the coefficients c_r may be very considerably larger than the coefficients a_r, even if $p(x)$ is small, and this may create difficulties of storage to the required precision. Second, the truncation of (40) at an earlier term, to give a poorer but perhaps contextually satisfactory precision for $p(x)$, involves a change of most of the coefficients c_r in (41), although the a_r retained in (40) have their original values. (This truncation, we note in passing, does not necessarily give the best polynomial approximation of degree $n-1$ to some function $f(x)$, even if $p(x)$ is the best polynomial approximation of degree n, but as we saw at the end of Chapter 1 the rapid convergence of the Chebyshev series guarantees an approximation near to the best, and in any case we know that the extra error cannot exceed $|a_n|$.)

3.12 We therefore seek a method which bypasses the polynomial form (41), and this is provided by the standard recurrence relation (2). In fact, following Clenshaw (1955), we can see quite easily that the sum $\sum_{r=0}^{n} a_r \phi_r(x)$ of any series of functions which satisfy a linear recurrence relation

$$\phi_{r+1}(x)+\alpha_r(x)\phi_r(x)+\beta_r(x)\phi_{r-1}(x) = 0 \qquad (43)$$

is given by

$$\sum_{r=0}^{n} a_r \phi_r(x) = b_0(x)\phi_0(x)+b_1(x)\{\phi_1(x)+\alpha_0(x)\phi_0(x)\}, \qquad (44)$$

where

$$\left.\begin{aligned} b_r(x)+\alpha_r(x)\,b_{r+1}(x)+\beta_{r+1}(x)\,b_{r+2}(x) &= a_r \\ b_{n+1}(x) = b_{n+2}(x) &= 0 \end{aligned}\right\}. \qquad (45)$$

For the Chebyshev case (40) we have $\alpha_r = -2x$, $\beta_r = 1$, and then

$$\sum_{r=0}^{n}{}' a_r T_r(x) = \{b_0(x)-\tfrac{1}{2}a_0\}T_0(x)+b_1(x)\{T_1(x)-2x\,T_0(x)\}, \qquad (46)$$

which, with the observations

$$\left.\begin{aligned} T_0(x) = 1, \qquad T_1(x) &= xT_0(x) \\ b_0 = a_0+2x\,b_1(x)-b_2(x) & \end{aligned}\right\}, \qquad (47)$$

reduces to

$$\sum_{r=0}^{n}{}' a_r T_r(x) = \tfrac{1}{2}\{b_0(x)-b_2(x)\}. \qquad (48)$$

We have replaced the summation by the evaluation of (48) from the recurrence system

$$\left.\begin{aligned} b_r(x) &= 2x\,b_{r+1}(x)-b_{r+2}(x)+a_r \\ b_{n+1}(x) &= b_{n+2}(x) = 0 \end{aligned}\right\}, \qquad (49)$$

and we easily produce, for the series $\sum_{r=0}^{n} a_r T_r^*(x)$, the result

$$\left.\begin{aligned}
\sum_{r=0}^{n} {}' a_r T_r^*(x) &= \tfrac{1}{2}\{b_0(x) - b_2(x)\} \\
b_r(x) &= 2(2x-1)b_{r+1}(x) - b_{r+2}(x) + a_r
\end{aligned}\right\}, \qquad (50)$$

with $b_{n+1}(x) = b_{n+2}(x) = 0$.

3.13 It is desirable to assess the possible errors in the computation of $b_0(x)$ and $b_2(x)$ from the recurrence systems of type (49). Individual errors arise through possible rounding errors in the coefficients a_r, or perhaps the inability to store them exactly in the computing machine, and through extra rounding errors involved in the computation of $b_r(x)$ from (49). All these combine to give a *local* error ε_r, whose maximum value can be guaranteed in any particular case in the computed b_r, that is from the accepted $b_{r+1}(x)$, $b_{r+2}(x)$ and a_r. We deduce that the combined error in $\bar{b}_s$, the finally computed value of b_s, is given by

$$b_s - \bar{b}_s = \varepsilon_n E_s(n) + \varepsilon_{n-1} E_s(n-1) + \ldots + \varepsilon_s E_s(s), \qquad (51)$$

where $E_s(r)$ is the exact value of the error at point s produced by zero error at point $r+1$ and unit error at point r.

Each $E_s(r)$ can obviously be computed separately from its recurrence system

$$\left.\begin{aligned}
E_t(r) &= 2x\, E_{t+1}(r) - E_{t+2}(r) \\
E_{r+1}(r) &= 0, \quad E_r(r) = 1, \quad t \leq r, \quad s \leq r
\end{aligned}\right\}, \qquad (52)$$

or we can use the well-known fact (see, for example, Fox, 1965) that we can produce them all with the single recurrence system

$$E_s(r+2) = 2x\, E_s(r+1) - E_s(r), \quad E_s(s-1) = 0, \quad E_s(s) = 1. \qquad (53)$$

Now the general solution of this recurrence is

$$E_s(r) = A\, T_r(x) + B\, U_r(x), \qquad (54)$$

and for the satisfaction of the initial conditions we find

$$E_s(r) = \frac{U_r(x)T_{s-1}(x) - T_r(x)U_{s-1}(x)}{U_s(x)T_{s-1}(x) - T_s(x)U_{s-1}(x)} = U_{r-s}(x). \qquad (55)$$

Since the maximum value of $|U_j(x)|$ is $j+1$, it follows from (51) that the error in each computed b_s could be quite large. On the other hand we find a significant and valuable cancellation in the required quantity $\frac{1}{2}\{b_0(x)-b_2(x)\}$, whose error is bounded by

$$\varepsilon \leq \frac{1}{2}\left[\sum_{r=n}^{2}|\varepsilon_r\{E_0(r)-E_2(r)\}| + |\varepsilon_1 E_0(1)| + |\varepsilon_0 E_0(0)|\right]. \quad (56)$$

From (55) we find $E_0(r)-E_2(r) = U_r(x)-U_{r-2}(x) = 2\,T_r(x)$, by an obvious identity, so that

$$\varepsilon \leq \sum_{r=n}^{2}|\varepsilon_r\,T_r(x)| + \tfrac{1}{2}|\varepsilon_1\,U_1(x)| + \tfrac{1}{2}|\varepsilon_0\,U_0(x)| \qquad (57)$$
$$\leq \sum_{r=1}^{n}|\varepsilon_r| + \tfrac{1}{2}|\varepsilon_0|,$$

since $U_1(x)$ has a maximum value of 2. We deduce that our recurrence process is perfectly stable, the local rounding errors are not amplified, and the upper bound to the error cannot exceed the arithmetic sum of the individual local rounding errors. The corresponding analysis for the $T_r^*(x)$ case obviously produces the same result.

3.14 At particular points the evaluation of the series is almost trivial, and we find

$$\left.\begin{aligned} p(1) &= \tfrac{1}{2}a_0+a_1+a_2+\ldots+a_n \\ p(-1) &= \tfrac{1}{2}a_0-a_1+a_2-\ldots+(-1)^n a_n \\ p(0) &= \tfrac{1}{2}a_0-a_2+a_4-\ldots+(-1)^n a_{2n} \end{aligned}\right\}, \qquad (58)$$

for the expansion in terms of $T_r(x)$, and for the $T_r^*(x)$ case the right-hand sides of (58) are the values of $p(1)$, $p(0)$ and $p(\frac{1}{2})$ respectively. These formulae, we shall find, are useful in certain methods of solving ordinary differential equations.

3.15 For the term-by-term indefinite integration of (40) we use the results (37) and (38), and deduce that if $p(x) = \sum_{r=0}^{n}{}'a_r\,T_r(x)$, then

$$\int_{-1}^{x}p(x)\,dx = \sum_{r=0}^{n+1}{}'b_r\,T_r(x), \qquad (59)$$

where

$$b_{n+1} = \frac{a_n}{2(n+1)}, \qquad b_n = \frac{a_{n-1}}{2n} \Bigg\}$$

$$b_r = \frac{1}{2r}(a_{r-1}-a_{r+1}), \qquad r = 1, 2,..., n-1 \tag{60}$$

and to make the result vanish at $x = -1$ we use the second of (58) to deduce that

$$\tfrac{1}{2}b_0 = b_1-b_2+b_3-...+(-1)^n b_{n+1}. \tag{61}$$

For the special case of definite integration when the upper limit x is unity, we find for the *infinite* series the result

$$\int_{-1}^{1} f(x)\, dx = 2(b_1+b_3+b_5+...)$$

$$= 2\left(\frac{1}{2}a_0-\frac{1}{1.3}a_2-\frac{1}{3.5}a_4-\frac{1}{5.7}a_6-...\right) \tag{62}$$

$$= a_0-\sum_{r=2}^{n}\left(\frac{1+(-1)^r}{r^2-1}\right)a_r,$$

which clearly converges much faster than the series for $f(x)$ itself.

3.16 For the range $0 \leq x \leq 1$ we similarly use the integral relation corresponding to (37), which is

$$\int T_r^*(x)\, dx = \frac{1}{4}\left\{\frac{T_{r+1}^*(x)}{r+1} - \frac{T_{r-1}^*(x)}{r-1}\right\}, \tag{63}$$

and find, for $p(x) = \sum_{r=0}^{n}{}' a_r T_r^*(x)$, the indefinite integral

$$\int_0^x p(x)\, dx = \sum_{r=0}^{n+1}{}' b_r T_r^*(x), \tag{64}$$

where

$$b_{n+1} = \frac{a_n}{4(n+1)}, \qquad b_n = \frac{a_{n-1}}{4n} \Bigg\}$$

$$b_r = \frac{1}{4r}(a_{r-1}-a_{r+1}), \qquad r = 1, 2,..., n-1 \tag{65}$$

and

$$\tfrac{1}{2}b_0 = b_1 - b_2 + b_3 - \ldots + (-1)^n b_{n+1}$$

$$= \tfrac{1}{4}a_0 - \tfrac{1}{8}a_1 - \tfrac{1}{2}\sum_{r=2}^{n} \frac{(-1)^r}{r^2 - 1}\, a_r. \tag{66}$$

For the definite integral, with upper limit unity, we find for the infinite series the result

$$\int_0^1 f(x)\, dx = 2(b_1 + b_3 + b_5 + \ldots)$$

$$= \frac{1}{2}a_0 - \frac{1}{1.3}a_2 - \frac{1}{3.5}a_4 - \frac{1}{5.7}a_6 - \ldots, \tag{67}$$

lacking only the factor 2 compared with (62).

3.17 These integration formulae are recommended by Clenshaw and Curtis (1960) as a general method for the indefinite or definite integration in a finite range of any function $f(x)$ which can be represented by a Chebyshev series. They note, for example, its advantage in respect of guaranteed accuracy, compared with the more standard quadrature formulae of Simpson and Gauss. With the latter it is common to judge the accuracy achieved by the consistency of computed results with different numbers of pivotal points, and they stress the dangers of this approach. For example, they observe that Simpson's rule, for $\int_{-1}^{1} (0.92 \cosh x - \cos x)\, dx$, gives 0·479 554 6 with interval 0·5, and the consistent 0·479 555 1 with interval 0·25, whereas the correct value to this precision is 0·479 428 2. Similarly for $\int_{-1}^{1} (x^4 + x^2 + 0.9)^{-1}\, dx$, they find that the Gauss three- and four-point formulae give respective consistent values of 1·585 026 and 1·585 060, compared with the correct 1·582 233.

Effectively, therefore, they replace the estimation of error of the quadrature formula by that of the adequacy of the computed truncated Chebyshev series for the approximation of the integrand, and the rapidity of the convergence of this series provides a more reliable guarantee. We return to this point in Chapter 4.

3.18 Turning finally to term-by-term differentiation of the finite Chebyshev series, we prefer not to introduce the function $U_{r-1}(x)$, involved in the derivative formula (39) for $T'_r(x)$, but to express the derived series, which is a polynomial of degree $n-1$, in terms of $T_r(x)$. We then write

$$p'(x) = \sum_{r=0}^{n-1}{}' c_r T_r(x), \tag{68}$$

and seek to compute the coefficients c_r in terms of the a_r of $p(x) = \sum_{r=0}^{n}{}' a_r T_r(x)$. To this end we integrate (68), using (37) and (38) for the integration of each $T_r(x)$, to give

$$\sum_{r=0}^{n}{}' a_r T_r(x) = \tfrac{1}{2}a_0 T_0(x) + \tfrac{1}{2}c_0 T_1(x) + \tfrac{1}{4}c_1 T_2(x) +$$
$$+ \frac{1}{2}\sum_{r=2}^{n-1} c_r \left\{ \frac{T_{r+1}(x)}{r+1} - \frac{T_{r-1}(x)}{r-1} \right\}, \tag{69}$$

and by equating coefficients of $T_r(x)$ on each side we find

$$\left.\begin{aligned} a_r &= \frac{1}{2r}(c_{r-1}-c_{r+1}), \qquad r = 1, 2,..., n-2 \\[2mm] a_{n-1} &= \frac{1}{2(n-1)}c_{n-2}, \qquad a_n = \frac{1}{2n}c_{n-1} \end{aligned}\right\}. \tag{70}$$

We can then calculate the c_r in succession, for decreasing r, from the general recurrence relation

$$c_{r-1} = c_{r+1} + 2ra_r, \tag{71}$$

with starting conditions given by the last two of (70), and find

$$\left.\begin{aligned} c_{n-1} &= 2na_n \\ c_{n-2} &= 2(n-1)a_{n-1} \\ c_{n-3} &= 2(n-2)a_{n-2} + 2na_n \\ &\cdot \quad \cdot \quad \cdot \quad \cdot \quad \cdot \quad \cdot \\ c_1 &= 4a_2 + 8a_4 + 12a_6 + ... \\ c_0 &= 2a_1 + 6a_3 + 10a_5 + ... \end{aligned}\right\}, \tag{72}$$

each series in (72) being finite, stopping at the term a_n or a_{n-1}.

For the derivative of $p(x) = \sum_{r=0}^{n}{}' a_r T_r^*(x)$ we proceed similarly, noting in virtue of (63) that the basic recurrence (71) is here replaced by

$$c_{r-1} = c_{r+1} + 4ra_r. \tag{73}$$

3.19 We note, as in all processes of differentiation, the amplification of possible rounding errors in the coefficients a_r of the given function. More important, perhaps, is the fact that for the term-by-term differentiation of the infinite Chebyshev series the formulae in (72) are infinite series. In fact for the range $-1 \leq x \leq 1$ we have the general expressions

$$c_{2r} = \sum_{s=r}^{\infty} 2(2s+1)a_{2s+1}, \qquad c_{2r+1} = \sum_{s=r}^{\infty} 2(2s+2)a_{2s+2} \left.\right\} \quad (74)$$
$$r = 0, 1,...$$

and we must take contextual care that the convergence of (74) is guaranteed. Even then the convergence may be slow and the error in the truncated approximation to the derivative can be quite large. For integration, on the other hand, the integrated series has smaller coefficients than that of the function, and our truncation error will be smaller by a factor of order n.

EXERCISES 3

1. Using the methods of **3.6**, establish the formulae

$$U_r(x) = (2x)^r - \binom{r-1}{1}(2x)^{r-2} + \binom{r-2}{2}(2x)^{r-4} - ...,$$

$$x^r = \frac{1}{2^r}\left[U_r(x) + \left\{\binom{r}{1} - \binom{r}{0}\right\}U_{r-2}(x) + \left\{\binom{r}{2} - \binom{r}{1}\right\}U_{r-4}(x) + ... \right].$$

2. Show that

$$U_{r-1}\{T_s(x)\}U_{s-1}(x) = U_{s-1}\{T_r(x)\}U_{r-1}(x) = U_{rs-1}(x),$$

and deduce the result

$$U_r^*(x) = U_r(2x-1) = \frac{U_{2r+1}(x^{\frac{1}{2}})}{2x^{\frac{1}{2}}}.$$

3. Show that

$$U_{s-1}(x)U_{r-1}(x) = \frac{1}{2(1-x^2)}\{T_{s-r}(x) - T_{s+r}(x)\},$$

$$T_r(x)U_{s-1}(x) = \tfrac{1}{2}\{U_{s+r-1}(x) + U_{s-r-1}(x)\},$$

and deduce an expansion for $x^r U_{s-1}(x)$ in terms of the $U_k(x)$ polynomials.

4. Show that the sum of the finite Legendre series $\sum\limits_{r=0}^{n} a_r P_r(x)$ is just $b_0(x)$, which is obtained from the recurrence

$$b_r(x) - \left(\frac{2r+1}{r+1}\right) x b_{r+1}(x) + \left(\frac{r+1}{r+2}\right) b_{r+2}(x) = a_r,$$

$$b_{n+1}(x) = b_{n+2}(x) = 0.$$

5. If the recurrence in (52) had the more general form

$$E_t(r) = \alpha_r E_{t+1}(r) - \beta_r E_{t+2}(r),$$

show that the corresponding recurrence in (53) is given by

$$E_s(r+2) = \alpha_r E_s(r+1) - \beta_{r-1} E_s(r).$$

6. Using the expansion for $|x|$ in Exercise 14, Chapter 1, and the integration formula (62), deduce the expansion

$$\frac{\pi}{4} = 1 - 2\left(\frac{1}{1^2 \cdot 3^2} - \frac{1}{3^2 \cdot 5^2} + \frac{1}{5^2 \cdot 7^2} - \cdots\right).$$

7. In the computation of the derivative of $\sum\limits_{r=0}^{n}{}' a_r T_r(x)$, in which each a_r has a possible rounding error of upper bound ε, show separately, from equations (72) and (39), that the upper bound for the rounding error in the derivative is of order $\frac{1}{3} n^3 \varepsilon$ at $x = \pm 1$, but of order $\frac{1}{4} n^2 \varepsilon$ at the point $x = 0$.

8. If $\sum\limits_{r=0}^{\infty} p^r f_r(x) = (1 - 2px + p^2)^{-\frac{1}{2}}$, show that

$$\int_{-1}^{1} \left(\sum_{r=0}^{\infty} p^r f_r(x)\right)\left(\sum_{s=0}^{\infty} q^s f_s(x)\right) dx = \sum_{n=0}^{\infty} \frac{2}{2n+1} p^n q^n,$$

and deduce that $f_r(x)$ is the Legendre polynomial $P_r(x)$. Hence determine a general formula for the coefficient of x^r in the expansion of $P_r(x)$.

9. Use the generating function in Exercise 8 to find the expression for x^r in a finite series $\sum\limits_{s=0}^{r} a_s P_s(x)$.

10. Show how the method of **3.12** can be adapted for the efficient computation of $\sum\limits_{r=0}^{n}{}' a_{2r} T_{2r}(x)$ and of $\sum\limits_{r=0}^{n} a_{2r+1} T_{2r+1}(x)$. (Hint: use the functional relation (21).)

11. If $(1-x^2)^{10} = \sum\limits_{r=0}^{10} a_{2r} x^{2r} = \sum\limits_{r=0}^{10'} b_{2r} T_{2r}(x)$, in $-1 \leq x \leq 1$, show that $\max |a_{2r}| = 252$, $\max |b_{2r}| \sim 0\cdot32$. Show also that if $(1-x^2)^{10} = \sum\limits_{r=0}^{10} c_r(2x^2-1)^r$, then $\max |c_r| \sim 0\cdot25$. (Expansion in powers of $(2x^2-1)$ often keeps the coefficients small (Beasley, 1965).)

12. In the formula (48) show that

$$|b_0| \leq |a_0| + 2|a_1| + \ldots + (n+1)|a_n| ,$$

and that, in (42),

$$|q_0| \leq |c_0| + |c_1| + \ldots + |c_n| .$$

13. Show that

$$\frac{d}{dx}\{T_r(x)\} = (\pm1)^{r+1} r^2 \text{ at } x = \pm1.$$

4

Chebyshev Approximations for Functions Defined Explicitly

Introduction

4.1 We turn now to the production of Chebyshev approximations for functions defined explicitly, that is, in closed form, so that we do not need to invert an operator. Such functions may include polynomials, infinite (Taylor's) series in powers of x, asymptotic (semi-convergent) series in powers of x^{-1}, rational functions, functions defined by definite or indefinite integrals, and so on. We also consider functions defined discretely, as in a mathematical table, and functions which may be defined as the result of measurement at an arbitrary selection of points.

The generally rapid convergence of the Chebyshev series has important advantages, both in the reduction in computational time and in the estimation of an accurate upper bound for the error. The resulting 'economization', in fact, has led to the almost exclusive use of Chebyshev-series sub-routines for evaluating the elementary functions by digital computer, in which the conservation of storage space and speed of computation are important considerations.

General methods

4.2 First we consider methods for general functions, for which our previous theory has produced two main possibilities for obtaining Chebyshev approximations. For $f(x)$ defined in $-1 \le x \le 1$, the *Chebyshev series* is given by

$$\left. \begin{aligned} f(x) &= \sum_{r=0}^{\infty}{}' a_r T_r(x) \\ a_r &= \frac{2}{\pi} \int_{-1}^{1} (1-x^2)^{-\frac{1}{2}} f(x) T_r(x)\, dx = \frac{2}{\pi} \int_{0}^{\pi} f(\cos\theta) \cos r\theta\, d\theta \end{aligned} \right\} . \quad (1)$$

In numerical practice we cannot use the infinite series, and we rely on a finite approximation of suitable accuracy. This is obtained most obviously by truncating the series (1) at a suitable point, giving the polynomial

$$p_n(x) = \sum_{r=0}^{n}{}' a_r T_r(x), \tag{2}$$

with error

$$\left.\begin{array}{c} e_n(x) = f(x) - p_n(x) = \displaystyle\sum_{r=n+1}^{\infty} a_r T_r(x) \\[2mm] |e_n(x)| \le \displaystyle\sum_{r=n+1}^{\infty} |a_r| \end{array}\right\}. \tag{3}$$

The formula for the coefficients, however, is not particularly attractive unless the integrations can be performed analytically with reasonably simple results. We may prefer to find a finite approximation to the Chebyshev series from one of the interpolation formulae (see **2.13**), which tend to the Chebyshev series as the number of matching points tends to infinity.

4.3 Equation (51) of Chapter 2 gives the approximation

$$\left.\begin{array}{c} p_n(x) = \displaystyle\sum_{r=0}^{n}{}'' b_r T_r(x) \\[3mm] b_r = \dfrac{2}{n}\displaystyle\sum_{k=0}^{n}{}'' f(x_k) T_r(x_k), \qquad x_k = \cos\dfrac{k\pi}{n} \end{array}\right\}, \tag{4}$$

and equation (52) gives the alternative

$$\left.\begin{array}{c} p_n(x) = \displaystyle\sum_{r=0}^{n}{}' c_r T_r(x) \\[3mm] c_r = \dfrac{2}{n+1}\displaystyle\sum_{k=0}^{n} f(x_k) T_r(x_k), \qquad x_k = \cos\left(\dfrac{2k+1}{n+1}\cdot\dfrac{\pi}{2}\right) \end{array}\right\}. \tag{5}$$

The resulting polynomials agree with $f(x)$ at the matching points, but we would like to know the magnitude of their discrepancies at other points.

To this end we find relations between the coefficients a_r of the infinite series and the coefficients b_r and c_r of the respective finite approximations. Using (1) and (4), we can write

$$b_r = \frac{2}{n} \sum_{k=0}^{n}{}'' \left\{ T_r(x_k) \sum_{r=0}^{\infty}{}' a_r T_r(x_k) \right\}, \qquad x_k = \cos \frac{k\pi}{n}. \qquad (6)$$

The orthogonality of the Chebyshev polynomials with regard to summation and the corresponding normalization factors, effectively given in equations (22) and (23) of Chapter 2, simplify considerably the expression (6) for b_r. With the observation that

$$\left.
\begin{aligned}
T_r(x_k) = \cos \frac{rk\pi}{n} &= \cos\left\{ (2pn \pm r)\frac{k\pi}{n} \right\} = T_{2pn \pm r}(x_k) \\
& \qquad\qquad p = 1, 2,\ldots
\end{aligned}
\right\}, \qquad (7)$$

we find the required expression

$$b_r = a_r + (a_{2n-r} + a_{2n+r}) + (a_{4n-r} + a_{4n+r}) + \ldots, \qquad (8)$$

which is valid for all r.

The corresponding analysis for c_r in (5), and the observation that

$$T_r(x_k) = \cos\left(\frac{2k+1}{n+1} \cdot \frac{r\pi}{2} \right) = (-1)^p \cos\left[\{2p(n+1) \pm r\} \left(\frac{2k+1}{n+1} \cdot \frac{\pi}{2} \right) \right]$$

$$= (-1)^p T_{2p(n+1) \pm r}(x_k), \qquad (9)$$

produces for c_r the expression

$$c_r = a_r - (a_{2n+2-r} + a_{2n+2+r}) + (a_{4n+4-r} + a_{4n+4+r}) - \ldots, \qquad (10)$$

also valid for all r.

4.4 If the truncation (2) is a satisfactory approximation to (1), so that a_r is negligible for $r > n$, it follows that the coefficients b_r and c_r differ from a_r by negligible amounts, and they can be computed conveniently from (4) and (5).

More generally, we have for the error the expressions

$$
\begin{aligned}
&f(x) - \sum_{r=0}^{n}{}'' b_r T_r(x) \\
&= \sum_{r=n+1}^{\infty} a_r T_r(x) - \\
&\quad - \sum_{r=0}^{n-1}{}' \left\{ \sum_{p=1}^{\infty} (a_{2pn-r} + a_{2pn+r}) \right\} T_r(x) - \left(\sum_{p=1}^{\infty} a_{2pn+n} \right) T_n(x) \\
&f(x) - \sum_{r=0}^{n}{}' c_r T_r(x) \\
&= \sum_{r=n+1}^{\infty} a_r T_r(x) - \\
&\quad - \sum_{r=0}^{n}{}' \left\{ \sum_{p=1}^{\infty} (-1)^p (a_{2p(n+1)-r} + a_{2p(n+1)+r}) T_r(x) \right\}
\end{aligned}
\tag{11}
$$

We deduce that

$$
\begin{aligned}
\left| f(x) - \sum_{r=0}^{n}{}'' b_r T_r(x) \right| &\le 2 \sum_{r=n+1}^{\infty} |a_r| \\
\left| f(x) - \sum_{r=0}^{n}{}' c_r T_r(x) \right| &< 2 \sum_{r=n+1}^{\infty} |a_r|
\end{aligned}
\tag{12}
$$

so that the error of (4) and (5) can never exceed twice the error of the truncated form (2) of the infinite series.

In the particular case in which the convergence of the infinite series is so fast that the coefficients $a_{n+2}, a_{n+3}, \ldots$, are negligible, we see from (8) that b_r agrees very closely with a_r except when $r = n-1$, where

$$ b_{n-1} = a_{n-1} + a_{n+1}. \tag{13} $$

The error in the first of (11) is then dominated by the term $a_{n+1}\{T_{n+1}(x) - T_{n-1}(x)\}$, with maximum value $2|a_{n+1}|$. None of the coefficients c_r, however, differs from the a_r by significant amounts, the maximum discrepancy being at $r = n$ where

$$ c_n = a_n - a_{n+2}. \tag{14} $$

The error in the second of (11) is then dominated by the single term $a_{n+1} T_{n+1}(x)$, with smaller maximum value $|a_{n+1}|$.

According to Elliott (1965), however, the formula (4) has a small theoretical advantage over (5) when the Chebyshev series converges slowly, and sometimes when $f(x)$ is either even or odd, and again if we seek an approximation to $\int_{-1}^{1} f(x)\,dx$ rather than to $f(x)$ itself. Moreover it has a practical advantage in that, if we decide to double the number of matching points to obtain better accuracy, the use of (4) involves less computation since the old matching points are included in the new set.

4.5 To illustrate these results we give some expansions for e^x in $-1 \le x \le 1$. Here we have, for the Chebyshev series, the coefficients

$$a_r = \frac{2}{\pi} \int_0^{\pi} e^{\cos \theta} \cos r\theta \, d\theta = 2I_r(1), \tag{15}$$

where $I_r(x)$ is a Bessel function of imaginary argument. To six decimals we find

$$e^x = 1 \cdot 266\ 066 T_0(x) + 1 \cdot 130\ 318 T_1(x) + 0 \cdot 271\ 495 T_2(x) +$$
$$+ 0 \cdot 044\ 337 T_3(x) + 0 \cdot 005\ 474 T_4(x) + 0 \cdot 000\ 543 T_5(x) +$$
$$+ 0 \cdot 000\ 045 T_6(x) + 0 \cdot 000\ 003 T_7(x), \tag{16}$$

further terms making negligible contribution.

Taking $n = 4$ in the first matching formula (4), we obtain the approximation

$$e^x \sim 1 \cdot 266\ 066 T_0(x) + 1 \cdot 130\ 321 T_1(x) + 0 \cdot 271\ 540 T_2(x) +$$
$$+ 0 \cdot 044\ 880 T_3(x) + 0 \cdot 005\ 474 T_4(x), \tag{17}$$

and the second matching formula (5) gives

$$e^x \sim 1 \cdot 266\ 066 T_0(x) + 1 \cdot 130\ 318 T_1(x) + 0 \cdot 271\ 495 T_2(x) +$$
$$+ 0 \cdot 044\ 334 T_3(x) + 0 \cdot 005\ 429 T_4(x). \tag{18}$$

We see that equations (8) and (10) are satisfied to six decimals, and that to this accuracy the errors in the approximations are

$$\left. \begin{aligned} e^x - \sum_{r=0}^{4}{}'' b_r T_r(x) &= 10^{-6}[3(T_7 - T_1) + 45(T_6 - T_2) + 543(T_5 - T_3)] \\[2mm] e^x - \sum_{r=0}^{4}{}' c_r T_r(x) &= 10^{-6}[3(T_7 + T_3) + 45(T_6 + T_4) + 543 T_5] \end{aligned} \right\} \tag{19}$$

with computed maximum values of about 0·001 2 and 0·000 6 respectively.

Again, taking $n = 1$ we have the linear approximations

$$e^x \sim 1 \cdot 543\ 081 T_0(x) + 1 \cdot 175\ 201 T_1(x) \atop e^x \sim 1 \cdot 260\ 592 T_0(x) + 1 \cdot 085\ 442 T_1(x) \Bigg\} , \qquad (20)$$

with maximum errors of about 0·644 and 0·372 respectively.

For the even function cosh x, which has the Chebyshev series (16) with the odd terms omitted, the matching approximations for $n = 4$ are obtained similarly by taking only the even terms in (17) and (18). The respective errors are here

$$0 \cdot 000\ 045\{T_6(x) - T_2(x)\}, \qquad 0 \cdot 000\ 045\{T_6(x) + T_4(x)\}, \qquad (21)$$

and the maximum value of the latter is some 30 per cent greater than that of the former. The corresponding results for the odd function sinh x, however, have errors little different from

$$0 \cdot 000\ 543\{T_5(x) - T_3(x)\}, \qquad 0 \cdot 000\ 543 T_5(x), \qquad (22)$$

and the maximum value of the former is about 1·8 times that of the latter. Corresponding analysis relevant to the linear approximations (20) gives the opposite results, that the second is here more accurate for cosh x, the first for sinh x.

In practice the differences in maximum error are rather small, and the *practical* advantage of fitting at the points in (4) is probably the most important consideration. The value of n needed for a given precision can usually be determined empirically by observing the rate of convergence of the coefficients of the finite approximation. In (17) and (18), for example, the ratios of successive coefficients after the first are about 4, 6 and 8 respectively, and we would expect the next coefficients to be approximately those of (16). As a check we can repeat the computation with larger values of n.

Polynomials and power series. Economization

4.6 For a polynomial of degree n the Chebyshev series (1) is of course a finite series, and is identical with the results obtained in (2) by truncation and in (4) and (5) by the matching methods. None of the corresponding methods for computing the coefficients, however, is particularly attractive. The use of (1), for $f(x) = \sum\limits_{r=0}^{n} \alpha_r x^r$, leads to the expression

$$a_r = \frac{2}{\pi} \int_0^\pi \cos r\theta \left(\sum_{r=0}^n \alpha_r \cos^r\theta \right) d\theta, \tag{23}$$

which we can evaluate rather tediously with the help of the orthogonality of $\cos r\theta$ and $\cos s\theta$ in $(0, \pi)$ and the identities

$$\left. \begin{aligned} \cos^{2s}\theta &= \frac{1}{2^{2s-1}} \sum_{r=0}^{s-1} \binom{2s}{r} \cos(2s-2r)\theta + \frac{1}{2^{2s}} \cdot \frac{(2s)!}{(s!)^2} \\ \cos^{2s+1}\theta &= \frac{1}{2^{2s}} \sum_{r=0}^s \binom{2s+1}{r} \cos(2s-2r+1)\theta \end{aligned} \right\}. \tag{24}$$

The expressions (4) and (5) for the coefficients b_r and c_r similarly lack attraction, and involve some lengthy computation.

In fact we proceed more easily by using the expansions for the powers x^r in terms of the Chebyshev polynomials $T_r(x)$, given in equation (18) of Chapter 3. For example, we easily find the representation

$$\begin{aligned} 1-x+x^2-x^3+x^4 &= T_0(x)-T_1(x)+\tfrac{1}{2}\{T_0(x)+T_2(x)\}- \\ &\quad -\tfrac{1}{4}\{3T_1(x)+T_3(x)\}+\tfrac{1}{8}\{3T_0(x)+4T_2(x)+T_4(x)\} \\ &= \tfrac{15}{8}T_0(x)-\tfrac{7}{4}T_1(x)+T_2(x)-\tfrac{1}{4}T_3(x)+\tfrac{1}{8}T_4(x), \end{aligned} \tag{25}$$

which is valid in $-1 \leq x \leq 1$.

The Chebyshev form has some advantages over the polynomial form. For example, (25) tells us immediately that we can get a cubic approximation to our quartic with an error of maximum absolute value $\tfrac{1}{8}$, whereas the omission of the term x^4 on the left of (25) gives a cubic with error as great as unity. Moreover a polynomial may have large coefficients even though its size throughout the range is small, and in this case the Chebyshev form will have much smaller coefficients and a greater possibility for significant truncation with little error. For example,

$$\begin{aligned} (1-x^2)^{10} &= 1-10x^2+45x^4-120x^6+210x^8-252x^{10}+ \\ &\quad +210x^{12}-120x^{14}+45x^{16}-10x^{18}+x^{20}, \end{aligned} \tag{26}$$

and in Chebyshev form this is

$$(1-x^2)^{10} = \frac{1}{524\,288}[92\,378T_0 - 167\,960T_2 + 125\,970T_4 - 77\,520T_6 +$$

$$+38\,760T_8 - 15\,504T_{10} + 4\,845T_{12} -$$

$$-1\,140T_{14} + 190T_{16} - 20T_{18} + T_{20}]. \quad (27)$$

The coefficients are much smaller, with a maximum of about 0·3. Further, the omission of the last three terms would produce an error of maximum value not greater than about 0·000 4.

4.7 This last device, called *economization* by Lanczos, is used mainly in connexion with finite Chebyshev approximations to infinite series. We could, for example, find an approximation to e^x from its Taylor's series

$$e^x = \sum_{r=0}^{n} \frac{x^r}{r!} + \frac{x^{n+1}}{(n+1)!}e^{\xi}, \quad -1 \leq \xi \leq 1. \quad (28)$$

For $n = 6$ the truncated approximation $\sum_{r=0}^{6}(x^r/r!)$ has an error certainly less than $(e/7!) \sim 0\cdot000\,5$. By the method of the previous paragraph we can express this approximation exactly in Chebyshev form, obtaining

$$\sum_{r=0}^{6}(x^r/r!) = 1\cdot266\,06T_0(x) + 1\cdot130\,21T_1(x) + 0\cdot271\,48T_2(x) +$$

$$+0\cdot044\,27T_3(x) + 0\cdot005\,47T_4(x) +$$

$$+0\cdot000\,52T_5(x) + 0\cdot000\,04T_6(x), \quad (29)$$

with the coefficients rounded to five decimals for easier inspection. This approximation already has an error of order 0·000 5, and we can certainly omit the T_6 term without introducing significant *additional* error: even the omission of T_5 does no more than increase the error to a maximum of about 0·001. The resulting approximation, which may be satisfactory for some purposes, has a far smaller error than that of the Taylor's series truncated after the term in x^4.

The disadvantage of this approach is that, having decided to truncate the Taylor's series at a particular point, any resulting approximation, however well economized, must have at least the error of the Taylor's series truncation. If the Taylor's series converges rapidly the truncation error may be small, but we have already remarked, in Chapter 1, on the generally poor performance of the Taylor's series in this connexion. Even for the exponential series we have noted that the truncation error for $n = 6$ in (29) can be as large as 5×10^{-4}, whereas the corresponding truncation of the Chebyshev series (16) gives an error hardly exceeding 3×10^{-6}.

Economization of (16) is then more valuable than that of (29), not particularly because we eliminate a smaller term but because its *initial* error is much smaller.

When the Taylor's series converges slowly, as for example in

$$\ln(1+x) = x - \tfrac{1}{2}x^2 + \tfrac{1}{3}x^3 - \dots, \quad 0 \leq x \leq 1, \tag{30}$$

we need many terms to guarantee a small truncation error. The economization may exclude quite a large number of Chebyshev terms of the appropriate series $\Sigma' \, a_r \, T_r^*(x)$, but the labour is large for a rather poor return. Moreover the Taylor's series may not even converge. For example if we wish to approximate to $(1+2x^2)^{-1}$ in $-1 \leq x \leq 1$, the series

$$(1+2x^2)^{-1} = 1 - 2x^2 + (2x^2)^2 - \dots \tag{31}$$

does not converge for $|x| \geq 1/\sqrt{2}$. In these circumstances, therefore, we seek more appropriate techniques, some of which are treated later in this chapter.

4.8 With this restriction, however, economization can also be applied to asymptotic (semi-convergent) series. Such a series is commonly used for computation of a function for large values of its argument. For example, for the exponential integral

$$-\mathrm{Ei}(-x) = \int\limits_x^\infty t^{-1} e^{-t} \, dt, \tag{32}$$

we can find the asymptotic series

$$-e^x \mathrm{Ei}(-x) \sim x^{-1} - (1!)x^{-2} + (2!)x^{-3} - \dots. \tag{33}$$

It is known that the error produced by truncation is smaller than the first neglected term. For small x this is quite large, but for $x = 4$, for example, the smallest term is $4!/4^5 \sim 0 \cdot 023$, and for $x \geq 4$ we can confidently use the first four terms of (33) and obtain a result with this maximum error.

The change of independent variable $y = 4/x$ permits the use of the $T^*(y)$ polynomial, and we find

$$x^{-1}-(1!)x^{-2}+(2!)x^{-3}-(3!)x^{-4} = \tfrac{1}{4}y-\tfrac{1}{16}y^2+\tfrac{1}{32}y^3-\tfrac{3}{128}y^4, \quad (34)$$

which in terms of $T_r^*(y)$ is approximately

$$0.104\,9T_0^*(y)+0.098\,1T_1^*(y)-0.007\,1T_2^*(y)-$$
$$-0.000\,5T_3^*(y)-0.000\,2T_4^*(y). \quad (35)$$

The omission of the last three terms gives a linear approximation with an extra error not exceeding 0·008 and a maximum total error not exceeding 0·032. Again we see that the economization error can be much smaller than the original truncation error.

The minimax polynomial

4.9 None of our finite approximations to infinite series have had exactly the minimax property, that the maximum error of the resulting polynomial is smaller than that of any other polynomial of the same degree. Truncation of the Chebyshev series at a point where the coefficients are decreasing rapidly will, of course, give a very close approximation to the minimax polynomial of corresponding degree, and in practice the effort to improve on this is rarely well rewarded. For functions whose early Chebyshev coefficients do not decrease rapidly, however, and for which we seek a good polynomial approximation of low degree, the true minimax polynomial may have a worth-while smaller maximum error. We therefore discuss a technique for finding it, and illustrate the method by obtaining the minimax linear fit to e^x in $-1 \leq x \leq 1$.

We have seen that the minimax polynomial $p_n(x)$, for a continuous function $f(x)$ in $-1 \leq x \leq 1$, is that polynomial for which $e_n(x) = f(x)-p_n(x)$ has equal and opposite maximum values $\pm M$ at $n+2$ successive points in $-1 \leq x \leq 1$. An algorithm for finding these points, the required polynomial and its maximum error $\pm M$, was suggested by Novodvorskii and Pinsker (1951). The algorithm is an iterative process with the following cycle of operations:

(i) Starting with an arbitrary selection $x_0, x_1, ..., x_{n+1}$, of $n+2$ points in $-1 \leq x \leq 1$, we find the polynomial $p_n^{(1)}(x)$ for which $e_n^{(1)}(x)$ has equal and successive opposite values $\pm M_1$ at these points.

(ii) We then find the position x_{n+2} of the maximum value of

$$|e_n^{(1)}(x)| = |f(x)-p_n^{(1)}(x)|,$$

which is either at a terminal point or at a zero of $\dfrac{de_n^{(1)}(x)}{dx}$.

(iii) If this maximum exceeds M_1, we replace one of the $x_0,...,x_{n+1}$ by x_{n+2}, in such a way that $e_n^{(1)}(x)$ has successively opposite signs at the new set of $n+2$ points.

(iv) With this new set we repeat steps (i), (ii) and (iii). The process converges uniformly to the required solution.

4.10 For the minimax linear fit to e^x we have to find the coefficients p and q such that the error function

$$e_1(x) = e^x-(p+qx) \tag{36}$$

has the required 'Chebyshev behaviour', with equal and opposite maximum values at three points in $-1 \leq x \leq 1$.

Step (i), with the arbitrary choice $x^{(0)} = \frac{1}{2}$, $x^{(1)} = 0$, $x^{(2)} = -\frac{1}{2}$, involves the solution of the three equations

$$e^{\frac{1}{2}}-(p+\tfrac{1}{2}q) = M, \qquad 1-p = -M, \qquad e^{-\frac{1}{2}}-(p-\tfrac{1}{2}q) = M. \tag{37}$$

To four decimals we find the solution

$$p = 1{\cdot}063\,8, \qquad q = 1{\cdot}042\,2, \qquad M = 0{\cdot}063\,8. \tag{38}$$

The resulting $e_1^{(1)}(x)$ has a turning point at about $x = 0{\cdot}04$, but its absolute maximum is at the terminal point $x = 1$, with approximate value $0{\cdot}61$. Step (iii) then requires that our new set of points should be

$$x_0 = 1, \qquad x_1 = 0, \qquad x_2 = -\tfrac{1}{2}, \tag{39}$$

and the new equations corresponding to (37) give the solution

$$p = 1{\cdot}155\,2, \qquad q = 1{\cdot}407\,9, \qquad M = 0{\cdot}155\,2. \tag{40}$$

The maximum of the new $e_1(x)$ is about $0{\cdot}620\,6$ at $x = -1$, and our new points are therefore $1, 0, -1$. The new approximation has the results

$$p = 1{\cdot}271\,5, \qquad q = 1{\cdot}175\,2, \qquad M = 0{\cdot}271\,5, \tag{41}$$

and the new maximum error, if greater than this M, must be at a turning point of the corresponding $e_1(x)$. We find the value $-0{\cdot}286\,0$ at $x = 0{\cdot}161\,4$, so that our new points are $1, 0{\cdot}161\,4, -1$. One further application of step (i) gives the final result

$$p_1(x) = 1 \cdot 264\ 3 + 1 \cdot 175\ 2x, \qquad M = 0 \cdot 278\ 8. \qquad (42)$$

4.11 It is interesting to examine the way in which the maximum errors get smaller and finally reach equality. Table 1 gives the errors at $x = -1 \cdot 0(0 \cdot 2)1 \cdot 0$ corresponding to the successive approximations $p_1^{(1)}(x)$, $p_1^{(2)}(x)$, $p_1^{(3)}(x)$, $p_1^{(4)}(x)$, given respectively by

$$\left. \begin{array}{ll} 1 \cdot 063\ 8 + 1 \cdot 042\ 2x, & 1 \cdot 155\ 2 + 1 \cdot 407\ 9x \\ 1 \cdot 271\ 5 + 1 \cdot 175\ 2x, & 1 \cdot 264\ 3 + 1 \cdot 175\ 2x \end{array} \right\}. \qquad (43)$$

From other known theorems we can from $p_1^{(3)}(x)$ be certain that the minimax fit will have an error lying between the extremes $0 \cdot 272$ and $0 \cdot 285$, and to this extent we may be content with $p_1^{(3)}(x)$.

TABLE 1

x	$e_1^{(1)}(x)$	$e_1^{(2)}(x)$	$e_1^{(3)}(x)$	$e_1^{(4)}(x)$
$-1 \cdot 0$	$+0 \cdot 346$	$+0 \cdot 621$	$+0 \cdot 272$	$+0 \cdot 279$
$-0 \cdot 8$	$+0 \cdot 219$	$+0 \cdot 420$	$+0 \cdot 118$	$+0 \cdot 125$
$-0 \cdot 6$	$+0 \cdot 110$	$+0 \cdot 238$	$-0 \cdot 018$	$-0 \cdot 010$
$-0 \cdot 4$	$+0 \cdot 023$	$+0 \cdot 078$	$-0 \cdot 131$	$-0 \cdot 124$
$-0 \cdot 2$	$-0 \cdot 037$	$-0 \cdot 055$	$-0 \cdot 218$	$-0 \cdot 211$
$0 \cdot 0$	$-0 \cdot 064$	$-0 \cdot 155$	$-0 \cdot 272$	$-0 \cdot 264$
$0 \cdot 2$	$-0 \cdot 051$	$-0 \cdot 215$	$-0 \cdot 285$	$-0 \cdot 278$
$0 \cdot 4$	$+0 \cdot 011$	$-0 \cdot 227$	$-0 \cdot 250$	$-0 \cdot 243$
$0 \cdot 6$	$+0 \cdot 133$	$-0 \cdot 178$	$-0 \cdot 155$	$-0 \cdot 147$
$0 \cdot 8$	$+0 \cdot 328$	$-0 \cdot 056$	$+0 \cdot 014$	$+0 \cdot 021$
$1 \cdot 0$	$+0 \cdot 612$	$+0 \cdot 155$	$+0 \cdot 272$	$+0 \cdot 279$

We also note that the end points are here points of maximum error. This is in general a likely event, since if the error curve is the Chebyshev polynomial $T_{n+1}(x)$ we should certainly have that result. Such an assumption, moreover, simplifies the computation, and in our example the second of two approximations would then be the minimax result. It cannot, however, be guaranteed. For example, the minimax linear fit in $-1 \leq x \leq 1$ to

$$f(x) = a + bx + \cos \tfrac{3}{2}\pi x \qquad (44)$$

is

$$p_1(x) = a + bx, \qquad (45)$$

since the error has equal and successive opposite values at $x = \tfrac{2}{3}$, 0, $-\tfrac{2}{3}$. At the ends of the range the error is here zero.

We also note that, if the Chebyshev series is known, its appropriate truncation will often give a very good starting approximation for a technique which is an obvious adaptation of that of **4.9**. In fact

$$p_1^{(1)}(x) = 1{\cdot}266\ 1 + 1{\cdot}130\ 3x, \qquad (46)$$

obtained by truncating the Chebyshev series (16), is fairly close to the minimax fit, and has an error of at most $0{\cdot}321\ 9$, compared with the optimum error of $0{\cdot}278\ 8$.

Interpolation in mathematical tables

4.12 The ideas of *economization* and *Chebyshev behaviour* can be adapted to provide powerful formulae for interpolation in a mathematical table. Here the function $f(x)$ is given numerically at selected points in some given range, and we shall assume that these points are equidistant. Our aim here is to provide easy facilities for interpolating between any successive pair of the equidistant 'pivotal' points, rather than to compute a single polynomial representation over the whole range.

Mathematical tables usually give some central differences, for use either with the Bessel interpolation formula

$$f_p = f_0 + p\ \delta f_{\frac{1}{2}} + B_2(\delta^2 f_0 + \delta^2 f_1) + B_3\ \delta^3 f_{\frac{1}{2}} + B_4(\delta^4 f_0 + \delta^4 f_1) + \dots, \quad (47)$$

or more likely with the Everett formula

$$f_p = (1-p)f_0 + pf_1 + E_2\ \delta^2 f_0 + F_2\ \delta^2 f_1 + E_4\ \delta^4 f_0 + F_4\ \delta^4 f_1 + \dots, \quad (48)$$

which needs only the even central differences. Here we are finding $f_p = f(x_p)$ at the point $x_p = x_0 + ph$, $0 \le p \le 1$, in terms of the values and the central differences of $f_0 = f(x_0)$ and $f_1 = f(x_0 + h) = f(x_1)$. The Bessel coefficients are given by

$$B_2 = \frac{p(p-1)}{2.2!}, \quad B_3 = \frac{p(p-1)(p-\frac{1}{2})}{3!}, \quad B_4 = \frac{(p+1)p(p-1)(p-2)}{2.4!}, \dots, \tag{49}$$

and the Everett coefficients by

$$\left. \begin{aligned} &E_2 = \frac{-p(p-1)(p-2)}{3!}, \qquad E_4 = \frac{-(p+1)p(p-1)(p-2)(p-3)}{5!}, \dots \\ &F_{2r}(p) = E_{2r}(1-p), \qquad E_{2r} = B_{2r} - B_{2r+1}, \qquad F_{2r} = B_{2r} + B_{2r+1} \end{aligned} \right\}. \tag{50}$$

With regard to the Bessel formula, Comrie (1931) observed that the ratio of $B_4(p)$ to $B_2(p)$ varies little in $0 \leq p \leq 1$, and proposed to use (47) in a form involving 'modified differences', given by

$$\left. \begin{array}{c} f_p = f_0 + p\ \delta f_{\frac{1}{2}} + B_2(\delta_m^2 f_0 + \delta_m^2 f_1) + B_3\ \delta^3 f_{\frac{1}{2}} + \varepsilon \\ \delta_m^2 f = \delta^2 f + C\ \delta^4 f \end{array} \right\}. \tag{51}$$

The error ε of (51), compared with the terms given explicitly in the infinite series (47), is then

$$\varepsilon = B_2\left(\frac{B_4}{B_2} - C\right)(\delta^4 f_0 + \delta^4 f_1) = 2(B_4 - CB_2)\mu\ \delta^4 f_{\frac{1}{2}}. \tag{52}$$

The choice $C = -0.184$ gives a very small value to $B_4 - CB_2$ in $0 \leq p \leq 1$. If fifth and higher differences are negligible in (47), therefore, we can tabulate modified instead of ordinary second differences, use them in (47), and economize by omitting the last term in (47) with a resulting small error.

If higher differences are significant we can eliminate their major effect by simultaneous *throwback* into lower-order differences (Miller 1946), and the device is applicable both to the Bessel formula and to the more attractive Everett variety. It turns out that this is part of a general theory (Fox 1956), of which we give here a summary.

4.13 We are trying to approximate $f_p = f(x_0 + ph)$, $0 \leq p \leq 1$, by a minimax polynomial $y_n(p)$, of degree n, *subject to the constraints* $y_n(0) = f_0$, $y_n(1) = f_1$. It is easy to see that for this minimax polynomial the error $e_n(p) = f_p - y_n(p)$ should have n turning points $p_1, p_2, \ldots, p_n$, $0 < p_1 < p_2 < \cdots < p_n < 1$, at which $e_n(p)$ has equal and successively opposite values. Instead of finding the true minimax polynomial of degree n, however, we rely on the rapid convergence of an appropriate Chebyshev series to give a close approximation by suitable truncation. The series $\sum_{r=0}^{\infty}{}' a_r\ T_r(2p-1)$ is not quite appropriate, since the dominant term after truncation, $a_{n+1}\ T_{n+1}(2p-1)$, does not vanish at $p = 0$ and 1. We therefore take a series in which every term vanishes at these points, given by

$$y(p) = \sum_{r=0}^{\infty}{}' a_r\ T_r\left\{(2p-1)\cos\frac{\pi}{2r}\right\}. \tag{53}$$

The points $x = \pm\cos(\pi/2r)$, corresponding to $p = 1$ and 0, coincide with the first and last zeros of $T_r(x)$, but we would still expect (53) to converge rapidly, and that its truncation after $r = n$ would give a polynomial of degree n close to the constrained minimax polynomial.

4.14 There are no obvious orthogonality properties of the functions in (53) which facilitate the computation of the coefficients. Our main interests, however, are the interpolation formulae, and the relations between the functions in (53) and the Bessel coefficients, for example, will enable us to express the Bessel formula (47) in the form (53).

Writing $t = 2p - 1$, we find

$$2B_2(t) = \frac{1}{2^2 \cdot 2!}(t^2 - 1^2), \qquad B_3(t) = \frac{1}{2^3 \cdot 3!}t(t^2 - 1^2) \left.\right\}$$
$$2B_4(t) = \frac{1}{2^4 \cdot 4!}(t^2 - 1^2)(t^2 - 3^2), \ldots \tag{54}$$

The even independent polynomials

$$\phi_{2r}(t) = T_{2r}\left(t \cos \frac{\pi}{4r}\right), \quad r = 0, 1, \ldots, s, \tag{55}$$

span the space of even polynomials of degree $2s$ which vanish at $t = -1$ and $+1$, corresponding to $p = 0$ and 1. Similarly the independent polynomials

$$\phi_{2r+1}(t) = T_{2r+1}\left(t \cos \frac{\pi}{4r+2}\right), \quad r = 0, 1, \ldots, s, \tag{56}$$

span the space of odd polynomials of degree $2s+1$ which vanish at $t = -1$ and $+1$. All such polynomials have $t^2 - 1$ as a factor.

We can then write

$$B_{2s}(t) = \sum_{r=1}^{s} a_{2r,2s} \, \phi_{2r}(t), \qquad B_{2s+1}(t) = \sum_{r=1}^{s} a_{2r+1,2s+1} \, \phi_{2r+1}(t), \tag{57}$$

and determine the coefficients by equating corresponding powers of t on each side. The resulting linear equations have a triangular matrix, which simplifies the computation. In particular we find

$$2B_2(t) = \frac{1}{8}\phi_2(t), \qquad B_3(t) = \frac{1}{72\sqrt{3}}\phi_3(t). \tag{58}$$

The Bessel formula (47) can then be written in the form

$$f_p = (1-p)f_0 + pf_1 + 2\phi_2 \, \mu\rho^2 f_{\frac{1}{2}} + \phi_3 \, \rho^3 f_{\frac{1}{2}} + \\ + 2\phi_4 \, \mu\rho^4 f_{\frac{1}{2}} + \phi_5 \, \rho^5 f_{\frac{1}{2}} + \ldots, \tag{59}$$

where the modified differences are defined by

$$\rho^{2s}f = \sum_{r=s}^{\infty} a_{2s,2r}\, \delta^{2r}f, \qquad \rho^{2s+1}f = \sum_{r=s}^{\infty} a_{2s+1,2r+1}\, \delta^{2r+1}f, \qquad (60)$$

and μ is the *averaging operator* defined by

$$\mu f_{\frac{1}{2}} = \tfrac{1}{2}(f_0 + f_1). \qquad (61)$$

4.15 It is rather more convenient in practice to associate the factor $a_{2s,2r}$ with ϕ_{2r}, and similarly with the odd functions, so that the expressions for the modified differences have leading coefficient unity. Equations (59) and (60), with obvious notation, then become

$$\left.\begin{array}{c} f_p = (1-p)f_0 + pf_1 + 2\psi_2\mu\,\bar{\delta}^2 f_{\frac{1}{2}} + \psi_3\,\bar{\delta}^3 f_{\frac{1}{2}} + \\[4pt] \qquad\qquad + 2\psi_4\,\bar{\delta}^4 f_{\frac{1}{2}} + \psi_5\,\bar{\delta}^5 f_{\frac{1}{2}} + \ldots \\[8pt] \bar{\delta}^{2s}f = \delta^{2s}f + \sum_{r=s+1}^{\infty} \alpha_{2s,2r}\, \delta^{2r}f \\[8pt] \bar{\delta}^{2s+1}f = \delta^{2s+1}f + \sum_{r=s+1}^{\infty} \alpha_{2s+1,2r+1}\, \delta^{2r+1}f \end{array}\right\}, \qquad (62)$$

and $2\,|a_{2r,2r}|$, $|a_{2r+1,2r+1}|$ are the maximum values of $2\,|\psi_{2r}|$ and $|\psi_{2r+1}|$ respectively.

Calculation gives results typified by

$$\left.\begin{array}{l} 2a_{2,2} = \dfrac{1}{8} = 12{\cdot}5 \times 10^{-2}, \quad a_{3,3} = \dfrac{1}{72\sqrt{3}} \sim 8{\cdot}02 \times 10^{-3} \\[12pt] 2a_{4,4} = \dfrac{3 - 2\sqrt{2}}{2^4.4!} \sim 4{\cdot}47 \times 10^{-4}, \quad a_{5,5} = \dfrac{\sec^5\dfrac{\pi}{10}}{2^9.5!} \sim 2{\cdot}09 \times 10^{-5} \\[16pt] 2a_{6,6} = \dfrac{26 - 15\sqrt{3}}{2^5.6!} \sim 8{\cdot}35 \times 10^{-7} \\[14pt] \bar{\delta}^2 = \delta^2 - \dfrac{3+\sqrt{2}}{4!}\delta^4 + \ldots \sim \delta^2 - 0{\cdot}183\,93\delta^4 + 0{\cdot}038\,06\delta^6 - \ldots \\[12pt] \bar{\delta}^3 = \delta^3 - \dfrac{6 + 2/\sqrt{5}}{2^6}\delta^5 + \ldots \sim \delta^3 - 0{\cdot}107\,73\delta^5 + \ldots \end{array}\right\}. \qquad (63)$$

Truncation after ψ_3, for example, then gives the valuable formula

$$\left.\begin{array}{l} f_p = (1-p)f_0 + pf_1 + 2\psi_2\,\mu\,\bar{\delta}^2 f_{\frac{1}{2}} + \psi_3\,\bar{\delta}^3 f_{\frac{1}{2}} + \varepsilon \\[4pt] \;\; = (1-p)f_0 + pf_1 + 2B_2\,\mu\,\bar{\delta}^2 f_{\frac{1}{2}} + B_3\,\bar{\delta}^3 f_{\frac{1}{2}} + \varepsilon \end{array}\right\}, \qquad (64)$$

and the error is approximately bounded by

$$\varepsilon \leq 4\cdot47 \times 10^{-4} \left| \mu \, \delta^4 f_{\frac{1}{2}} \right| + 2\cdot09 \times 10^{-5} \left| \delta^5 f_{\frac{1}{2}} \right|. \tag{65}$$

Later truncation produces even more powerful results, but for their effective use we need tables of the interpolating coefficients ψ_4, $\psi_5,\ldots,$ in addition to the already well-tabulated B_2 and B_3.

Similar results were obtained by Fox (1956) for the economized Everett formula. Corresponding to the truncation (64) he obtains

$$f_p = (1-p)f_0 + pf_1 + E_2 \, \bar{\delta}^2 f_0 + F_2 \, \bar{\delta}^2 f_1 + \varepsilon, \tag{66}$$

where the modified even differences are the same as those for the Bessel formula, the odd differences do not appear, and ε is approximately bounded by the rather larger quantity

$$\varepsilon \leq 4\cdot47 \times 10^{-4} \left| \mu \, \delta^4 f_{\frac{1}{2}} \right| + 6\cdot1 \times 10^{-4} \left| \delta^5 f_{\frac{1}{2}} \right|. \tag{67}$$

Since the tabulation of mathematical functions is now a rather obsolescent practice we omit here the details of the analysis.

Curve fitting

4.16 Of more practical importance is the production of a single polynomial approximation to a function given numerically at a set of arbitrary points in $-1 \leq x \leq 1$. This is generally performed by the least-squares method of **2.8**, and here we give the details of a suitable practical process.

We recall that we are given values $f(x_k)$, $k = 0, 1,\ldots, N$, and seek as approximation to $f(x)$ that linear combination $\sum\limits_{r=0}^{n} c_r \, \psi_r(x)$, of suitable independent functions, such that

$$S = \sum_{k=0}^{N} w(x_k) \left\{ f(x_k) - \sum_{r=0}^{n} c_r \, \psi_r(x_k) \right\}^2 = \text{minimum}. \tag{68}$$

In the language of matrix algebra the minimization problem leads to the normal equations

$$\mathbf{A'WAc = A'Wf}, \tag{69}$$

where $\mathbf{c}$ is the vector of constants c_0, $c_1,\ldots, c_n$, $\mathbf{f}$ the vector of given values $f(x_0),\ldots,f(x_N)$, $\mathbf{W}$ the diagonal matrix with elements w_0, $w_1,\ldots, w_N$, and $\mathbf{A}$ is the $(N+1) \times (n+1)$ matrix whose rth column is the vector with elements $\psi_r(x_0),\ldots, \psi_r(x_N)$. The prime denotes matrix transposition.

We also noted the advantage, for the solution of the linear equations (69), in choosing the functions $\psi_r(x)$ so that the matrix $\mathbf{A'WA}$ is diagonal, that is we seek to satisfy the orthogonality relations

$$\sum_{k=0}^{N} w(x_k)\psi_r(x_k)\psi_s(x_k) = 0, \quad r \neq s. \tag{70}$$

The minimum sum of squares of residuals is then

$$S_{\min} = \sum_{k=0}^{N} w(x_k)\left\{ f^2(x_k) - \sum_{r=0}^{n} c_r^2 \psi_r^2(x_k) \right\}. \tag{71}$$

4.17 We are interested in polynomial approximation, and therefore choose $\psi_r(x)$, a polynomial of degree r, to be a member of a set of orthogonal polynomials which satisfy (70). The required approximation is then

$$p_n(x) = \sum_{r=0}^{n} c_r \psi_r(x), \qquad c_r = \frac{\displaystyle\sum_{k=0}^{N} w(x_k) f(x_k)\psi_r(x_k)}{\displaystyle\sum_{k=0}^{N} w(x_k)\psi_r^2(x_k)}. \tag{72}$$

It is desirable that none of the $\psi_r(x)$ should have large absolute values in the range of the data points x_k, and if we take this to be $-1 \leq x \leq 1$ it is convenient to normalize $\psi_r(x)$ so that, like the Chebyshev polynomial, its leading coefficient is 2^{r-1}.

Following Forsythe (1957), we generate successive polynomials from the recurrence system

$$\left.\begin{aligned} \psi_0(x) &= \tfrac{1}{2}, \qquad \psi_1(x) = 2x\,\psi_0(x) + \beta_0\,\psi_0(x) \\ \psi_{r+1}(x) &= (2x + \beta_r)\psi_r(x) + \gamma_{r-1}\,\psi_{r-1}(x) \end{aligned}\right\}. \tag{73}$$

Every pair of these polynomials is to satisfy (70), and an obvious adaptation of the analysis of **1.13** shows that the coefficients of the expected additions $\sum_{s=r-2}^{0} \gamma_s \psi_s(x)$ on the right of (73) are all zeros. The other coefficients are given by

$$\left.\beta_r = \frac{-2\displaystyle\sum_{k=0}^{N} w(x_k) x_k \psi_r^2(x_k)}{\displaystyle\sum_{k=0}^{N} w(x_k)\psi_r^2(x_k)}, \qquad \gamma_{r-1} = \frac{-\displaystyle\sum_{k=0}^{N} w(x_k)\psi_r^2(x_k)}{\displaystyle\sum_{k=0}^{N} w(x_k)\psi_{r-1}^2(x_k)} \right\}, \tag{74}$$
$$r = 1, 2, \dots$$

and the first of (74) also applies for $r = 0$.

In practice we do not normally know in advance what value of n will achieve a satisfactory $S_{\min}$ in (71). The use of orthogonal polynomials has the advantage that an increase in n does not affect the previous coefficients c_r, and as n changes to $n+1$ the value of $S_{\min}$ is reduced by the single quantity $c_{n+1}^2 \sum_{k=0}^{N} w(x_k)\psi_{n+1}^2(x_k)$.

4.18 A computer programme will therefore calculate the relevant β_r, γ_{r-1}, c_r, and the values of the $\psi_r(x_k)$ for $k = 0, 1, ..., N$, and will stop when $S_{\min}$ is sufficiently small. The calculation of $\psi_r(x_k)$ can be performed from the recurrence (73), so that $\psi_{r-1}(x_k)$ and $\psi_{r-2}(x_k)$ must be stored at any stage. Since x_k and $f(x_k)$ must be retained, we have at any time to store at least $4(N+1)$ numbers. When subsequently we wish to compute $p_n(x)$ in (72) for any arbitrary x we can again use the recurrence (73) to find each $\psi_r(x)$, and then compute the linear combination $\sum_{r=0}^{n} c_r \psi_r(x)$.

Clenshaw (1960) proposed to reduce the storage requirements, though usually at the expense of increasing the computing time, by expressing each $\psi_r(x)$ in terms of its $r+1$ Chebyshev coefficients, one of which is always unity, rather than by its $N+1$ values at the data points. We write

$$\psi_r(x) = \sum_{i=0}^{r-1}{}' a_i^{(r)}T_i(x) + T_r(x), \tag{75}$$

the unit coefficient of $T_r(x)$ arising from our requirement that the coefficient of x^r in $\psi_r(x)$ should be 2^{r-1}. The coefficients $a_i^{(r)}$ may themselves be generated by recurrence. For if we substitute (75) in (73), use the relation $2x\,T_s(x) = T_{s+1}(x) + T_{s-1}(x)$, and observe that $a_i^{(i)} = 1$, $a_i^{(s)} = 0$ for $s < i$, we find the relation

$$a_i^{(s+1)} = a_{i-1}^{(s)} + a_{i+1}^{(s)} + \beta_s a_i^{(s)} + \gamma_{s-1} a_i^{(s-1)}, \tag{76}$$

which is true for all i and s.

He also proposes to store the Chebyshev coefficients of the accepted approximation

$$p_k(x) = \sum_{r=0}^{k} c_r \psi_r(x) = \sum_{r=0}^{k}{}' \alpha_r^{(k)}T_r(x), \tag{77}$$

noting that the change from k to $k+1$ is performed easily with the formula

$$\alpha_i^{(k+1)} = \alpha_i^{(k)} + c_{k+1} a_i^{(k+1)}. \tag{78}$$

The calculation of $p_k(x)$ from its Chebyshev form is then effected by the recurrence process outlined in **3.12**.

4.19 Finally, we note that the deliberate attempt to ensure that the normal equations (69) should have a diagonal matrix not only simplifies the computation of the coefficients c_r but also has a beneficial effect on their accuracy. Suppose, for example, that the weights are all unity and that we seek the coefficients of the approximating polynomial expressed directly in powers of x in the form

$$p_n(x) = \sum_{r=0}^{n} a_r x^r. \tag{79}$$

In this case the matrix of the normal equations is

$$\mathbf{A'A} = \begin{bmatrix} s_0 & s_1 & \cdot & s_{n-1} \\ s_1 & s_2 & \cdot & s_n \\ \cdot & \cdot & \cdot & \cdot \\ s_{n-1} & s_n & \cdot & s_{2n-2} \end{bmatrix}, \qquad s_r = \sum_{k=0}^{N} x_k^r. \tag{80}$$

There is a strong tendency, increasing rapidly with n, for the inverse of this matrix to have very large coefficients. Small errors in the right-hand sides of the linear equations then cause much larger errors in the solution, the coefficients a_r, and in this sense the problem is ill-conditioned.

Suppose, for example, that we take the range $0 \le x \le 1$, with $n = 2$ and $x_k = 0{\cdot}2k$ for $k = 0, 1, \ldots, 5$. We find

$$\mathbf{A'A} = \begin{bmatrix} 6 & 3 & 2{\cdot}2 \\ 3 & 2{\cdot}2 & 1{\cdot}8 \\ 2{\cdot}2 & 1{\cdot}8 & 1{\cdot}566\,4 \end{bmatrix}$$

$$(\mathbf{A'A})^{-1} = \tfrac{1}{7} \begin{bmatrix} 5{\cdot}75 & -20{\cdot}625 & 15{\cdot}625 \\ -20{\cdot}625 & 127{\cdot}187\,5 & -117{\cdot}187\,5 \\ 15{\cdot}625 & -117{\cdot}187\,5 & 117{\cdot}187\,5 \end{bmatrix}. \tag{81}$$

Errors bounded by $|\varepsilon|$ on the right-hand side of the normal equations could give rise to errors almost as large as 6ε, 38ε and 36ε in a_0, a_1 and a_2 respectively, and as n and N increase this effect is magnified substantially.

In fact if N is large, and the x_k are at equal intervals in $0 \leq x \leq 1$, the quantity $\sum\limits_{k=0}^{N} x_k^r$ will not differ greatly from $(N+1)\int\limits_0^1 x^r \, dx = (N+1)/(r+1)$. The corresponding matrix $\mathbf{A'A}$ is then a segment of the Hilbert matrix, which is notorious, in the literature of linear algebra, for its degree of ill-conditioning in respect to the solution of linear equations.

Methods for rational functions

4.20 We now turn to methods of a rather different nature, and we introduce them near the end of the chapter because they are analogous to the methods used in the next chapter for functions defined implicitly as solutions of certain types of differential equations. They are suitable for rational functions

$$f(x) = P(x)/Q(x), \tag{82}$$

where $P(x)$ and $Q(x)$ are polynomials.

There are two main approaches. First, we can seek to generate the coefficients of the infinite Chebyshev series by solving certain difference equations. Second, we can seek deliberately a polynomial approximation of fixed degree and find an upper bound for its maximum error. The first method has less general easy application, but in suitable cases is particularly elegant. We illustrate it by finding the Chebyshev series, in $0 \leq x \leq 1$, for the function $(1+x)^{-1}$.

4.21 Here we try to determine the coefficients in the equation

$$(1+x)^{-1} - \sum_{r=0}^{\infty} {}' a_r T_r^*(x) = 0. \tag{83}$$

Multiplying by $1+x$, using the identity

$$x \, T_r^*(x) = \tfrac{1}{4}\{T_{r-1}^*(x) + 2T_r^*(x) + T_{r+1}^*(x)\}, \tag{84}$$

and equating to zero the coefficient of $T_r^*(x)$, we find the general equation

$$\tfrac{1}{4}(a_{r-1} + 6a_r + a_{r+1}) = 0, \quad r = 1, 2, \ldots. \tag{85}$$

For $r = 0$ we have the particular equation

$$\tfrac{1}{4}(3a_0 + a_1) = 1. \tag{86}$$

Equation (85) is a difference equation with constant coefficients, with general solution

$$a_r = A(-3 + 2\sqrt{2})^r + B(-3 - 2\sqrt{2})^r. \tag{87}$$

We must clearly take $B = 0$, since otherwise a_r would oscillate and increase unboundedly in magnitude, and we know that the Chebyshev series will converge. The coefficient A is then obtained from (86), and we deduce the Chebyshev series

$$(1 + x)^{-1} = \sqrt{2} \sum_{r=0}^{\infty}{}' (-1)^r (3 - 2\sqrt{2})^r T_r^*(x). \tag{88}$$

We note its rapid convergence, and contrast it favourably with the Taylor's series

$$(1 + x)^{-1} = 1 - x + x^2 - \dots, \tag{89}$$

which does not converge at all at $x = 1$.

4.22 The second method, applied to the same function, seeks a finite approximation

$$(1 + x)^{-1} \sim \sum_{r=0}^{n}{}' a_r T_r^*(x), \qquad 1 \sim (1 + x) \sum_{r=0}^{n}{}' a_r T_r^*(x). \tag{90}$$

The previous approach now produces the equations

$$\left. \begin{array}{l} \tfrac{1}{4}(3a_0 + a_1) = 1 \\[4pt] \tfrac{1}{4}(a_{r-1} + 6a_r + a_{r+1}) = 0, \quad r = 1, 2, \dots, n-1 \\[4pt] \tfrac{1}{4}(a_{n-1} + 6a_n) = 0 \\[4pt] \tfrac{1}{4}a_n = 0 \end{array} \right\}. \tag{91}$$

These equations, of course, have no solution, since the two sides of (90) can never agree exactly for finite n. We can, however, find a solution of the slightly perturbed problem

$$1 + p_{n+1}(x) = (1 + x) \sum_{r=0}^{n}{}' a_r T_r^*(x), \tag{92}$$

where $p_{n+1}(x)$ is a polynomial of degree $n+1$ which ensures that a_n in (91) is not zero. Since (91) contains $n+2$ equations for $n+1$

unknowns we can introduce a further parameter. Following Lanczos (1957) we call the parameter τ, and to keep the perturbation as small as possible we choose

$$p_{n+1}(x) = \tau_{n+1} T_{n+1}^*(x). \tag{93}$$

The equations corresponding to (91) are now unchanged, except that the last becomes

$$\tfrac{1}{4}a_n = \tau_{n+1}. \tag{94}$$

We can now compute $a_n, a_{n-1}, \ldots, a_0$ in terms of τ_{n+1}, working backwards in (91) as far as the second equation, and the first will then evaluate τ_{n+1}.

With $n = 4$, for example, we find

$$\left.\begin{array}{lll} a_4 = 4\tau_5, & a_3 = -24\tau_5, & a_2 = 140\tau_5 \\ a_1 = -816\tau_5, & a_0 = 4\,756\tau_5, & \tau_5 = 1/3\,363 \end{array}\right\}, \tag{95}$$

and we have the identity

$$\frac{1}{1+x}\left\{1 + \frac{1}{3\,363} T_5^*(x)\right\}$$
$$= \frac{1}{3\,363}\{2\,378 T_0^*(x) - 816 T_1^*(x) + 140 T_2^*(x) - 24 T_3^*(x) + 4 T_4^*(x)\}. \tag{96}$$

The error of the right of (96), in relation to $(1+x)^{-1}$, is then just

$$\varepsilon = \tau_5(1+x)^{-1} T_5^*(x), \tag{97}$$

with an upper bound of amount $\tau_5 = 1/3\,363 \sim 3 \times 10^{-4}$, at $x = 0$.

This finite approximation, of course, is not just a truncation of the Chebyshev series. To six decimals the former is

$$(1+x)^{-1} \sim 0{\cdot}707\,107 T_0^*(x) - 0{\cdot}242\,640 T_1^*(x) + 0{\cdot}041\,629 T_2^*(x) -$$
$$-0{\cdot}007\,136 T_3^*(x) + 0{\cdot}001\,189 T_4^*(x), \tag{98}$$

while the truncated Chebyshev series gives, to the same precision,

$$(1+x)^{-1} \sim 0{\cdot}707\,107 T_0^*(x) - 0{\cdot}242\,641 T_1^*(x) + 0{\cdot}041\,631 T_2^*(x) -$$
$$-0{\cdot}007\,143 T_3^*(x) + 0{\cdot}001\,225 T_4^*(x). \tag{99}$$

This finite approximation, in fact, will usually have a slightly larger maximum error than the truncated series, but its upper bound is completely determined without reference to the Chebyshev series.

4.23 The extension to the more general rational function (82) is almost obvious. We seek to satisfy exactly the equation

$$P(x)+E(x) = Q(x) \sum_{r=0}^{n}{}' a_r T_r(x), \tag{100}$$

where $E(x)$ is a perturbing polynomial which makes this possible. For $E(x)$ we take a combination of Chebyshev polynomials

$$E(x) = \sum_{m=p}^{q} \tau_m T_m(x), \tag{101}$$

where p and q are chosen so that the resulting equations for the coefficients a_r and τ_m have a unique solution. The error of the approximation is then

$$\varepsilon(x) = \frac{E(x)}{Q(x)}, \qquad |\varepsilon(x)| \leq \frac{\sum_{m=p}^{q} |\tau_m|}{|\min Q(x)|}. \tag{102}$$

It is unusual to need more than one or two terms in (101).

For example, the approximation

$$(1+x+x^2)^{-1} \sim \sum_{r=0}^{n}{}' a_r T_r(x), \quad 0 \leq x \leq 1, \tag{103}$$

gives rise to $n+3$ equations for $n+1$ coefficients, and we have to use two terms in (101). One of them must clearly be $\tau_{n+2} T_{n+2}(x)$. It is preferable to take the other as $\tau_{n+1} T_{n+1}(x)$, since the computed τ_{n+1} is likely to be much smaller than the coefficient τ_1, say, of a second perturbation $\tau_1 T_1(x)$.

Other methods for elementary functions

4.24 There is a variety of other methods for the determination of the Chebyshev series or a finite approximation for elementary functions. The most obvious is the indefinite integration of a known series. For example, the indefinite integration of the Chebyshev series (88), using an obvious extension of the method of **3.16**, produces the Chebyshev series for $\ln(1+x)$ in $0 \leq x \leq 1$. After a little manipulation we find

$$\left. \begin{aligned} \ln(1+x) = \ln\left(\frac{3+2\sqrt{2}}{4}\right) T_0^*(x)+ \\ + 2\{\lambda T_1^*(x) - \tfrac{1}{2}\lambda^2 T_2^*(x) + \tfrac{1}{3}\lambda^3 T_3^*(x) - \dots\} \\ \lambda = 3-2\sqrt{2} \end{aligned} \right\}. \tag{104}$$

Again, the known expansion for $(1+x)^{-1}$ in $0 \leq x \leq 1$ will serve to produce an expansion for $\tan^{-1}x$ in $-1 \leq x \leq 1$. We write

$$\tan^{-1}x = \int (1+x^2)^{-1}\, dx = \sqrt{2} \int \{\tfrac{1}{2} - \lambda\, T_1^*(x^2) + \lambda^2 T_2^*(x^2) - ...\}\, dx,$$

(105)

and use the results of **3.7** to express this as

$$\tan^{-1}x = \sqrt{2} \int \{\tfrac{1}{2} - \lambda\, T_2(x) + \lambda^2 T_4(x) - ...\}\, dx. \qquad (106)$$

Integration then gives

$$\tan^{-1}x = 2\{\mu\, T_1(x) - \tfrac{1}{3}\mu^3 T_3(x) + \tfrac{1}{5}\mu^5 T_5(x) - ...\}, \quad \mu = \sqrt{2} - 1. \quad (107)$$

We note, with Lanczos, that the Chebyshev series often have forms analogous to the Taylor's series, the term x^r in the latter being replaced by $\nu^r T_r(x)$ in the former, the powers ν^r acting as 'converging factors'.

A summary of other methods, and collections of series for various functions occurring frequently in numerical analysis, has been given by Clenshaw (1962). According to him one of the most convenient methods is the solution of a differential equation satisfied by the function, and this is the topic of the next chapter.

EXERCISES 4

1. The formula

$$p_{n-1}^{(1)}(x) = \sum_{r=0}^{n-1}{}' c_r^{(1)} T_r(x), \qquad c_r^{(1)} = \frac{2}{n}\sum_{k=0}^{n-1} p_n(x_k^{(1)}) T_r(x_k^{(1)}),$$

matches $p_n(x)$ exactly at the points

$$x_k^{(1)} = \cos\left(\frac{2k+1}{n}\cdot\frac{\pi}{2}\right), \qquad k = 0, 1,..., n-1,$$

the zeros of the Chebyshev polynomial $T_n(x)$. If $p_n(x)$ is a polynomial of degree n, show that $p_{n-1}^{(1)}(x)$ is the minimax polynomial of degree $n-1$. Verify this for the quadratic $p_2(x) = x^2 + x$.

The formula

$$p_{n-1}^{(2)}(x) = \sum_{r=0}^{n-1}{}'' c_r^{(2)} T_r(x), \qquad c_r^{(2)} = \frac{2}{n-1}\sum_{k=0}^{n-1}{}'' p_n(x_k^{(2)}) T_r(x_k^{(2)}),$$

matches $p_n(x)$ exactly at the points

$$x_k^{(2)} = \cos\left(\frac{k\pi}{n-1}\right).$$

Find this approximation for $p_2(x)$, and verify that its maximum error is twice that of $p_{n-1}^{(1)}(x)$.

We can also match at the zeros of $U_n(x)$. Find this approximation, $p_{n-1}^{(3)}(x)$, and its maximum error, for $p_2(x)$.

Verify the statement, implied in **2.15**, that the maximum error of the integrated approximation, $\int_{-1}^{1} \{p_2(x)-p_1^{(r)}(x)\}\, dx$, is smallest for $r = 3$.

Show finally that the points $x_k^{(2)}$ are at $x = 1, -1$, and the zeros of $U_{n-2}(x)$.

(This gives intuitive backing to a result of Elliott (1965) that collocation at the points $x_k^{(2)}$ is better than collocation at the Chebyshev points if we are interested more in the integral of a general $f(x)$ than in $f(x)$ itself.)

2. In a certain Chebyshev series, $f(x) = \sum_{r=0}^{\infty}{}' a_r T_r(x)$, the coefficients are negligible after the term $a_{n+3} T_{n+3}(x)$. Two finite approximations, of order n, are

$$p_n^{(1)}(x) = \sum_{r=0}^{n}{}' c_r T_r(x), \qquad c_r = \frac{2}{n+1} \sum_{k=0}^{n} f(x_k)T_r(x_k),$$

$$x_k = \cos\left(\frac{2k+1}{n+1}\cdot\frac{\pi}{2}\right),$$

$$p_n^{(2)}(x) = \sum_{r=0}^{n}{}'' b_r T_r(x), \qquad b_r = \frac{2}{n} \sum_{k=0}^{n} f(x_k)T_r(x_k),$$

$$x_k = \cos\frac{k\pi}{n}.$$

Show that, if n is even,

$$\left|\int_{-1}^{1} \{f(x)-p_n^{(2)}(x)\}\, dx\right| \sim \frac{8}{n^3}\left|a_{n+2}\right|,$$

$$\left|\int_{-1}^{1} \{f(x)-p_n^{(1)}(x)\}\, dx\right| \sim \frac{2}{n^2}\left|a_{n+2}\right|,$$

and if n is odd,

$$\left|\int_{-1}^{1}\{f(x)-p_n^{(2)}(x)\}\,dx\right| \sim \frac{4}{n^3}\{|a_{n+1}|+3\,|a_{n+3}|\},$$

$$\left|\int_{-1}^{1}\{f(x)-p_n^{(1)}(x)\}\,dx\right| \sim \frac{1}{n^2}\{|a_{n+1}|+2\,|a_{n+3}|\}.$$

(This again shows the slight advantage of the form $p_n^{(2)}(x)$, if the approximation is used as a step in the calculation of a definite integral.)

3. For the minimax linear fit $p+qx$ to a continuous function $f(x)$ in $-1 \leq x \leq 1$, the points of maximum error are known to include $x = -1$ and $x = 1$. Show that

$$q = \tfrac{1}{2}\{f(1)-f(-1)\}, \qquad p = \tfrac{1}{4}\{f(1)+f(-1)+2f(x_c)-2qx_c\},$$
$$f'(x_c) = q,$$

and the maximum error is

$$M = |p+qx_c-f(x_c)|.$$

4. Find the linear minimax fit to e^x in $-1 \leq x \leq 1$, with an adaptation of the method of **4.9**, starting with the appropriate truncated Chebyshev series as first approximation.

5. The alternating series

$$\ln(1+x) = x-\tfrac{1}{2}x^2+\tfrac{1}{3}x^3-..., \quad 0 \leq x \leq 1,$$

has the property that the error of truncation is smaller than the first neglected term. We can then write, for example,

$$\ln(1+x) = x-\tfrac{1}{2}x^2+\tfrac{1}{3}x^3+\varepsilon, \quad |\varepsilon| < \tfrac{1}{4}.$$

Show that this can be economized to

$$\ln(1+x) = \tfrac{13}{16}x+\eta, \quad |\eta| < \tfrac{13}{48}.$$

6. Find the results of equation (63).

7. Discuss the economization of the Everett interpolation formula (48).

8. A function $f(x)$ is obtained by measurement with the following results:

x	$-1\cdot0$	$-0\cdot9$	$-0\cdot5$	$-0\cdot2$	$0\cdot1$	$0\cdot4$	$0\cdot7$	$0\cdot8$
$f(x)$	$0\cdot54$	$0\cdot62$	$0\cdot77$	$0\cdot98$	$1\cdot00$	$0\cdot92$	$0\cdot75$	$0\cdot70$

Find the least-squares solutions, of orders 0, 1, 2, 3, with unit weight function, by the method of **4.17**. By computing the individual residuals at each stage, and assuming that a quadratic is expected to give a good fit, determine one reading which is probably incorrect.

Find also the Chebyshev forms of the expansions by the method of **4.18**.

9. Invert the matrix

$$\mathbf{A'A} = \begin{bmatrix} 6 & 3 & 2 \\ 3 & 2 & 1\cdot5 \\ 2 & 1\cdot5 & 1 \end{bmatrix},$$

the Hilbert matrix corresponding to (81).

10. Find the fifth degree approximation, by the Lanczos τ method, to the function $(1+x)^{-1}$ in $0 \le x \le 1$.

11. By performing a Lanczos process for $(p+x)^{-1}$, in $0 \le x \le 1$, show that

$$\tau_{n+1} = \frac{-1}{T^*_{n+1}(-p)},$$

and hence determine the polynomial form of $T_7^*(x)$.

12. Find the approximation

$$(1+x+x^2)^{-1} \sim \sum_{r=0}^{8}{}'a_r\,T_r(x), \quad -1 \le x < 1,$$

and determine an upper bound for the error.

13. In Exercise 12 we use the perturbation $\tau_9\,T_9(x)+\tau_{10}\,T_{10}(x)$. Find the corresponding result for a perturbation $\tau_1\,T_1(x)+\tau_{10}\,T_{10}(x)$. Why cannot we use the perturbation $\tau_0\,T_0(x)+\tau_{10}\,T_{10}(x)$?

14. Discuss the determination of the Chebyshev series for $(1+x+x^2)^{-1}$ in $-1 \le x \le 1$.

15. Prove the results of **4.24**.

16. Use equation (106) to produce the series

$$\tan^{-1}x = x \sum_{r=0}^{\infty}{}' a_{2r} T_{2r}(x),$$

$$a_{2r} = (-1)^r \sum_{s=r}^{\infty} \frac{4}{2r+1} \mu^{2r+1}, \quad \mu = \sqrt{2}-1.$$

(Hint: use the relation $T_{2r+1} = 2x\{T_{2r}-T_{2r-2}+...+(-1)^r\tfrac{1}{2}T_0\}$. Note that this form gives better relative accuracy for small x.)

17. The series (107) provides for $x = 1$ the expression

$$\frac{\pi}{4} = 2(\mu-\tfrac{1}{3}\mu^3+\tfrac{1}{5}\mu^5-...), \quad \mu = \sqrt{2}-1.$$

The corresponding Taylor's series gives

$$\frac{\pi}{4} = 1-\tfrac{1}{3}+\tfrac{1}{5}-....$$

Show that the former converges faster than the Euler transform of the latter. (The Euler transform of $\sum\limits_{r=0}^{\infty} (-1)^r a_r$ is $\sum\limits_{r=0}^{\infty} \frac{(-1)^r}{2^{r+1}} \Delta^r a_0$, where Δ is the forward difference operator.)

18. Find in $0 \le x \le 1$ the approximation

$$(1+x)^{-1} \sim a_0+a_1 x+a_2 x^2+a_3 x^3+a_4 x^4,$$

using an adaptation of the Lanczos τ method, without first producing the corresponding Chebyshev series. (Hint: write

$$(1+x)(a_0+a_1 x+a_2 x^2+a_3 x^3+a_4 x^4) = 1+\tau_5 T_5^*(x),$$

and equate powers of x on each side.)

19. Repeat Exercise 18 for the range $0 \le x \le \tfrac{1}{2}$, and show that the maximum error hardly exceeds 2×10^{-5}. (Hint: use the perturbation $\tau_5 T_5^*(2x)$.)

20. Find a fourth-order approximation for $(1+z)^{-1}$ in the complex plane. (Hint: use the perturbation $\tau_5 T_5^*(x/z)$ for the function $(1+x)^{-1}$, and put $x = z$ in the result. We find the *rational*

approximation

$$\frac{1}{1+z} \sim \frac{512+768z+352z^2+48z^3+2z^4}{512+1\,280z+1\,120z^2+400z^3+50z^4+z^5}.$$

At $z = i$, for example, this gives $0 \cdot 500\,15 - 0 \cdot 500\,66i$, compared with the true $\frac{1}{2}(1-i)$. The error is still bounded by

$$\frac{\tau}{1+z} = \frac{z^5}{(1+z)(512+1\,280z+1\,120z^2+400z^3+50z^4+z^5)}.$$

5

Ordinary Differential Equations

Introduction

5.1 In **4.20** and **4.21** we discussed methods for finding the Chebyshev series for rational functions in a finite range $-1 \leq x \leq 1$ or $0 \leq x \leq 1$. Basically we produced for the coefficients of the Chebyshev series an infinite set of linear algebraic equations, which could be treated as a recurrence relation with constant coefficients and with certain associated conditions. In the first part of this chapter we show that the solution of a certain type of differential system, that is a differential equation with specified associated conditions, can be calculated in much the same way, though here the recurrence relation has non-constant coefficients.

5.2 In **4.22** and **4.23** we also considered the computation of a finite polynomial as an approximation to the rational function, showing that the polynomial obtained was the exact representation of a slight perturbation of the given function. For example, if

$$f(x) = P(x)/Q(x), \qquad (1)$$

where P and Q are polynomials, our computed polynomial satisfies exactly the equation

$$p_n(x) = \sum_{r=0}^{n}{}' a_r T_r(x) = \frac{P(x)}{Q(x)} + \frac{E(x)}{Q(x)}, \qquad E(x) = \sum_{s=p}^{q} \tau_s T_s(x). \quad (2)$$

Here p and q depend on the relative degrees of $P(x)$ and $Q(x)$, and the τ_s are computed in the process. The absolute maximum of the error $e_n(x) = p_n(x) - f(x)$ is then easily obtained as the largest value of $|E(x)/Q(x)|$.

For the linear differential system *with polynomial coefficients* we can similarly find a $p_n(x)$ which satisfies exactly a slightly different system. If we represent by

$$f(D)y = g(x) \tag{3}$$

the combination of differential equation and associated conditions, our polynomial solution will satisfy exactly the perturbed system

$$f(D)p_n(x) = g(x) + \sum_{s=p}^{q} \tau_s T_s(x). \tag{4}$$

It is here more difficult to estimate the error $e_n(x)$, since this depends on a knowledge or reasonable estimate of the inverse of the operator f. This type of problem, of course, occurs in other areas of numerical analysis in the determination of the error of an approximation to a quantity which is defined implicitly rather than explicitly.

Methods for finding polynomial approximations, with some attempts at error analysis, are treated in the second part of this chapter.

5.3 When the linear differential equation has more general coefficients we have two possible methods. In the first we approximate to the coefficients by finite polynomials, say truncated Chebyshev series, and thereby transform this problem to the simple form. This needs no separate discussion.

It is usually necessary, however, to consider a different method, and we borrow an idea corresponding to the treatment of the interpolating polynomial for an explicit function. In Chapter 2 we showed that in the Lagrange interpolation formula

$$\left.\begin{aligned} f(x) &= p_n(x) + \frac{1}{(n+1)!} f^{(n+1)}(\xi) \, \Pi(x) \\ \Pi(x) &= (x-x_0)...(x-x_n) \end{aligned}\right\}, \tag{5}$$

in which all the x_r and ξ lie in $-1 \leq x \leq 1$, a good choice for the matching points x_r, at which $p_n(x)$ agrees with $f(x)$, is the set of zeros of the Chebyshev polynomial $T_{n+1}(x)$. At least one of the factors of the error $f(x) - p_n(x)$ is thereby made as small as possible.

For the implicit problem we proceed in an analogous way, satisfying the differential equation at the zeros of a Chebyshev polynomial, thereby producing a set of algebraic equations for the determination of the coefficients of the approximating polynomial.

Corresponding to (4), and in analogy with (5), we now have the exact solution of something like

$$f(D)p_n(x) = g(x)+T_s(x)E(x), \tag{6}$$

where $E(x)$ is determined implicitly in the course of computation. Again, for the implicit problem, the determination of the difference $y(x)-p_n(x)$ is a more formidable task.

These problems we discuss in the last part of this chapter, and we append some notes on recent work on the corresponding treatment of non-linear differential equations. Throughout we restrict attention to equations of first and second orders, since the techniques apply without change, though with extra labour, to systems of higher orders.

Chebyshev series for rational functions

5.4 We observed in Chapter 4 that the Chebyshev series for (1) is obtained by expressing each side of the identity

$$Q(x) \sum_{r=0}^{\infty} {}' a_r T_r(x) = P(x) \tag{7}$$

as a series of Chebyshev polynomials, which is easy since $Q(x)$ and $P(x)$ are themselves polynomials. The various relevant expressions for $x^r T_s(x)$ and $T_r(x)T_s(x)$ were given in **3.8** for both our basic selected ranges of x. We can now equate coefficients of $T_r(x)$ on both sides of (7), and hence obtain an infinite set of linear equations, with a finite number of terms in each equation, for the coefficients a_r.

For example, for

$$f(x) = (1+x)^{-1}, \quad 0 \le x \le 1, \tag{8}$$

we have $Q(x) = (1+x)$, $P(x) = 1$, and

$$Q(x) \sum_{r=0}^{\infty} {}' a_r T_r^*(x) = \sum_{r=0}^{\infty} {}' (\tfrac{1}{4}a_{r-1}+ \tfrac{3}{2}a_r+\tfrac{1}{4}a_{r-1})T_r^*(x). \tag{9}$$

The algebraic equations are then given by

$$\left.\begin{aligned} \tfrac{3}{4}a_0+\tfrac{1}{4}a_1 &= 1 \\ \tfrac{1}{4}a_{r-1}+\tfrac{3}{2}a_r+\tfrac{1}{4}a_{r+1} &= 0, \quad r = 1, 2,... \end{aligned}\right\}. \tag{10}$$

Similarly, for $f(x) = 1/(1+x+x^2)$, in $-1 \leq x \leq 1$, with $f(x) = \sum_{r=0}^{\infty} {}' a_r T_r(x)$, we find

$$\left.\begin{array}{r}
\tfrac{3}{4}a_0 + \tfrac{1}{2}a_1 + \tfrac{1}{4}a_2 = 1 \\[2mm]
\tfrac{1}{2}a_0 + \tfrac{7}{4}a_1 + \tfrac{1}{2}a_2 + \tfrac{1}{4}a_3 = 0 \\[2mm]
\tfrac{1}{4}a_{r-2} + \tfrac{1}{2}a_{r-1} + \tfrac{3}{2}a_r + \tfrac{1}{2}a_{r+1} + \tfrac{1}{4}a_{r+2} = 0 \\[2mm]
r = 2, 3, \ldots
\end{array}\right\}. \tag{11}$$

5.5 In theory we can solve equations like (10) or (11) by invoking the theory of difference equations with constant coefficients. For example, the general solution of the third of (11) is

$$a_r = A_1 p_1^r + A_2 p_2^r + A_3 p_3^r + A_4 p_4^r, \tag{12}$$

where p_1, p_2, p_3 and p_4 are the roots of the equation

$$\tfrac{1}{4} + \tfrac{1}{2}p + \tfrac{3}{2}p^2 + \tfrac{1}{2}p^3 + \tfrac{1}{4}p^4 = 0. \tag{13}$$

Now two of the roots of this equation have moduli greater than unity, and since we seek a convergent Chebyshev series the corresponding coefficients in (12) must be taken to be zero. The other two coefficients, and hence the required solution, are obtained by substituting (12) into the first two of (11), which for this purpose serve as 'initial conditions'.

We shall rarely be able to solve equations like (13), and we look for alternative methods of treating the infinite set of equations of type (11). A first obvious method is to solve successive subsets of equations, involving successive leading submatrices of the infinite matrix, and we assume, without proof, that this process will converge whenever a convergent Chebyshev series exists. The calculation can be arranged so that the labour of solving the first $n+1$ equations is not significantly greater than that of solving the first n equations.

The set (10) is simple, but will illustrate the process. We start with

$$\tfrac{3}{4}a_0 = 1, \qquad a_0 = \tfrac{4}{3}. \tag{14}$$

We then consider the 2×2 set

$$\left.\begin{array}{r}
\tfrac{3}{4}a_0 + \tfrac{1}{4}a_1 = 1 \\[2mm]
\tfrac{1}{4}a_0 + \tfrac{3}{2}a_1 + \tfrac{1}{4}a_2 = 0
\end{array}\right\}, \tag{15}$$

eliminate a_0, and find

$$\left.\begin{aligned}\tfrac{3}{4}a_0 + \tfrac{1}{4}a_1 \quad\quad &= 1 \\ \tfrac{17}{12}a_1 + \tfrac{1}{4}a_2 &= -\tfrac{1}{3}\end{aligned}\right\}. \tag{16}$$

Ignoring a_2, we back-substitute in the 2×2 upper triangular set, and find

$$a_1 = -\tfrac{4}{17}, \quad a_0 = \tfrac{24}{17}. \tag{17}$$

Introducing the next row, we have

$$\left.\begin{aligned}\tfrac{3}{4}a_0 + \tfrac{1}{4}a_1 \quad\quad\quad\quad &= 1 \\ \tfrac{17}{12}a_1 + \tfrac{1}{4}a_2 \quad\quad &= -\tfrac{1}{3} \\ \tfrac{1}{4}a_1 + \tfrac{3}{2}a_2 + \tfrac{1}{4}a_3 &= 0\end{aligned}\right\}, \tag{18}$$

and a single operation, the elimination of a_1 from the third equation, using the second as pivotal row, produces

$$\left.\begin{aligned}\tfrac{3}{4}a_0 + \tfrac{1}{4}a_1 \quad\quad\quad &= 1 \\ \tfrac{17}{12}a_1 + \tfrac{1}{4}a_2 \quad &= -\tfrac{1}{3} \\ \tfrac{99}{68}a_2 + \tfrac{1}{4}a_3 &= \tfrac{1}{17}\end{aligned}\right\}. \tag{19}$$

We ignore a_3, and back-substitute in the leading 3×3 set to find

$$a_2 = \tfrac{4}{99}, \quad a_1 = -\tfrac{24}{99}, \quad a_0 = \tfrac{140}{99}. \tag{20}$$

The results (14), (17) and (20) are converging rapidly to the true Chebyshev solutions.

Application to the more 'difficult' system (11) is obvious, and we observe the economies in the computation of successive approximations.

5.6 A second method borrows the classic device of *backward recurrence*. If we take $a_{n+1} = a_{n+2} = \ldots = 0$, $a_n = 1$, and recur backwards with the second of (10), we can find $a_{n-1}, \ldots, a_0$ without using the first of (10). The satisfaction of the latter is achieved merely by multiplying our solution by a computable factor. For example, taking $a_2 = a_3 = \ldots = 0$, $a_1 = 1$, we find $a_0 = -6$ from the second of (10) with $r = 1$. The first equation then gives the multiplier $1/(\tfrac{3}{4}a_0 + \tfrac{1}{4}a_1) = -4/17$, and the corresponding solution is identical with (17).

To find the next approximation we repeat the whole calculation, finding in turn

$$a_2 = 1, \quad a_1 = -6, \quad a_0 = 35. \tag{21}$$

The corresponding multiplier is 4/99, and we have the solution (20). In virtue of the fact that the coefficients in (10) are independent of r, the numbers $1, -6, 35,...$ in the 'trial' solutions are the same in each case, which again provides economies in the arithmetic.

For the system (11) we clearly need two independent trial solutions at each stage, and their required linear combination is computed by satisfying the first two of (11). We might, for example, take the two solutions with initial conditions

$$\left.\begin{array}{ll} a_{n-1} = 1, & a_n = a_{n+1} = ... = 0 \\ a_n = 1, & a_{n+1} = a_{n+2} = ... = 0 \end{array}\right\}, \tag{22}$$

which are certainly independent. The number of trial solutions clearly depends on the number of 'initial rows' in the infinite matrix prior to the incidence of the upper triangular form. If any of the upper triangular equations have a non-zero right-hand side, however, we must take yet another solution, corresponding to a 'particular solution' of the recurrence relation. If the two general solutions are called I and II, and the particular solution III, the required linear combination is $A_1(\text{I}) + A_2(\text{II}) + (\text{III})$, and A_1 and A_2 are chosen so that the 'initial equations' are satisfied. The treatment of the general situation should be obvious from these considerations of particular cases.

Our success corresponds to the fact that by backward recurrence we effectively eliminate the unwanted terms in an expression like (12). Certainly the trial solutions contain multiples of all the solutions p_1^r, p_2^r, p_3^r and p_4^r, but if $|p_3| > 1$, $|p_4| > 1$, say, then the factors A_3 and A_4 must be small. Backward recurrence ensures that rounding errors do not *increase* the contributions from these unwanted terms, and the final small multiplying factors associated with the trial solutions further suppress their total contribution.

Chebyshev series for differential systems. The integrated system

5.7 We consider the first-order differential equation

$$p_1(x)y' + p_2(x)y = p_3(x), \tag{23}$$

where $p_1(x)$, $p_2(x)$ and $p_3(x)$ are polynomials, and the second-order equation

$$q_1(x)y'' + q_2(x)y' + q_3(x)y = q_4(x), \tag{24}$$

where the $q_r(x)$ are also polynomials. With (23) we shall have one associated condition, and (24) will generally have two, to provide a unique solution to the problem.

If we seek a solution of the form $y = \sum\limits_{r=0}^{\infty}{}' a_r\, T_r(x)$, in $-1 \leq x \leq 1$, or the corresponding form with $T_r^*(x)$ in $0 \leq x \leq 1$, and substitute in the differential equation, we are faced with the problem of differentiating a Chebyshev series. This we consider in **5.18** below. Since the coefficients are polynomials, however, we can easily integrate (23), to produce

$$p_1\, y + \int (p_2 - p_1')y\, dx = \int p_3\, dx + A, \qquad (25)$$

where A is an arbitrary constant. From (24) we similarly obtain

$$q_1\, y' + (q_2 - q_1')y + \int (q_1'' - q_2' + q_3)y\, dx = \int q_4\, dx + A, \qquad (26)$$

and a second integration gives

$$q_1\, y + \int (q_2 - 2q_1')y\, dx + \iint (q_1'' - q_2' + q_3)y\, dxdx$$
$$= \iint q_4\, dxdx + Ax + B, \qquad (27)$$

where A and B are arbitrary constants.

The known formulae for products $x^r T_s(x)$ in terms of Chebyshev polynomials, and the integrals of such quantities, enable us to express the left-hand sides of equations like (25) and (27) as infinite Chebyshev series, in which the coefficient of $T_r(x)$ is a *finite* linear combination of coefficients a_r. The right-hand sides are finite series, and the comparison of corresponding terms produces an infinite set of linear equations of a form very similar to those of the third of (11) for the direct problem. There may also be some 'special' equations, such as the second of (11), with a finite number of terms.

Finally there are extra equations coming from the 'conditions', which will usually involve an infinite number of terms. We note the important fact that *any* form of linear condition is acceptable. In particular we do not even mind a very 'mixed' condition such as

$$\alpha_0\, y(0) + \alpha_1\, y'(0) + \alpha_2\, y(1) + \alpha_3\, y'(-1) = \alpha_4, \qquad (28)$$

which would complicate severely most numerical methods for ordinary differential equations. The only criterion is that we must be able to express the conditions as linear combinations of the Chebyshev coefficients a_r.

Example, first-order system

5.8 Consider, for example, the first-order system

$$(1+x)y'+(1+x+x^2)y = 1-x, \qquad \left.\begin{array}{c} y(0)-\tfrac{3}{4}y(1) = 1 \\ 0 \le x \le 1 \end{array}\right\} \tag{29}$$

This is a reasonably difficult problem, with a condition as complicated as possible for a first-order system. With $y = \sum\limits_{r=0}^{\infty}{}' a_r T_r^*(x)$, a single integration gives a system in which the coefficient of $T_r^*(x)$ on the left-hand side is

$$\frac{1}{64r}a_{r-3}+\frac{1}{8r}a_{r-2}+\left(\frac{1}{4}+\frac{13}{64r}\right)a_{r-1}+\frac{3}{2}a_r+$$

$$+\left(\frac{1}{4}-\frac{13}{64r}\right)a_{r+1}-\frac{1}{8r}a_{r+2}-\frac{1}{64r}a_{r+3}. \tag{30}$$

We need not use the equation for $r = 0$, since this would serve only to determine the constant A in the integrated equation (25). We therefore deduce the infinite set of linear equations

$$
\begin{array}{llllllll}
\tfrac{1}{8}a_0- & \tfrac{7}{4}a_1+ & \tfrac{1}{4}a_2- & \tfrac{7}{4}a_3+ & \tfrac{1}{4}a_4- & \tfrac{7}{4}a_5+\ldots & & = 1 \\
\tfrac{29}{64}a_0+ & \tfrac{13}{8}a_1+ & \tfrac{1}{16}a_2- & \tfrac{1}{8}a_3- & \tfrac{1}{64}a_4 & & & = \tfrac{1}{4} \\
\tfrac{1}{16}a_0+ & \tfrac{23}{64}a_1+ & \tfrac{3}{2}a_2+\tfrac{19}{128}a_3- & \tfrac{1}{16}a_4-\tfrac{1}{128}a_5 & & & & = -\tfrac{1}{16} \\
\tfrac{1}{192}a_0+ & \tfrac{1}{24}a_1+\tfrac{61}{192}a_2+ & \tfrac{3}{2}a_3+\tfrac{35}{192}a_4- & \tfrac{1}{24}a_5-\tfrac{1}{192}a_6 & & & & = 0 \\
& \tfrac{1}{256}a_1+ & \tfrac{1}{32}a_2+\tfrac{77}{256}a_3+ & \tfrac{3}{2}a_4+\tfrac{51}{256}a_5- & \tfrac{1}{32}a_6-\tfrac{1}{256}a_7 & & & = 0 \\
& & \tfrac{1}{320}a_2+ & \tfrac{1}{40}a_3+\tfrac{93}{320}a_4+ & \tfrac{3}{2}a_5+\ldots & & & = 0 \\
& & & \tfrac{1}{384}a_3+\ldots & & & & = 0
\end{array}
$$

$$\tag{31}$$

Here the first equation comes from the condition, the next two are the special forms of (30) for $r = 1$ and 2, and the rest come from the use of $r = 3, 4,\ldots$ in (30). We note the characteristic upper triangular form, following some initial equations, and the only significant differences from that of a set like (11), for the direct problem, are that the first equation has an infinite number of terms, and the coefficients in the general equations are not constant but depend on r.

5.9 Again we have two possible methods of solution, and they are virtually identical with those for the direct problem. The elimination method, unfortunately, immediately introduces an infinity of terms in rows other than the first, but this gives no serious problem for the modern computing machine. Indeed if we remember the multipliers and the interchanges in the elimination method we can add an extra column whenever we add an extra row, and again keep the extra computation to a minimum in the evaluation of successive approximate solutions.

It is even better to use the *compact* elimination methods, based on the well-known decomposition of a matrix into the product of a unit lower triangular matrix and an upper triangular matrix. Though we should use interchanges to preserve numerical stability, it is clear that these will affect only the first few rows, since after a time the diagonal elements in the matrix will dominate the rows. In (31), for example, we find it necessary to interchange only the first two rows. The triangular decomposition of the permuted leading submatrix of order three can then be performed, and that for the next submatrix is easily obtained in the partitioned form

$$
\begin{array}{cc}
\mathbf{A} & \mathbf{b} \\
\begin{bmatrix}
\cdot453\,125 & 1\cdot625 & \cdot062\,5 & -\cdot125 \\
\cdot125 & -1\cdot75 & \cdot25 & -1\cdot75 \\
\cdot062\,5 & \cdot359\,375 & 1\cdot5 & \cdot148\,437 \\
\cdot005\,208 & \cdot041\,667 & \cdot317\,708 & 1\cdot5
\end{bmatrix}
\begin{bmatrix}
\cdot25 \\
1 \\
-\cdot062\,5 \\
0
\end{bmatrix}
\end{array}
=
\begin{array}{c}
\mathbf{L} \\
\begin{bmatrix}
1 & & & \\
\cdot275\,862 & 1 & & \\
\cdot137\,931 & -\cdot061\,520 & 1 & \\
\cdot011\,494 & -\cdot010\,458 & \cdot212\,143 & 1
\end{bmatrix}
\end{array}
$$

$$
\times
\begin{array}{cc}
\mathbf{U} & \mathbf{c} \\
\begin{bmatrix}
\cdot453\,125 & 1\cdot625 & \cdot062\,5 & -\cdot125 \\
& -2\cdot198\,276 & \cdot232\,759 & -1\cdot715\,517 \\
& & 1\cdot505\,699 & \cdot060\,140 \\
& & & 1\cdot470\,738
\end{bmatrix}
\begin{bmatrix}
\cdot25 \\
\cdot931\,034 \\
-\cdot039\,706 \\
\cdot015\,287
\end{bmatrix}
\end{array}.
$$

$$(32)$$

Only the numbers outside the partitioning lines have to be computed, and we can take full advantage of the extra accuracy obtained by accurate accumulation of inner products. The corresponding elements of the vector **c** are produced from **b**, in exact analogy with the columns of **U**, and back-substitution in $\mathbf{Ux} = \mathbf{c}$ easily gives the successive approximations

$$a_2 = -0\cdot026\,37, \quad a_1 = -0\cdot426\,32, \quad a_0 = 2\cdot084\,24$$
$$a_3 = 0\cdot010\,39, \quad a_2 = -0\cdot026\,79, \quad a_1 = -0\cdot434\,48, \quad a_0 = 2\cdot116\,41 \Big\}.$$

$$(33)$$

5.10 The second method uses backward recurrence to compute independent solutions of the homogeneous equations. Obviously

8

three such solutions are needed, and their linear combination comes from the satisfaction of the first three 'initial equations' in (31).

Table 1 gives four independent solutions of the general recurrence relation, with obvious starting conditions.

TABLE 1

r	$a_r(\text{IV})$	$a_r(\text{III})$	$a_r(\text{II})$	$a_r(\text{I})$
5	0			
4	1	0		
3	−8	1	0	
2	−29	−8	1	0
1	464	−13	−8	1
0	326	304	3	−8

Taking the last three, and evaluating the left-hand sides of the first three of (31) (with multiplying factors used to retain integer numbers), we find the equations

$$
\left.
\begin{aligned}
456A_3 + 117A_2 - 22A_1 &= 8 \\
7\,424A_3 - 741A_2 - 128A_1 &= 16 \\
317A_3 - 152A_2 - 18A_1 &= -8
\end{aligned}
\right\}. \tag{34}
$$

The corresponding solution $A_3\,a_r(\text{III}) + A_2\,a_r(\text{II}) + A_1\,a_r(\text{I})$ is identical with the second of (33). Indeed we have merely used a different method of solving the equations corresponding to the first four rows and columns in (31).

To get the next solution we would use $a_r(\text{IV})$, $a_r(\text{III})$ and $a_r(\text{II})$ in Table 1. Only one extra recurrence is needed, and only one more new column of coefficients is required for the new equations of type (34). We therefore have savings in computation similar to those of the more obvious $\mathbf{A} = \mathbf{LU}$ method.

Example, second-order system

5.11 No particular difference in technique is required for a second-order system, though two conditions are required and in the corresponding algebraic equations there will usually be two initial equations which contain an infinite number of terms. Consider, for example, the system

$$
\left.
\begin{aligned}
y'' + xy' + xy &= 1 + x + x^2, \quad -1 \le x \le 1 \\
y(0) = 1, \quad y'(0) + 2y(1) - y(-1) &= -1
\end{aligned}
\right\}, \tag{35}
$$

where again the rather strange second condition will cause no problems. The twice-integrated equation is

$$y+\int xy\,dx+\iint (xy-y)\,dxdx = A+Bx+\tfrac{1}{2}x^2+\tfrac{1}{6}x^3+\tfrac{1}{12}x^4. \qquad (36)$$

With $y = \sum\limits_{r=0}^{\infty}{}' a_r T_r(x)$, the coefficient of $T_r(x)$ on the left of (36) is

$$\frac{1}{8r(r-1)}a_{r-3}+\frac{r-2}{4r(r-1)}a_{r-2}-\frac{1}{8r(r+1)}a_{r-1}+\left\{1+\frac{1}{2(r^2-1)}\right\}a_r-$$

$$-\frac{1}{8r(r-1)}a_{r+1}-\frac{r+2}{4r(r+1)}a_{r+2}+\frac{1}{8r(r+1)}a_{r+3}. \qquad (37)$$

From the given conditions we obtain two algebraic equations, and the rest come from the use of (37) with $r = 2, 3,\dots.$ The first of the latter is an 'extra' initial row before the start of the triangular set, and the complete equations are given by

$$\left.\begin{array}{l}
\tfrac{1}{2}a_0 \quad\quad -a_2 \quad\quad +a_4 \quad\quad -a_6+\dots \quad\quad\quad = 1\\[4pt]
\tfrac{1}{2}a_0 +4a_1 +a_2 \quad\quad +a_4 +8a_5 +a_6+\dots \quad\quad = -1\\[4pt]
\tfrac{1}{24}a_1 +\tfrac{7}{6}a_2 -\tfrac{1}{16}a_3 -\tfrac{1}{6}a_4+\tfrac{1}{48}a_5 \quad\quad\quad = \tfrac{7}{24}\\[4pt]
\tfrac{1}{48}a_0+\tfrac{1}{24}a_1 -\tfrac{1}{96}a_2 +\tfrac{17}{16}a_3 -\tfrac{1}{48}a_4-\tfrac{5}{48}a_5 +\tfrac{1}{96}a_6 \quad = \tfrac{1}{24}\\[4pt]
\tfrac{1}{96}a_1 +\tfrac{1}{24}a_2 -\tfrac{1}{160}a_3 +\tfrac{31}{30}a_4 -\tfrac{1}{96}a_5 -\tfrac{3}{40}a_6+\tfrac{1}{160}a_7 = \tfrac{1}{96}\\[4pt]
\tfrac{1}{160}a_2 +\tfrac{3}{80}a_3 -\tfrac{1}{240}a_4+\tfrac{49}{48}a_5-\tfrac{1}{160}a_6-\tfrac{7}{120}a_7+\tfrac{1}{240}a_8 = 0
\end{array}\right\} . \quad (38)$$

5.12 The direct method of solution is performed precisely as before, and we need not pursue the arithmetic. There is, however, one point of detail in relation to the backward recurrence method. We clearly need three independent solutions of the upper triangular set of equations, but these are non-homogeneous. We must therefore take three independent solutions, (I), (II) and (III), of this set with zeros on the right-hand side, and one particular solution, say (0), of the non-homogeneous set. The latter, for example, can here be as simple as $a_0 = 0$, $a_1 = 1$, $a_2 = a_3 = \dots = 0$. In the usual way we then find constants such that $A_1 a_r(\mathrm{I})+A_2 a_r(\mathrm{II})+A_3 a_r(\mathrm{III})+a_r(0)$ satisfies the first three of (38).

Alternatively, it is here very satisfactory to use the Gauss-Seidel iterative method. In four cycles we converge to the four-decimal solution

$$a_0 = 2{\cdot}537\,9, \quad a_1 = -0{\cdot}637\,2, \quad a_2 = 0{\cdot}274\,5 \Big\}, \tag{39}$$
$$a_3 = 0{\cdot}017\,2, \quad a_4 = 0{\cdot}005\,5$$

of the leading 5×5 set of equations in (38).

This iterative process is always likely to work well for the computation of the later coefficients, since the rows are almost certainly diagonally dominant at some stage. It is not certain, however, that the first few coefficients can be obtained in this way, since the early rows may not be dominated by the diagonal terms.

An eigenvalue problem

5.13 We consider next a simple eigenvalue problem, given by

$$y'' + \lambda xy = 0, \quad y(0) = 0, \quad y(1) = 0, \quad 0 \le x \le 1. \tag{40}$$

With $y = \sum\limits_{r=0}^{\infty}{}' a_r T_r^*(x)$, the coefficient of $T_r^*(x)$ on the left of the twice-integrated system is

$$a_r + \tfrac{1}{64}\lambda \Bigg\{ \frac{a_{r-3}}{r(r-1)} + \frac{2a_{r-2}}{r(r-1)} - \frac{a_{r-1}}{r(r+1)} - \frac{4a_r}{r^2-1} - \\ - \frac{a_{r+1}}{r(r-1)} + \frac{2a_{r+2}}{r(r+1)} + \frac{a_{r+3}}{r(r+1)} \Bigg\}. \tag{41}$$

We therefore have the homogeneous equations

$$\begin{aligned}
\tfrac{1}{2}a_0 \;-a_1 \;+a_2 \;-a_3 \;+a_4 - \ldots &= 0 \\
\tfrac{1}{2}a_0 \;+a_1 \;+a_2 \;+a_3 \;+a_4 + \ldots &= 0 \\
a_0 +\tfrac{1}{3}a_1 + (\mu - \tfrac{4}{3})a_2 \;-\tfrac{1}{2}a_3 \;+\tfrac{1}{3}a_4 +\tfrac{1}{6}a_5 &= 0 \\
\tfrac{1}{6}a_0 +\tfrac{1}{3}a_1 \;-\tfrac{1}{12}a_2 + (\mu - \tfrac{1}{2})a_3 \;-\tfrac{1}{6}a_4 +\tfrac{1}{6}a_5 +\tfrac{1}{12}a_6 &= 0 \\
\tfrac{1}{12}a_1 \;+\tfrac{1}{6}a_2 \;-\tfrac{1}{20}a_3 + (\mu - \tfrac{4}{15})a_4 -\tfrac{1}{12}a_5 +\tfrac{1}{10}a_6 +\tfrac{1}{20}a_7 &= 0
\end{aligned} \Bigg\}, \tag{42}$$

where $\mu = 64/\lambda$. In analogy with our previous methods we try to find those values of λ for which the determinants of successive submatrices vanish, and the corresponding solutions of the subsets of homogeneous equations.

There are various possible methods, of which the one selected in any context will depend on the precise nature of the matrices involved.

Basically, however, we seek the eigensolutions of the matrix equation

$$(A - B\lambda)a = 0, \tag{43}$$

and shall usually be interested in the first few eigenvalues of smallest modulus. This suggests the methods of either direct or inverse iteration, which are particularly suitable for the treatment of successive submatrices.

5.14 In (42) we do well to eliminate the first two rows and columns, which do not contain μ, to find the equations

$$\left.\begin{array}{l} (\mu - \tfrac{10}{3})a_2 \qquad -\tfrac{5}{6}a_3 \qquad -\tfrac{5}{3}a_4 + \ldots = 0 \\[4pt] -\tfrac{5}{12}a_2 + (\mu - \tfrac{5}{6})a_3 \qquad -\tfrac{1}{2}a_4 + \ldots = 0 \\[4pt] \tfrac{1}{6}a_2 \qquad -\tfrac{2}{15}a_3 + (\mu - \tfrac{4}{15})a_4 + \ldots = 0 \\[4pt] \quad\cdot \qquad\qquad \cdot \qquad\qquad \cdot \qquad\qquad \cdot \qquad\qquad \cdot \end{array}\right\}. \tag{44}$$

The first solution is

$$\left.\begin{array}{l} \mu = \tfrac{10}{3}, \quad \lambda = 19{\cdot}2, \quad a_0 = 1 \\[4pt] a_1 = 0, \quad a_2 = -\tfrac{1}{2}, \quad y = x(x-1) \end{array}\right\}. \tag{45}$$

For the next approximation it is easy to find and solve the relevant quadratic equation, and we find

$$\left.\begin{array}{ll} \mu_1 = \tfrac{1}{12}(25 + 5\sqrt{11}) \sim 3{\cdot}465, & \lambda_1 \sim 18{\cdot}47 \\[4pt] \mu_2 = \tfrac{1}{12}(25 - 5\sqrt{11}) \sim 0{\cdot}701\,4, & \lambda_2 \sim 91{\cdot}25 \end{array}\right\}. \tag{46}$$

The eigenvector corresponding to μ_1 is approximately

$$a_0 = 1, \quad a_1 = 0{\cdot}079, \quad a_2 = -0{\cdot}5, \quad a_3 = -0{\cdot}079. \tag{47}$$

For the next approximation to this eigensolution, which corresponds to the *largest* eigenvalue μ, we can use direct iteration with the 3×3 matrix in (44). Starting with

$$\mathbf{a}^{(0)} = (a_2^{(0)}, a_3^{(0)}, a_4^{(0)}) = (1, 0.16, 0),$$

we find successive vectors from the iteration

$$\mathbf{a}^{(r+1)} = \begin{bmatrix} \tfrac{10}{3} & \tfrac{5}{6} & \tfrac{5}{3} \\[6pt] \tfrac{5}{12} & \tfrac{5}{6} & \tfrac{1}{2} \\[6pt] -\tfrac{1}{6} & \tfrac{2}{15} & \tfrac{4}{15} \end{bmatrix} \mathbf{a}^{(r)}. \tag{48}$$

These are normalized to have their first component unity, and the number by which we divide to obtain this is the current approximation to μ_1 in the array

$$\left.\begin{array}{ll} \mathbf{a}^{(1)} = (1, 0\cdot159, -0\cdot042), & \mu = 3\cdot467 \\ \mathbf{a}^{(2)} = (1, 0\cdot154, -0\cdot045), & \mu = 3\cdot396 \\ \mathbf{a}^{(3)} = (1, 0\cdot154, -0\cdot047), & \mu = 3\cdot387 \end{array}\right\} \tag{49}$$

We have virtually converged already to a three-figure solution.

The three eigenvalues of (44) are approximately

$$\left.\begin{array}{ll} \mu_1 = 3\cdot387, & \lambda_1 = 18\cdot9 \\ \mu_2 = 0\cdot796\,7, & \lambda_2 = 80\cdot3 \\ \mu_3 = 0\cdot252\,2, & \lambda_3 = 253\cdot8 \end{array}\right\} \tag{50}$$

These are approximations to the three smallest eigenvalues λ of the differential system, and they are associated with the 'smoothest' eigenfunctions, most accurately representable by a polynomial of small degree, here a quartic polynomial. For self-adjoint second-order systems successive eigenfunctions will have $0, 1, 2,\ldots$ zeros in the relevant interval.

Some special examples

5.15 So far our examples have been fairly general, and typical of the problems which arise in practice. We now give some special cases for which one or other of our methods of solution might have particular advantages.

We consider first the system

$$y'' + y = 1, \quad y(0) = 0, \quad y(1) = 1, \quad -1 \leq x \leq 1, \tag{51}$$

in which we seek the Chebyshev series $y = \sum_{r=0}^{\infty}{}' a_r T_r(x)$. With our previous methods we find the algebraic equations

$$\left.\begin{array}{llllll} \tfrac{1}{2}a_0 & -a_2 & +a_4 & -a_6+\ldots & =0 \\ \tfrac{1}{2}a_0 & +a_1+a_2 & +a_3 & +a_4 & +a_5+a_6+\ldots & =0 \\ \tfrac{1}{8}a_0 & +\tfrac{5}{6}a_2 & +\tfrac{1}{24}a_4 & & =\tfrac{1}{4} \\ & \tfrac{1}{24}a_1 & +\tfrac{15}{16}a_3 & +\tfrac{1}{48}a_5+\ldots & =0 \end{array}\right\} \tag{52}$$

$$\cdot \qquad \cdot \qquad \cdot \qquad \cdot \qquad \cdot \qquad \cdot \qquad \cdot \qquad \cdot$$

The matrix is 'sparse', and we can take full advantage of this in the backward recurrence process. The direct elimination, on the other hand, 'fills in' the zeros and in effect performs unnecessary work. In the case of a genuinely even or odd solution we can, of course, omit entirely the respective even and odd Chebyshev coefficients, and the matrix has then no particularly sparse form.

5.16 A second special example occurs when the upper triangular part of the relevant linear equations is singular, with embarrassment for the method of backward recurrence. For example, with the system

$$xy'-y = x, \quad y(1) = 0, \quad 0 \le x \le 1, \tag{53}$$

we find after integration the algebraic equations

$$\left.\begin{aligned}
\tfrac{1}{2}a_0 +a_1 +a_2 +a_3+\ldots &= 0 \\
-\tfrac{1}{4}a_0+\tfrac{1}{2}a_1 +\tfrac{3}{4}a_2 &= \tfrac{1}{4} \\
0a_1 +\tfrac{1}{2}a_2+\tfrac{1}{2}a_3 &= \tfrac{1}{16} \\
\tfrac{1}{12}a_2+\tfrac{1}{2}a_3+\tfrac{5}{12}a_4 &= 0 \\
\tfrac{1}{8}a_3 +\tfrac{1}{2}a_4+\tfrac{3}{8}a_5 &= 0
\end{aligned}\right\}, \tag{54}$$

the general equation having the form

$$\left(\frac{1}{4}-\frac{1}{2r}\right)a_{r-1}+\tfrac{1}{2}a_r+\left(\frac{1}{4}+\frac{1}{2r}\right)a_{r+1} = 0. \tag{55}$$

We would normally expect to use the recurrence relation, representing the upper triangular part of (54), to find both a general solution $a_r(\mathrm{I})$ and a particular solution $a_r(0)$, and we would then obtain $a_r = A\,a_r(\mathrm{I})+a_r(0)$ so that the first of (54) is satisfied. But the zero coefficient of a_1 in the third of (54) prohibits this method, and the best we can do is to write (54) in the form

$$\left.\begin{aligned}
\tfrac{1}{2}a_2+\tfrac{1}{2}a_3 &= \tfrac{1}{16} \\
\tfrac{1}{2}a_0+a_1 +a_2 +a_3+\ldots &= 0 \\
a_1 +\tfrac{5}{4}a_2+\tfrac{1}{2}a_3+\ldots &= \tfrac{1}{4} \\
\tfrac{1}{12}a_2+\tfrac{1}{2}a_3+\tfrac{5}{12}a_4 &= 0
\end{aligned}\right\}, \tag{56}$$

$$\cdot \quad \cdot \quad \cdot \quad \cdot \quad \cdot \quad \cdot$$

the third of which comes from eliminating a_0 from the first two of (54). The recurrence method can now be applied in the usual way, though we are here using one equation which has no connexion with the general recurrence relation.

Circumstances of this kind complicate the programming of the recurrence method. With the direct elimination, of course, no change of method is required. Indeed the only embarrassment of the latter method is the possible 'accidental' singularity of a leading submatrix, and if this happens we merely introduce successive rows and columns, with 'interchanges', until we find a non-singular submatrix. This must ultimately exist if the solution of the differential equation has a convergent Chebyshev series.

5.17 Finally, we mention a type of problem in which there is no need to satisfy any initial condition. In **4.8** we used economization to approximate to the asymptotic series for the exponential integral, given by

$$-e^x \text{Ei}(-x) = x^{-1} - (1!)x^{-2} + (2!)x^{-3} - \dots . \qquad (57)$$

We saw that the success of this method is limited by the point of truncation of the series, and we can eliminate this difficulty by by-passing the computation of the infinite series.

If we write

$$-e^x \text{Ei}(-x) = x^{-1} y(x^{-1}), \qquad (58)$$

we can find the differential equation

$$z^2 y' + (1+z)y = 1, \quad z = x^{-1}, \qquad (59)$$

and the range $0 \le z \le 1$ corresponds to $\infty \ge x \ge 1$. In this range there is a convergent Chebyshev expansion $y = \sum\limits_{r=0}^{\infty}{}' a_r T_r^*(z)$, and we find it by performing our standard process of integration. In the resulting equation the coefficient of $T_r^*(z)$ on the left is

$$a_{r-2}\left(\frac{1}{16} - \frac{1}{16r}\right) + a_{r-1}\left(\frac{1}{4} + \frac{1}{8r}\right) + \frac{3}{8}a_r + a_{r+1}\left(\frac{1}{4} - \frac{1}{8r}\right) + a_{r+2}\left(\frac{1}{16} + \frac{1}{16r}\right), \qquad (60)$$

and on the right we have just $z = \frac{1}{2}\left(T_1^*(z) + T_0^*(z)\right)$. The resulting algebraic equations are given by

$$\left.\begin{array}{l} \frac{3}{8}a_0 + \frac{3}{8}a_1 + \frac{1}{8}a_2 + \frac{1}{8}a_3 \qquad\qquad = \frac{1}{2} \\[2mm] \frac{1}{32}a_0 + \frac{5}{16}a_1 + \frac{3}{8}a_2 + \frac{3}{16}a_3 + \frac{3}{32}a_4 \qquad = 0 \\[2mm] \qquad \frac{1}{24}a_1 + \frac{7}{24}a_2 + \frac{3}{8}a_3 + \frac{5}{24}a_4 + \frac{1}{12}a_5 = 0 \end{array}\right\} \qquad (61)$$

$$\cdot \qquad \cdot \qquad \cdot \qquad \cdot \qquad \cdot \qquad \cdot \qquad \cdot$$

We need not satisfy any initial condition since we seek only the convergent solution of (59), and the relevant initial condition $y(0) = 1$ is inherent in (59). This means, effectively, that we seek only the particular integral of the differential equation.

With the forward elimination method, for example, we find successive solutions

$$\left.\begin{array}{l} a_0 = \dfrac{4}{3}, \qquad\qquad\qquad\qquad\qquad\qquad y(0) = \dfrac{2}{3} \\[3mm] a_0 = \dfrac{40}{27}, \quad a_1 = -\dfrac{4}{27}, \qquad\qquad\qquad y(0) = \dfrac{8}{9} \\[3mm] a_0 = \dfrac{116}{77}, \quad a_1 = \dfrac{-14}{77}, \quad a_2 = \dfrac{2}{77}, \quad y(0) = \dfrac{74}{77} \end{array}\right\}, \qquad (62)$$

and we are clearly converging to the correct initial condition. The backward recurrence process, of course, needs just one solution and a simple multiplying factor.

Note that we have here obtained satisfactory Chebyshev approximations for a function whose Taylor's series does not exist.

Chebyshev series for differential systems. The original system

5.18 The main reason for treating first the integrated system is that the general equation, of the infinite set of equations for the Chebyshev coefficients, contains a finite number of terms. If we are prepared to forego this requirement we can treat the original system directly. For this purpose we write, for example,

$$\left.\begin{array}{l} y(x) = \displaystyle\sum_{r=0}^{\infty}{}' a_r T_r(x) \\[3mm] y'(x) = \displaystyle\sum_{r=0}^{\infty}{}' a_r^{(1)} T_r(x) \\[3mm] y''(x) = \displaystyle\sum_{r=0}^{\infty}{}' a_r^{(2)} T_r(x) \end{array}\right\}, \qquad (63)$$

for the Chebyshev series in the range $-1 \leq x \leq 1$. When we substitute in the differential equation, and equate corresponding coefficients of $T_r(x)$, the resulting equations will contain the coefficients a_r, $a_r^{(1)}$ and $a_r^{(2)}$ for a second-order system, and the 'conditions' will involve a_r and $a_r^{(1)}$.

We can express the $a_r^{(1)}$ and $a_r^{(2)}$ in terms of the a_r from the formulae

$$\left.\begin{aligned}a_r^{(1)} &= 2\{(r+1)a_{r+1}+(r+3)a_{r+3}+(r+5)a_{r+5}+\ldots\} \\ a_r^{(2)} &= 4\{(r+1)(r+2)a_{r+2}+2(r+2)(r+4)a_{r+4}+ \\ &\qquad\qquad\qquad +3(r+3)(r+6)a_{r+6}+\ldots\}\end{aligned}\right\}, \quad (64)$$

(see **3.18**), in which the factors 2 and 4 are replaced by 4 and 16 respectively for the $T_r^*(x)$ polynomials. For the problem of equation (29), for example, the coefficient of $T_r^*(x)$ on the left of the differential equation is

$$\tfrac{1}{4}a_{r-1}^{(1)}+\tfrac{3}{2}a_r^{(1)}+\tfrac{1}{4}a_{r+1}^{(1)}+\tfrac{1}{4}a_{r-2}+\tfrac{1}{2}a_{r-1}+\tfrac{15}{8}a_r+\tfrac{1}{2}a_{r+1}+\tfrac{1}{16}a_{r+2}. \quad (65)$$

Substituting from (64), this becomes

$$\tfrac{1}{16}a_{r-2}+\tfrac{1}{2}a_{r-1}+(\tfrac{15}{8}+r)a_r+\{\tfrac{1}{2}+6(r+1)\}a_{r+1}+$$
$$+\{\tfrac{1}{16}+2(r+2)\}a_{r+2}+6(r+3)a_{r+3}+2(r+4)a_{r+4}+\ldots. \quad (66)$$

We must now compare coefficients for all $r = 0, 1, 2, \ldots$, and adding the condition we find the algebraic equations

$$\left.\begin{aligned}\tfrac{1}{8}a_0 &-\tfrac{7}{4}a_1 +\tfrac{1}{4}a_2 -\tfrac{7}{4}a_3 +\tfrac{1}{4}a_4 -\tfrac{7}{4}a_5+\ldots = 1 \\ \tfrac{15}{8}a_0 &+7a_1+\tfrac{33}{8}a_2+18a_3 +8a_4+30a_5+\ldots = 1 \\ \tfrac{1}{2}a_0&+\tfrac{47}{16}a_1+\tfrac{25}{2}a_2+\tfrac{97}{16}a_3 +24a_4+10a_5+\ldots = -\tfrac{1}{2} \\ \tfrac{1}{16}a_0 &+\tfrac{1}{2}a_1+\tfrac{31}{8}a_2+\tfrac{37}{2}a_3+\tfrac{129}{16}a_4+30a_5+\ldots = 0 \\ \tfrac{1}{16}a_1 &+\tfrac{1}{2}a_2+\tfrac{39}{8}a_3 +\tfrac{49}{2}a_4+\tfrac{161}{16}a_5+\ldots = 0\end{aligned}\right\}. \quad (67)$$

$$\cdot\quad\cdot\quad\cdot\quad\cdot\quad\cdot\quad\cdot\quad\cdot\quad\cdot$$

We can use the same elimination method as before, introducing successive rows and columns, and inspecting the rate of convergence. The third and fourth solutions are approximately

$$\left.\begin{aligned}a_0 &= 2\cdot165\,10, \quad a_1 = -0\cdot420\,74, \quad a_2 = -0\cdot027\,73 \\ a_0 &= 2\cdot116\,75, \quad a_1 = -0\cdot434\,54, \quad a_2 = -0\cdot027\,58, \quad a_3 = 0\cdot010\,37\end{aligned}\right\},$$
$$(68)$$

which may be compared with those of (33) for the previous method.

5.19 We are, of course, rather uneasy about the large coefficients in equations like (67), both practically with respect to the rounding errors of the elimination method, and theoretically with respect to the convergence of the series in the rows of (67). This danger is intensified in the corresponding solution of second-order systems. For the equation (35), for example, the coefficient of $T_r(x)$ on the left is

$$a_r^{(1)}+\tfrac{1}{2}(a_{r-1}^{(1)}+a_{r+1}^{(1)})+\tfrac{1}{2}(a_{r-1}+a_{r+1}), \tag{69}$$

which with the use of (64) becomes

$$\tfrac{1}{2}a_{r-1}+ra_r+\tfrac{1}{2}a_{r+1}+(4r+6)(r+2)a_{r+2}+(8r+18)(r+4)a_{r+4}+$$
$$+(12r+38)(r+6)a_{r+6}+\ldots. \tag{70}$$

For the system (35) we then find the algebraic equations

$$\left.\begin{array}{l}
\tfrac{1}{2}a_0 \quad\quad -a_2 \quad\quad +a_4 \quad\quad\quad -a_6+\ldots = 1 \\[4pt]
\tfrac{1}{2}a_0+4a_1 \ +a_2 \quad\quad +a_4 \ +8a_5 \ \ +a_6+\ldots = -1 \\[4pt]
\quad\quad a_1+12a_2 \quad +72a_4 \quad\quad +228a_6+\ldots = 3 \\[4pt]
\tfrac{1}{2}a_0 \ +a_1 \ +\tfrac{1}{2}a_2+30a_3 \quad\quad +130a_5 \quad\quad +\ldots = 1 \\[4pt]
\quad\quad \tfrac{1}{2}a_1 \ +2a_2 \ +\tfrac{1}{2}a_3+56a_4 \quad\quad +204a_6+\ldots = \tfrac{1}{2} \\[4pt]
\quad\quad\quad \tfrac{1}{2}a_2 \ +3a_3 \ +\tfrac{1}{2}a_4 \ +90a_5 \quad\quad +\ldots = 0 \\[4pt]
\ \cdot\quad\ \cdot\quad\ \cdot\quad\quad \cdot\quad\quad \cdot\quad\quad \cdot\quad\quad \cdot\quad\quad \cdot\quad\quad \cdot
\end{array}\right\}, \tag{71}$$

and we note the presence of some very large coefficients.

The solution of the leading 5×5 equations is approximately

$$\left.\begin{array}{l}
a_0 = 2{\cdot}539\ 8, \quad a_1 = -0{\cdot}637\ 3, \quad a_2 = 0{\cdot}274\ 7 \\[4pt]
\quad\quad a_3 = 0{\cdot}007\ 7, \quad a_4 = 0{\cdot}004\ 7
\end{array}\right\}, \tag{72}$$

which is not significantly different from that of (39) obtained by the previous method. There is, however, a marked difference in the computed value of a_3, and examination of (71) shows the reason for this. If $a_6, a_7,\ldots$ are negligible, the last of (71) shows that a_5 is approximately $-0{\cdot}002$, and from this perturbation alone we see from the fourth of (71) that a_3 should be increased by approximately $0{\cdot}009$, bringing its value more into line with that of (39). In the integrated equations (38), with very 'diagonally-dominant' coefficients, the neglect of a_5 has a very much smaller effect.

In both sets of equations, of course, a_1 is somewhat affected by the neglect of a_5, and this can hardly be avoided since the relevant equation comes from the second given condition. The latter involves a derivative, with consequent larger coefficients in some of the terms.

Chebyshev series for differential systems. The mixed system

5.20 Clenshaw (1957) uses a rather different method, specifically in conjunction with the process of backward recurrence, for finding the Chebyshev series. Here we use the original differential system, and the assumptions (63) for the range $-1 \leq x \leq 1$, but instead of the 'infinite' relations (64) we now take the finite relations

$$\left.\begin{aligned} a_{r-1}^{(1)} - a_{r+1}^{(1)} &= 2ra_r \\ a_{r-1}^{(2)} - a_{r+1}^{(2)} &= 2ra_r^{(1)} \end{aligned}\right\}, \tag{73}$$

to connect the Chebyshev coefficients of the function with those of its derivatives. For the range $0 \leq x \leq 1$ the factors 2 in (73) are replaced by 4.

Substituting (63) into the differential system, and equating corresponding coefficients of $T_r(x)$, $r = 0, 1, \ldots$, we can with the aid of (73) build up by backward recurrence both general and particular solutions of the recurrence, and find the appropriate linear combination to satisfy the various initial equations.

5.21 Consider, for example, the system (29). With $y = \sum\limits_{r=0}^{\infty}{}' a_r T_r^*(x)$, $y' = \sum\limits_{r=0}^{\infty}{}' a_r^{(1)} T_r^*(x)$, the coefficient of $T_r^*(x)$ on the left of the differential equation in (29) is

$$\tfrac{1}{4}a_{r-1}^{(1)} + \tfrac{3}{2}a_r^{(1)} + \tfrac{1}{4}a_{r+1}^{(1)} + \tfrac{1}{16}a_{r-2} + \tfrac{1}{2}a_{r-1} + \tfrac{15}{8}a_r + \tfrac{1}{2}a_{r+1} + \tfrac{1}{16}a_{r+2}, \tag{74}$$

this representing twice the coefficient of $T_0^*(x)$ for $r = 0$. On the right of the differential equation we have $\tfrac{1}{2}T_0^*(x) - \tfrac{1}{2}T_1^*(x)$, so that, with the initial condition and the equations corresponding to (74) for $r = 0, 1, 2, \ldots$, we find the algebraic equations

$$\left.\begin{aligned} \tfrac{1}{8}a_0 \; -\tfrac{7}{4}a_1 \; +\tfrac{1}{4}a_2 \; -\tfrac{7}{4}a_3 +\tfrac{1}{4}a_4 \; -\tfrac{7}{4}a_5 + \ldots \qquad\qquad &= 1 \\ \tfrac{3}{4}a_0^{(1)} + \tfrac{1}{4}a_1^{(1)} + \tfrac{15}{16}a_0 \; +\tfrac{1}{2}a_1 + \tfrac{1}{16}a_2 \qquad\qquad\qquad &= \tfrac{1}{2} \\ \tfrac{1}{4}a_0^{(1)} + \tfrac{3}{2}a_1^{(1)} \; +\tfrac{1}{4}a_2^{(1)} \; +\tfrac{1}{2}a_0 + \tfrac{31}{16}a_1 \; +\tfrac{1}{2}a_2 + \tfrac{1}{16}a_3 \qquad &= -\tfrac{1}{2} \\ \tfrac{1}{4}a_1^{(1)} + \tfrac{3}{2}a_2^{(1)} \; +\tfrac{1}{4}a_3^{(1)} + \tfrac{1}{16}a_0 \; +\tfrac{1}{2}a_1 + \tfrac{15}{8}a_2 \; +\tfrac{1}{2}a_3 + \tfrac{1}{16}a_4 &= 0 \end{aligned}\right\}. \tag{75}$$

We observe that we can compute $a_n, a_{n-1}, \ldots, a_0$ by backward recurrence, from successive homogeneous equations, without using the first three 'initial equations' of (75), so that we need three trial solutions and a linear combination thereof.

Starting, for example, with $a_n = 1, a_{n+1} = \ldots = 0$, $a_n^{(1)} = a_{n+1}^{(1)} = \ldots = 0$, we can 'build up' $a_r^{(1)}$ and a_r by using the first of (73) (with 2 replaced by 4) and (75) in turn. This is clearly possible without further adjustment of the equations, since $a_{r-1}^{(1)}$ is deduced from a_r and $a_{r+1}^{(1)}$, and the computation of a_{r-2} follows directly from

TABLE 2

	(I)		(II)		(III)	
r	a_r	$a_r^{(1)}$	a_r	$a_r^{(1)}$	a_r	$a_r^{(1)}$
0	323	1792	312	−44	2	−32
1	472	−224	−14	−64	−8	8
2	−30	−96	−8	12	1	0
3	−8	16	1	0	0	0
4	1	0	0	0	0	0
5	0	0	0	0	0	0

the equation corresponding to (74). In particular we do not need a knowledge of $a_{r-2}^{(1)}$ for this purpose. Three trial solutions, with the starting conditions similar to those of Table 1 in **5.10**, are shown in Table 2.

Substituting in the first three of (75), we then find the equations

$$\left. \begin{array}{rrr} -778 \cdot 875 A_1 & +59 \cdot 75 A_2 & +14 \cdot 5 A_3 = 1 \\ 1\,824 \cdot 937\,5 A_1 & +236 A_2 - 24 \cdot 062\,5 A_3 = \tfrac{1}{2} \\ 1\,148 \cdot 5 A_1 + 20 \cdot 937\,5 A_2 & -10 A_3 = -\tfrac{1}{2} \end{array} \right\}. \qquad (76)$$

The solution $A_1 a_r(\text{I}) + A_2 a_r(\text{II}) + A_3 a_r(\text{III})$ is approximately

$$\left. \begin{array}{lll} a_0 = 2 \cdot 116\,5, & a_1 = -0 \cdot 434\,5, & a_2 = -0 \cdot 026\,8 \\ & a_3 = 0 \cdot 010\,4, & a_4 = -0 \cdot 000\,4 \end{array} \right\}, \qquad (77)$$

which is very similar to that of (33) for the integrated method.

5.22 There is in fact a very close connexion between this approach and the integrated method. If we take the two equations corresponding to (74) for $r-1$ and $r+1$, subtract and use the relevant first of (73), we eliminate the $a_r^{(1)}$ terms and produce exactly $4r$ times the general equation (30) for the integrated system. The only reason for the slight disagreement between the first of Table 2 and the corresponding part of Table 1 is that the initial conditions for solution I do not quite satisfy (74) with $r = 6$, and the corresponding integrated equation, the first not given explicitly in (31), is therefore also not quite satisfied. The trial solutions II and III, correspondingly, do not quite satisfy the fifth and fourth respectively of (31), so that our result (77) is not quite the exact solution of the leading 5×5 set of equations obtained from (31). This is no particular disadvantage in practice, and indeed Clenshaw takes quite arbitrary starting conditions for the backward recurrence, the only criterion being that the required trial solutions must be linearly independent.

In this example we can proceed without eliminating the $a_r^{(1)}$ coefficients, but in other cases the elimination simplifies the computation of this method. For the equation (59), for example, our basic equation has on the left the term

$$\tfrac{1}{16}(a_{r-2}^{(1)}+4a_{r-1}^{(1)}+6a_r^{(1)}+4a_{r+1}^{(1)}+a_{r+2}^{(1)})+\tfrac{1}{4}(a_{r-1}+6a_r+a_{r+1}). \quad (78)$$

This we want to use to find a_{r-1}, but $a_{r-2}^{(1)}$ also depends on a_{r-1}, and we must either replace $a_{r-2}^{(1)}$ by $a_r^{(1)}+4(r-1)a_{r-1}$ and adjust (78) accordingly, or eliminate altogether the $a_r^{(1)}$ coefficients, obtaining effectively the integrated form (60).

5.23 The solution of second-order systems is obtained in a similar manner. For the differential system (35), for example, we have the 'conditions', given by

$$\left.\begin{aligned}
\tfrac{1}{2}a_0-a_2+a_4-\ldots &= 1 \\
\tfrac{1}{2}a_0^{(1)}-a_2^{(1)}+a_4^{(1)}-\ldots+\tfrac{1}{2}a_0+3a_1+a_2+\ldots &= -1
\end{aligned}\right\}, \quad (79)$$

the particular equations

$$\left.\begin{aligned}
\tfrac{1}{2}a_0^{(2)}+\tfrac{1}{2}a_1^{(1)}+\tfrac{1}{2}a_1 &= \tfrac{3}{2} \\
a_1^{(2)}+\tfrac{1}{2}a_0^{(1)}+\tfrac{1}{2}a_2^{(1)}+\tfrac{1}{2}a_0+\tfrac{1}{2}a_2 &= 1 \\
a_2^{(2)}+\tfrac{1}{2}a_1^{(1)}+\tfrac{1}{2}a_3^{(1)}+\tfrac{1}{2}a_1+\tfrac{1}{2}a_3 &= \tfrac{1}{2}
\end{aligned}\right\}, \quad (80)$$

and the general equation

$$a_r^{(2)}+\tfrac{1}{2}(a_{r-1}^{(1)}+a_{r+1}^{(1)})+\tfrac{1}{2}(a_{r-1}+a_{r+1}) = 0, \quad r = 3, 4, \ldots. \quad (81)$$

Starting with arbitrary conditions, such as

$$\left.\begin{array}{c} a_n = 1, \qquad a_{n+1} = a_{n+2} = \dots = 0 \\ a_n^{(1)} = a_{n+1}^{(1)} = \dots = 0 \\ a_n^{(2)} = a_{n+1}^{(2)} = \dots = 0 \end{array}\right\}, \tag{82}$$

we can build up the table of $a_r^{(2)}$, $a_r^{(1)}$ and a_r by using in turn the second of (73), the first of (73), and the equations of type (81). Here, we note, we must use the last two of (80) to find a_1 and a_0, and these equations are not homogeneous. As in **5.12** we therefore need three trial solutions of the homogeneous set, and one for the non-homogeneous set, and a linear combination which will satisfy

TABLE 3

		(I)			(O)	
r	a_r	$a_r^{(1)}$	$a_r^{(2)}$	a_r	$a_r^{(1)}$	$a_r^{(2)}$
0	1017	−632	440	0	2	0
1	−292	196	−192	1	0	0
2	47	−48	48	0	0	0
3	−8	8	0	0	0	0
4	1	0	0	0	0	0

(79) and the first of (80). We show in Table 3 one possible general solution (I) and a particular solution (0). We suppress the rest of the arithmetic, since no point of substance is introduced therein.

5.24 Again, however, we shall in some cases prefer to eliminate the $a_r^{(2)}$ and perhaps also the $a_r^{(1)}$. Consider, for example, the equation

$$(1+x^2)y''+y'+y = 0, \quad -1 \le x \le 1. \tag{83}$$

The relevant algebraic equations contain on the left-hand side the terms

$$\tfrac{1}{4}a_{r-2}^{(2)}+\tfrac{3}{2}a_r^{(2)}+\tfrac{1}{4}a_{r+2}^{(2)}+a_r^{(1)}+a_r, \tag{84}$$

and we cannot find a_r directly from the corresponding equation. Changing r to $r+2$ in (84), and subtracting these two equations, we eliminate the $a_r^{(2)}$ terms and obtain

$$\tfrac{1}{2}(r-1)a_{r-1}^{(1)}+3(r+1)a_{r+1}^{(1)}+\tfrac{1}{2}(r+3)a_{r+3}^{(1)}+a_r^{(1)}-a_{r+2}^{(1)}+a_r-a_{r+2}. \tag{85}$$

This is effectively equivalent to a single integration of the differential equation. But we still cannot compute a_r directly, and must either replace $a_{r-1}^{(1)}$ by $a_{r+1}^{(1)}+2ra_r$ in (85), or eliminate the $a_r^{(1)}$ coefficients altogether by means of a second integration.

Evaluation of methods

5.25 These various considerations suggest, for a general-purpose computer programme for first-order and second-order systems, that the most convenient formulation of the corresponding algebraic problem is obtained from the singly and doubly integrated systems respectively. No special cases have to be considered, and we always obtain equations containing only the required Chebyshev coefficients a_r.

For the solution of the algebraic problem, again, the forward elimination method, or preferably the *compact* elimination associated with the matrix decomposition $\mathbf{A} = \mathbf{LU}$, is probably the best all-purpose process. There are no special cases which need special consideration, and although we may do a little more arithmetic than is strictly necessary, as indicated in **5.15**, this is a very small price to pay.

5.26 The use of the mixed system, with backward recurrence, is particularly valuable for desk computation. Here we do not mind special cases; we can keep the arithmetic to a minimum in all cases, and it usually involves 'easier' numbers. If we are looking for the Chebyshev series, and are prepared to assess its accuracy by inspection, the use of mixed equations is no particular disadvantage.

On the other hand, for the purpose of investigating the rate of convergence of different orders of approximation to the true Chebyshev series, it is desirable to use equations containing the a_r coefficients only. We discuss this and allied matters, for example the accuracy of successive solutions for the integrated and original systems, in **5.37** *et seq.* below.

The finite approximation $\sum\limits_{r=0}^{n} {}' a_r T_r(x)$

5.27 So far we have concentrated on finding the Chebyshev series by a method of successive approximation involving the solution of successive subsets of equations drawn from the infinite set. Each such solution provides a polynomial approximation of the form

$$p_n(x) = \sum_{r=0}^{n} {}' a_r^{(n+1)} T_r(x), \qquad (86)$$

where the notation $a_r^{(n+1)}$ indicates that these coefficients are the solutions of the leading $n+1$ equations. (In the mixed system this statement may not be quite accurate, but this is a detail which need not concern us. The statement is true for the methods involving only the a_r coefficients, obtained either from the integrated or original system.)

Now in Chapter 4, for the direct problem of approximating to a rational function, we produced this polynomial approximation by the τ method, and it is interesting to connect together these two approaches. We first consider the direct problem.

5.28 From the analysis of Chapter 4 we know, for the problem of equation (8), that there exists a finite approximation (86) which satisfies exactly the perturbed equation

$$(1+x)p_n(x) = 1+\tau_{n+1} T^*_{n+1}(x), \tag{87}$$

for which we can compute τ_{n+1} together with the coefficients of $p_n(x)$. For $n = 2$, for example, the relevant equations are

$$\left.\begin{aligned}
\tfrac{3}{4}a_0+\tfrac{1}{4}a_1 \quad\quad\ &= 1\\
\tfrac{1}{4}a_0+\tfrac{3}{2}a_1+\tfrac{1}{4}a_2 &= 0\\
\tfrac{1}{4}a_1+\tfrac{3}{2}a_2 &= 0\\
\tfrac{1}{4}a_2 &= \tau_3
\end{aligned}\right\}, \tag{88}$$

which we can solve without difficulty.

We see that this approach is effectively identical with our standard method of finding an approximation to the Chebyshev series by solving the relevant equations involving the leading 3×3 submatrix of the infinite system (10) for the Chebyshev coefficients. For suppose that in the latter we *assume* that $a_3 = a_4 = \ldots = 0$. Then the first three equations in (10) can be solved for a_0, a_1 and a_2, and the only equation unsatisfied in the complete set is the fourth. This will be satisfied if we add to its right-hand side the term $\tfrac{1}{4}a_2$, and this corresponds to solving exactly the perturbed equation

$$(1+x)p_2(x) = 1+\tfrac{1}{4}a_2 T^*_3(x). \tag{89}$$

The computed coefficients, of course, are the $a_r^{(3)}$ of (86).

In all cases, we have observed, the infinite set of equations has one or more 'special' equations, followed by an upper triangular set. The number of special equations determines in an obvious way the number of equations unsatisfied by the assumption $a_{n+1} = a_{n+2} = \ldots = 0$, and therefore the number of perturbing terms present in an equation like (89). For the system (11), for example, we have

$$
\left.
\begin{aligned}
\tfrac{3}{4}a_0 + \tfrac{1}{2}a_1 + \tfrac{1}{4}a_2 \qquad\qquad\quad &= 1 \\
\tfrac{1}{2}a_0 + \tfrac{7}{4}a_1 + \tfrac{1}{2}a_2 + \tfrac{1}{4}a_3 \qquad\quad &= 0 \\
\tfrac{1}{4}a_0 + \tfrac{1}{2}a_1 + \tfrac{3}{2}a_2 + \tfrac{1}{2}a_3 + \tfrac{1}{4}a_4 &= 0 \\
\tfrac{1}{4}a_1 + \tfrac{1}{2}a_2 + \tfrac{3}{2}a_3 + \tfrac{1}{2}a_4 + \ldots &= 0 \\
\tfrac{1}{4}a_2 + \tfrac{1}{2}a_3 + \tfrac{3}{2}a_4 + \ldots &= 0 \\
\tfrac{1}{4}a_3 + \tfrac{1}{2}a_4 + \ldots &= 0 \\
\cdot\quad\cdot\quad\cdot\quad\cdot\quad
\end{aligned}
\right\}
\tag{90}
$$

The solution of the leading 3×3 set leaves two equations unsatisfied, so that the resulting solution, $p_2(x)$, is the exact solution of

$$
\left.
\begin{aligned}
(1 + x + x^2)p_2(x) &= 1 + \tau_3 T_3(x) + \tau_4 T_4(x) \\
\tau_3 = \tfrac{1}{4}a_1 + \tfrac{1}{2}a_2, \quad &\tau_4 = \tfrac{1}{4}a_2
\end{aligned}
\right\}
\tag{91}
$$

and these perturbations are therefore easily calculable. Again the computed a_r are the $a_r^{(3)}$ of (86).

5.29 The approximations obtained for the differential system have precisely the same connexion with the corresponding τ method for computing directly a polynomial approximation (86) of specified degree n. For the integrated method, for example, the algebraic equations (31) for the first-order system (29) show that the solution $a_r^{(3)}$, $r = 0, 1, 2$, of the leading 3×3 equations gives a quadratic approximation which satisfies exactly the integrated system

$$
\left.
\begin{aligned}
(1 + x)p_2(x) + \int (x + x^2)p_2(x)\,dx &= B + x - \tfrac{1}{2}x^2 + E_2(x) \\
E_2(x) = \tau_3 T_3^*(x) + \tau_4 T_4^*&(x) + \tau_5 T_5^*(x) \\
\tau_3 = \tfrac{1}{192}a_0^{(3)} + \tfrac{1}{24}a_1^{(3)} + \tfrac{61}{192}a_2^{(3)}, \quad &\tau_4 = \tfrac{1}{256}a_1^{(3)} + \tfrac{1}{32}a_2^{(3)} \\
\tau_5 = \tfrac{1}{320}a_2^{(3)}&
\end{aligned}
\right\}
\tag{92}
$$

where the arbitrary constant is adjusted so that the given associated condition is satisfied. The corresponding solution of the original system can be treated in precisely the same manner.

In the direct application of the τ method we observe that the attempt to solve the first of (92) without the $E_2(x)$ term would require the addition of precisely this term. We then record corresponding to (31) the equations

$$
\left.
\begin{aligned}
\tfrac{1}{8}a_0 \quad &-\tfrac{7}{4}a_1 \quad +\tfrac{1}{4}a_2 = 1 \\
\tfrac{29}{64}a_0 \quad &+\tfrac{13}{8}a_1 \quad +\tfrac{1}{16}a_2 = \tfrac{1}{4} \\
\tfrac{1}{16}a_0 \quad &+\tfrac{23}{64}a_1 \quad +\tfrac{3}{2}a_2 = -\tfrac{1}{16} \\
\tfrac{1}{192}a_0 \quad &+\tfrac{1}{24}a_1 +\tfrac{61}{192}a_2 = \tau_3 \\
&\tfrac{1}{256}a_1 \quad +\tfrac{1}{32}a_2 = \tau_4 \\
&\tfrac{1}{320}a_2 = \tau_5
\end{aligned}
\right\},
\tag{93}
$$

and solve six equations in the six unknowns $a_0, a_1, a_2, \tau_3, \tau_4, \tau_5$. Our more direct approach simplifies both the analysis and the computation, though the results, of course, are identical.

The finite approximation $\overset{n}{\underset{r=0}{\Sigma}} b_r x^r$

5.30 The corresponding method of finding a finite polynomial approximation in the form

$$
p_n(x) = \sum_{r=0}^{n} b_r x^r,
\tag{94}
$$

which was used by Lanczos (1957) in his original τ method, can also be considered in this way, though the situation is here more interesting. We observe in advance that x^r can be differentiated as easily as it can be integrated, so that the original system is as easy to treat as the integrated system. In some problems, moreover, we might like to cancel out a common power of x, which is less easy with the Chebyshev form.

Considering first the integrated system, we take the problem of **5.11** in the integrated form (36). Substituting (94) in (36), and comparing coefficients of x^2, x^3,..., in the result, we produce a set of algebraic equations for the coefficients b_r. To these we add two further equations deduced from the given conditions, and the full set is given by

$$\left.\begin{array}{l}
b_0 \qquad\qquad\qquad\qquad\qquad\qquad\qquad = 1 \\
b_0 +4b_1 +b_2 +3b_3 +b_4 +3b_5+b_6+3b_7+\dots = -1 \\
\qquad\qquad b_2 \qquad\qquad\qquad\qquad\qquad = \tfrac{1}{2} \\
\tfrac{1}{6}b_0 +\tfrac{1}{6}b_1 \qquad +b_3 \qquad\qquad\qquad = \tfrac{1}{6} \\
\qquad \tfrac{1}{12}b_1 +\tfrac{1}{6}b_2 \qquad +b_4 \qquad\qquad = \tfrac{1}{12} \\
\qquad\qquad \tfrac{1}{20}b_2+\tfrac{3}{20}b_3 \qquad +b_5 \qquad = 0 \\
\qquad\qquad\qquad \tfrac{1}{30}b_3+\tfrac{4}{30}b_4 \qquad +b_6 \quad = 0 \\
\qquad\qquad\qquad\qquad \tfrac{1}{42}b_4+\tfrac{5}{42}b_5 \qquad +b_7 = 0 \\
\qquad\qquad\cdot\quad\cdot\quad\cdot\quad\cdot\quad\cdot\quad\cdot
\end{array}\right\}. \qquad (95)$$

The general term on the left, for the coefficient of x^r, has the form

$$\frac{b_{r-3}}{r(r-1)}+\frac{r-2}{r(r-1)}b_{r-2}+b_r, \qquad (96)$$

and we note its simplicity compared with the corresponding Chebyshev form (37).

The equations, of course, are of precisely the same general form as those for the Chebyshev coefficients, an upper triangular set following three initial rows. On the other hand, the solution of successive leading subsets no longer gives successive approximations to the polynomial form of the Chebyshev series, but only to the Taylor's series, which may not even converge.

5.31 For example if we solve the leading 5×5 equations, taking $b_5 = b_6 = \dots = 0$, we have the exact solution of a system perturbed by

$$(\tfrac{1}{20}b_2+\tfrac{3}{20}b_3)x^5+(\tfrac{1}{30}b_3+\tfrac{4}{30}b_4)x^6+(\tfrac{1}{42}b_4)x^7. \qquad (97)$$

The corresponding Chebyshev result has perturbations

$$\tau_5 T_5(x)+\tau_6 T_6(x)+\tau_7 T_7(x), \qquad (98)$$

and to achieve the same effect we have to add on the right of (95), in rows three to eight, the numbers

$$c_s = \tau_5 c_5^{(s)} + \tau_6 c_6^{(s)} + \tau_7 c_7^{(s)}, \quad s = 2, 3, ..., 7, \qquad (99)$$

where $c_r^{(s)}$ is the coefficient of x^s in $T_r(x)$.

The standard τ method then solves the resulting eight equations in eight unknowns. Again we can avoid the explicit introduction of these τ unknowns, though perhaps not here so conveniently, by observing immediately that

$$\left. \begin{aligned} 64\tau_7 &= \tfrac{1}{42}b_4 \\ 32\tau_6 &= \tfrac{1}{30}b_3 + \tfrac{4}{30}b_4 \\ -112\tau_7 + 16\tau_5 &= \tfrac{1}{20}b_2 + \tfrac{3}{20}b_3 \end{aligned} \right\} . \qquad (100)$$

We can therefore express the perturbation explicitly in terms of the b_r, and here reduce the problem to the solution of the 5×5 set

$$\left. \begin{aligned} b_0 &&&&&&&& = 1 \\ b_0 &+4b_1 &+b_2 &+3b_3 &+b_4 &= -1 \\ & &b_2 &-\tfrac{3}{160}b_3 &-\tfrac{3}{40}b_4 &= \tfrac{1}{2} \\ \tfrac{1}{6}b_0 &+\tfrac{1}{6}b_1 &+\tfrac{1}{16}b_2 &+\tfrac{19}{16}b_3 &+\tfrac{1}{32}b_4 &= \tfrac{1}{6} \\ &\tfrac{1}{12}b_1 &+\tfrac{1}{6}b_2 &+\tfrac{1}{20}b_3 &+\tfrac{6}{5}b_4 &= \tfrac{1}{12} \end{aligned} \right\} . \qquad (101)$$

The solution gives a polynomial approximation of degree 4 identical with that obtained from the leading 5×5 Chebyshev set (38).

For the next approximation, of course, the perturbation is different, and in particular the resulting 6×6 equations of type (101) do not have the same coefficients as (101) in the leading 5×5 subset. It is this variation which leads us ultimately to the Chebyshev series rather than the Taylor's series. On the other hand, this variation here perhaps makes the original τ method more attractive, particularly since the sparse nature of the typical matrix in (95) simplifies an obvious method of computation. If we back-substitute in the upper triangular set we easily obtain the b_r in terms of τ_r (with adjustment similar to that of **5.16** if the upper triangular matrix is singular), and then solve for the τ_r from the remaining equations.

5.32 We can treat the original system in precisely the same way. We obtain directly from (35) the equations

$$\left.\begin{aligned}
b_0 &= 1 \\
b_0+4b_1+b_2+3b_3+b_4+3b_5+b_6+3b_7+\ldots &= -1 \\
2b_2 &= 1 \\
b_0+b_1+6b_3 &= 1 \\
b_1+2b_2+12b_4 &= 1 \\
b_2+3b_3+20b_5 &= 0 \\
\cdot \quad \cdot \quad \cdot \quad \cdot \quad \cdot \quad \cdot \quad \cdot \quad \cdot \quad \cdot
\end{aligned}\right\}, \quad (102)$$

of which the general term on the left is

$$b_{r-1}+rb_r+(r+1)(r+2)b_{r+2}, \quad r = 0, 1,\ldots, \quad (103)$$

for the coefficient of x^r, with $b_s = 0$ for negative s.

This may be compared favourably with the corresponding Chebyshev system (71). We now have a *finite* number of terms in each equation, and indeed the rows of (102) are merely constant multiples of those of (95). The method of solution is exactly the same, though for a polynomial approximation of degree four we have to perturb the right-hand side of (102), in rows starting with the third, with the terms

$$c_s = \tau_3 c_3^{(s)}+\tau_4 c_4^{(s)}+\tau_5 c_5^{(s)}, \quad s = 0, 1,\ldots, 5. \quad (104)$$

The perturbation is different, and our solution is correspondingly a little different from that of the integrated system. It is, of course, exactly equivalent to that of (72) for the solution $\sum_{r=0}^{4}{}' a_r T_r(x)$ of the original system, and obtained rather more easily.

5.33 Finally, the flexibility of the polynomial x^r easily permits the cancellation of a power of x, whenever this seems desirable. Consider, for example, the system

$$xy''+y'+16xy = 0, \quad y(0) = 1, \quad y'(0) = 0. \quad (105)$$

There is obviously an even solution, and if we seek the approximation

$$y = \sum_{r=0}^{n} b_{2r} x^{2r} \quad (106)$$

the general equation of the infinite algebraic set is given by

$$16b_{2r}+4(r+1)^2b_{2r+2} = 0, \qquad (107)$$

relevant to the coefficient of x^{2r+1}. The single perturbation required for an exact solution (106) is $\tau_{2n+1} T_{2n+1}(x)$. On the other hand we can divide (105) by x; the equation (107) then refers to the coefficient of x^{2r}, and the required perturbation is $\tau_{2n} T_{2n}(x)$.

Similarly, the first integration of (105) gives

$$xy'+ \int_0^x 16xy \, dx = 0, \qquad (108)$$

which satisfies the second given condition. A second integration gives

$$xy- \int y \, dx+ \int\int_0^x 16xy \, dxdx = A, \qquad (109)$$

where the constant is to be determined so that $y(0) = 1$. But we might prefer to divide (108) by x before integrating again, to obtain

$$y+ \int g(x) \, dx = A, \qquad g(x) = x^{-1} \int_0^x 16xy \, dx, \qquad (110)$$

in which again we can cancel the x in the numerator and denominator of $g(x)$.

This cancellation, difficult to organize with the Chebyshev form, has some significant effects on the accuracy of successive approximations. We return to this point in **5.47** below.

Error analysis

5.34 Various questions of error analysis merit some consideration. For example, with any of the methods which obtain successive approximate solutions $p_n(x)$ of increasing degree, either of the form $\sum_{r=0}^{n}{}' a_r T_r(x)$ or $\sum_{r=0}^{n} b_r x^r$, we would like to know the smallest value of n for which the error

$$e_n(x) = p_n(x)-y(x) \qquad (111)$$

is such that $\max |e_n(x)|$ is smaller than some given quantity. As a corollary, we would like to be able to estimate $\max |e_n(x)|$ for any given n. Moreover we get different polynomials $p_n(x)$ with the solution of the leading $n+1$ equations of the integrated and original systems, and we are naturally interested in which of these has the smaller max $|e_n(x)|$. Finally, we might ask for the best polynomial approximation of given degree n, which we must here take to be the corresponding truncated Chebyshev series. The minimax polynomial, which is obviously 'better', can hardly be obtained by this process, and in any case it will rarely be considerably better than the truncated Chebyshev series.

For most of these problems the easiest solution, and perhaps the most practical with modern computing power, is to calculate enough successive approximations, by any method, so that we can estimate our requirements by inspection of the computed coefficients. It is, however, interesting and instructive to apply mathematical analysis in various situations and for various problems.

We are effectively asking, in all cases, for a good estimate of the difference between our computed coefficients of the form $\sum_{r=0}^{n}{}' a_r T_r(x)$ and the true Chebyshev coefficients, together with an estimate of the neglected coefficients $a_{n+1}, a_{n+2}, \ldots$. In one particular case some relevant analysis has been supplied by Miller (1952), Olver (1964) and Makinouchi (1965). This refers to the method of backward recurrence, on the lines of **5.6** and **5.10**, for the computation of the Chebyshev series represented by a *three-term* homogeneous recurrence relation with one computable normalizing factor. Under certain conditions, the analysis shows that in each computed coefficient the number of significant figures which agree with the true value is equal to the number of figures in front of the decimal point in the trial solution, that is before the multiplier is applied. This analysis is of restricted application, and even then we have to do some inspection, or find other knowledge of the Chebyshev series, in order to estimate the effect of the neglected terms.

An alternative to extensive computation and inspection is an analysis relevant to the perturbations induced by approximate solutions. For the direct problem, the approximation of a rational function, this immediately supplies all the relevant answers, and this we discuss first.

Perturbation theory for rational functions

5.35 From the content of **5.28**, we can conclude immediately that the error in the approximation $\sum_{r=0}^{n}{}' a_r^{(n+1)} T_r^*(x)$ to the rational function

$1/(1+x)$, computed from the leading $n+1$ equations in (88), is given by

$$(1+x)e_n(x) = \tau_{n+1} T^*_{n+1}(x) = \tfrac{1}{4}a_n^{(n+1)} T^*_{n+1}(x), \quad 0 \le x \le 1, \quad (112)$$

so that we can easily estimate max $|e_n(x)|$, or even compute the value of $e_n(x)$ at any point, *without* knowing the Chebyshev series. Our first question, of how to determine a suitable n for any given accuracy criterion, can then also be answered without excessive computation. The problem, simple for this particular example, is obviously not much more difficult for the more elaborate example of equations (11). From (90) and (91) we have

$$(1+x+x^2)e_n(x) = (\tfrac{1}{4}a_{n-1}^{(n+1)} + \tfrac{1}{2}a_n^{(n+1)})T_{n+1}(x) + \tfrac{1}{4}a_n^{(n+1)}T_{n+2}(x) \atop -1 \le x \le 1 \Big\}, \quad (113)$$

and all the required coefficients are computed successively and economically. Certainly

$$\max |e_n(x)| \le \frac{\tfrac{1}{4}|a_{n-1}^{(n+1)}| + \tfrac{3}{4}|a_n^{(n+1)}|}{\min_{-1 \le x \le 1}(1+x+x^2)} = \tfrac{1}{3}|a_{n-1}^{(n+1)}| + |a_n^{(n+1)}|, \quad (114)$$

and we can bound $|e_n(x)|$ more closely by direct computation of (113).

5.36 If we seek a polynomial of degree n closer to the truncated Chebyshev series for $(1+x)^{-1}$, the easiest approach is to compute $p_{n+1}(x)$ and then to neglect the term $a_{n+1}^{(n+2)}T^*_{n+1}(x)$. Then this polynomial is

$$\bar{p}_n(x) = \sum_{r=0}^{n+1}{}' a_r^{(n+2)}T^*_r(x) - a_{n+1}^{(n+2)}T^*_{n+1}(x), \quad (115)$$

and the new error satisfies the equation

$$(1+x)\bar{e}_n(x) = \tfrac{1}{4}a_{n+1}^{(n+2)}T^*_{n+2}(x) - (1+x)a_{n+1}^{(n+2)}T^*_{n+1}(x)$$

$$= a_{n+1}^{(n+2)}\{-\tfrac{1}{4}T^*_n(x) - \tfrac{3}{2}T^*_{n+1}(x)\}. \quad (116)$$

Again we can easily compute $\bar{e}_n(x)$ at every point or estimate its maximum value directly.

This approach, of course, is equivalent to solving a perturbed set of $n+1$ equations to produce the approximation of degree n.

The leading 4×4 equations, for example, are

$$\left. \begin{array}{l} \tfrac{3}{4}a_0^{(4)} + \tfrac{1}{4}a_1^{(4)} = 1 \\ \tfrac{1}{4}a_0^{(4)} + \tfrac{3}{2}a_1^{(4)} + \tfrac{1}{4}a_2^{(4)} = 0 \\ \tfrac{1}{4}a_1^{(4)} + \tfrac{3}{2}a_2^{(4)} + \tfrac{1}{4}a_3^{(4)} = 0 \\ \tfrac{1}{4}a_2^{(4)} + \tfrac{3}{2}a_3^{(4)} = 0 \end{array} \right\}, \qquad (117)$$

and we are effectively substituting for $a_3^{(4)}$ from the last equation to produce the 3×3 set

$$\left. \begin{array}{l} \tfrac{3}{4}a_0^{(4)} + \tfrac{1}{4}a_1^{(4)} = 1 \\ \tfrac{1}{4}a_0^{(4)} + \tfrac{3}{2}a_1^{(4)} + \tfrac{1}{4}a_2^{(4)} = 0 \\ \tfrac{1}{4}a_1^{(4)} + \tfrac{35}{24}a_2^{(4)} = 0 \end{array} \right\}. \qquad (118)$$

We easily deduce that the resulting quadratic has the error

$$(1+x)\bar{e}_2(x) = \tfrac{1}{24}a_2^{(4)}T_2^*(x) + \tfrac{1}{4}a_2^{(4)}T_3^*(x), \qquad (119)$$

which is equivalent to (116) with $a_3^{(4)} = -a_2^{(4)}/6$.

We can pursue further this process of successive approximation, at each stage truncating the series after the first $n+1$ terms, to produce better approximations to the 'best' polynomial of degree n. For $(1+x)^{-1}$, for example, the Chebyshev series rounded to five decimals is

$$y(x) = 0.707\,11T_0^* - 0.242\,64T_1^* + 0.041\,63T_2^* - ..., \qquad (120)$$

and the corresponding quadratic approximations obtained from the first two steps of the process outlined are respectively

$$\left. \begin{array}{l} p_2(x) = 0.707\,07T_0^* - 0.242\,42T_1^* + 0.040\,40T_2^* \\ \bar{p}_2(x) = 0.707\,11T_0^* - 0.242\,63T_1^* + 0.041\,59T_2^* \end{array} \right\}. \qquad (121)$$

The 'perturbation' $(1+x)e_n(x)$ is also converging to the 'true perturbation', which for the Chebyshev series is

$$-(1+x)\sum_{r=3}^{\infty} a_r T_r^*(x) = -\tfrac{1}{4}a_3 T_2^* - (\tfrac{3}{2}a_3 + \tfrac{1}{4}a_5)T_3^* - ...,$$

$$\sim 0.001\,79T_2^* + 0.009\,76T_3^* + ... \qquad (122)$$

For (121) we have the respective perturbations

$$0.010\,10T_3^*(x), \qquad 0.001\,73T_2^*(x) + 0.010\,40T_3^*. \qquad (123)$$

We repeat, however, that this error analysis is rigorous and does not depend on any sort of knowledge of the Chebyshev series.

Perturbation theory for differential systems. The integrated system

5.37 We consider first the treatment of the integrated system, since this is most nearly analogous to the corresponding direct problem. For the first-order system (29), for example, the algebraic equations (31) for the integrated system are similar in most respects to those say of (11) for the rational function $1/(1+x+x^2)$. The main difference is that the equation corresponding to the given condition has an infinity of terms, and with second-order systems the first two equations are usually of this type.

Nevertheless, successive approximate solutions, obtained from leading subsets of equations of the set (31), converge to the Chebyshev series. From (33), for example, we find

$$\left.\begin{aligned}
p_2(x) &= 1\cdot042\,12T_0^*(x)-0\cdot426\,32T_1^*(x)-0\cdot026\,37T_2^*(x) \\
p_3(x) &= 1\cdot058\,20T_0^*(x)-0\cdot434\,48T_1^*(x)-0\cdot026\,79T_2^*(x)+ \\
&\qquad\qquad +0\cdot010\,39T_3^*(x)
\end{aligned}\right\}, \quad (124)$$

and more extensive computation gives the Chebyshev series

$$y(x) = 1\cdot058\,31T_0^*(x)-0\cdot434\,54T_1^*(x)-0\cdot026\,80T_2^*(x)+$$
$$+0\cdot010\,45T_3^*(x)-0\cdot000\,40T_4^*(x)-0\cdot000\,04T_5^*(x).... \quad (125)$$

Each successive solution of (124) is the exact solution of a perturbed system. For example, $p_2(x)$ is obtained by assuming $a_3 = a_4 = \ldots = 0$ in (31). Only three equations are unsatisfied, and we find that $p_2(x)$ satisfies exactly the perturbed integrated system

$$\left.\begin{aligned}
(1+x)p_2(x)+ &\int (x+x^2)p_2(x)\,dx = A+x-\tfrac{1}{2}x^2+E_2(x) \\
E_2(x) &= \tau_3 T_3^*(x)+\tau_4 T_4^*(x)+\tau_5 T_5^*(x) \\
\tau_3 = \tfrac{1}{192}a_0+\tfrac{1}{24}a_1&+\tfrac{61}{192}a_2, \qquad \tau_4 = \tfrac{1}{256}a_1+\tfrac{1}{32}a_2 \\
\tau_5 &= \tfrac{1}{320}a_2
\end{aligned}\right\}. \quad (126)$$

We have also effectively chosen the constant A so that $p_2(x)$ satisfies exactly the given condition for $y(x)$, that is we are satisfying exactly the algebraic equation representing this condition.

The error $e_2(x)$ then satisfies the equation

$$(1+x)e_2(x) + \int (x+x^2)e_2(x)\,dx = E_2(x) + \alpha, \qquad (127)$$

where α is chosen so that

$$e_2(0) - \tfrac{3}{4}e_2(1) = 0. \qquad (128)$$

5.38 The solution of equations like (127) and (128) is not particularly easy, but the nature of $E_2(x)$ often enables us to find a good estimate for $e_2(x)$ from the iterative scheme defined here by

$$(1+x)e_2^{(r+1)}(x) = E_2(x) + \alpha_r - \int (x+x^2)e_2^{(r)}(x)\,dx, \qquad (129)$$

with the arbitrary constant adjusted so that (128) is satisfied at every stage.

With $e_2^{(0)}(x) = 0$, the next iterate is

$$(1+x)e_2^{(1)}(x) = E_2(x) + \alpha_0$$
$$= -0{\cdot}015\,3T_3^*(x) - 0{\cdot}002\,5T_4^*(x) -$$
$$-0{\cdot}000\,1T_5^*(x) - 0{\cdot}031\,4. \qquad (130)$$

In this example we can express the integral in (129) in closed analytical form, but it is just as easy, and usually necessary, to use simple quadrature formulae such as the trapezium rule. The iterative sequence, with the α_r adjusted at each stage, has the following approximate values:

x	0·0	·1	·2	·3	·4	·5	·6	·7	·8	·9	1·0
$(1+x)e_2^{(1)}$	−018 5	−034 7	−043 6	−045 7	−041 8	−033 9	−024 4	−016 8	−015 0	−023 9	−049
$(1+x)e_2^{(2)}$	−010 0	−026 0	−034 3	−035 3	−029 9	−020 3	−009 2	−000 3	+002 7	−004 5	−026
$(1+x)e_2^{(3)}$	−014 9	−030 9	−039 4	−040 6	−035 6	−026 6	−016 3	−008 4	−006 7	−015 5	−039
$(1+x)e_2^{(4)}$	−012 4	−028 4	−036 8	−037 9	−032 7	−023 4	−012 7	−004 3	−002 0	−009 9	−033

$$(131)$$

At this stage successive changes are oscillatory, and in the form of a geometric progression with common factor $\tfrac{1}{2}$. Taking advantage of this, and dividing finally by $1+x$, we obtain the error distribution

x	0·0	·1	·2	·3	·4	·5	·6	·7	·8	·9	1·0
$e_2(x)$	−013 3	−026 5	−031 4	−029 8	−024 1	−016 3	−008 7	−003 4	−002 0	−006 2	−017

$$(132)$$

This answer is more than a good estimate. It is in fact the accurate difference, with a maximum discrepancy of one unit in the fourth decimal place, between $y(x)$ in (125) and the $p_2(x)$ of (124). We have obtained it with little effort, and without knowing any more about the Chebyshev series than the approximation $p_2(x)$. In particular we have no idea at this stage about the accuracy of the coefficients of $p_2(x)$ compared with the Chebyshev coefficients, nor could we estimate with any confidence the behaviour of the neglected terms $a_3, a_4, \ldots$ in the Chebyshev series.

5.39 With a view to finding a better quadratic approximation we might take the second of (124), which is obtained from the leading 4×4 set of equations in (31), and omit the term in $T_3^*(x)$. This polynomial,

$$\bar{p}_2(x) = \tfrac{1}{2}a_0^{(4)}T_0^*(x) + a_1^{(4)}T_1^*(x) + a_2^{(4)}T_2^*(x)$$
$$= 1{\cdot}058\,20T_0^*(x) - 0{\cdot}434\,48T_1^*(x) - 0{\cdot}026\,79T_2^*(x), \quad (133)$$

has an error $\bar{e}_2(x) = \bar{p}_2(x) - y(x)$ which is clearly the exact solution of the perturbed integrated system

$$
(1+x)\bar{e}_2(x) + \int (x+x^2)\bar{e}_2(x)\,dx = \alpha + \tau_4 T_4^*(x) + \tau_5 T_5^*(x) + \\
+\tau_6 T_6^*(x) - a_3^{(4)}\Big\{(1+x)\,T_3^*(x) + \int (x+x^2)\,T_3^*(x)\,dx\Big\} \\
\left.\begin{array}{l} \\ \\ \\ \tau_4 = \tfrac{1}{256}a_1^{(4)} + \tfrac{1}{32}a_2^{(4)} + \tfrac{77}{256}a_3^{(4)} \\ \\ \tau_5 = \tfrac{1}{320}a_2^{(4)} + \tfrac{1}{40}a_3^{(4)}, \qquad \tau_6 = \tfrac{1}{384}a_3^{(4)} \end{array}\right\} \quad (134)
$$

In analogy with the discussion centred on equations (117)–(119) we can also deduce the result (134) directly from equations (31). For in this set we are taking $a_4 = a_5 = \ldots = 0$, expressing a_3 in terms of a_0, a_1 and a_2 from the fourth of (31), and thereby implicitly obtaining a perturbed leading 3×3 set for the new a_0, a_1 and a_2. The resulting error equation is (134) written in the form

$$
(1+x)\bar{e}_2(x) + \int (x+x^2)\bar{e}_2(x)\,dx \\
= \alpha + a_3^{(4)}\{\tfrac{1}{8}T_1^*(x) - \tfrac{19}{128}T_2^*(x) - \tfrac{3}{2}T_3^*(x)\} + \\
+ (\tfrac{1}{256}a_1^{(4)} + \tfrac{1}{32}a_2^{(4)})T_4^*(x) + \tfrac{1}{320}a_2^{(4)}T_5^*(x) \\
\left.\begin{array}{l} \\ \\ \\ a_3^{(4)} = -\tfrac{2}{3}(\tfrac{1}{192}a_0^{(4)} + \tfrac{1}{24}a_1^{(4)} + \tfrac{61}{192}a_2^{(4)}) \end{array}\right\} \quad (135)
$$

Another interesting point, obtained by inspecting the first of (31), is that we are also now perturbing the given condition. This comes as no surprise, since we quite reasonably expect that the 'best' polynomial will not satisfy exactly the associated condition, but now we have quantitative as well as qualitative verification for this conjecture.

The resulting condition, which specifies α in (135), is

$$\bar{e}_2(0) - \tfrac{3}{4}\bar{e}_2(1) = \tfrac{7}{4}a_3^{(4)}. \tag{136}$$

From (133) and (134), and with the iterative method used in **5.38**, we find, for the first approximation to the error, the expression

$$(1+x)\bar{e}_2^{(1)}(x) = 0\cdot001\ 4 + \cdot001\ 3T_1^* - \cdot001\ 5T_2^* -$$

$$- \cdot015\ 6T_3^* - \cdot002\ 5T_4^* - \cdot000\ 1T_5^*, \tag{137}$$

and corresponding to (131) we obtain successive approximations

x	$0 \cdot 0$	$\cdot 1$	$\cdot 2$	$\cdot 3$	$\cdot 4$	$\cdot 5$	$\cdot 6$	$\cdot 7$	$\cdot 8$	$\cdot 9$	$1 \cdot 0$
$(1+x)\bar{e}_2^{(1)}$	$\cdot011\ 8$	$-\cdot003\ 5$	$-\cdot011\ 5$	$-\cdot012\ 6$	$-\cdot008\ 0$	$\cdot000\ 4$	$\cdot010\ 1$	$\cdot017\ 8$	$\cdot019\ 3$	$\cdot009\ 7$	$-\cdot017$
$(1+x)\bar{e}_2^{(2)}$	$\cdot010\ 3$	$-\cdot005\ 0$	$-\cdot012\ 9$	$-\cdot013\ 6$	$-\cdot008\ 7$	$-\cdot000\ 1$	$\cdot009\ 2$	$\cdot016\ 0$	$\cdot016\ 1$	$\cdot005\ 3$	$-\cdot021$
$(1+x)\bar{e}_2^{(3)}$	$\cdot011\ 0$	$-\cdot004\ 3$	$-\cdot012\ 2$	$-\cdot012\ 8$	$-\cdot007\ 9$	$\cdot000\ 7$	$\cdot010\ 1$	$\cdot016\ 9$	$\cdot017\ 2$	$-\cdot006\ 8$	$-\cdot019$
$(1+x)\bar{e}_2^{(4)}$	$\cdot010\ 7$	$-\cdot004\ 6$	$-\cdot012\ 5$	$-\cdot013\ 1$	$-\cdot008\ 3$	$\cdot000\ 3$	$\cdot009\ 7$	$\cdot016\ 4$	$\cdot016\ 6$	$\cdot006\ 1$	$-\cdot019$

$$(138)$$

Again we have virtually converged to the solution, and the result

x	$0 \cdot 0$	$\cdot 1$	$\cdot 2$	$\cdot 3$	$\cdot 4$	$\cdot 5$	$\cdot 6$	$\cdot 7$	$\cdot 8$	$\cdot 9$	$1 \cdot 0$
$\bar{e}_2(x)$	$\cdot010\ 7$	$-\cdot004\ 2$	$-\cdot010\ 4$	$-\cdot010\ 1$	$-\cdot005\ 9$	$\cdot000\ 2$	$\cdot006\ 1$	$\cdot009\ 6$	$\cdot009\ 2$	$\cdot003\ 2$	$-\cdot010\ 0$

$$(139)$$

again agrees almost exactly with the correct solution of (135) and (136). We note, moreover, that the error has very nearly equal and opposite values at four points in the range, so that our solution (133) is very near indeed to the minimax polynomial, which here almost coincides with the truncated Chebyshev series. Again, we do not require any independent knowledge of the Chebyshev series to confirm this analysis.

5.40 For the general first-order system (23), with its integrated form (25), the equation for the error of a polynomial approximation of degree n is given by

$$p_1(x)e_n(x) + \int (p_2 - p_1')e_n(x)\,dx = E_n(x), \tag{140}$$

where $E_n(x)$ is composed of a number of terms $\tau_p T_p^*(x)$, and an arbitrary constant in (140) is adjusted so that the initial condition, or a perturbation thereof, is satisfied exactly. We would expect the iterative scheme

$$p_1(x)e_n^{(r+1)}(x) + \int (p_2 - p_1')e_n^{(r)}(x)\, dx = E_n(x) \qquad (141)$$

to converge whenever the term p_1 in the 'operator' in (140) is 'more important' than its partner $\int (p_2 - p_1')$ when applied to $e_n(x)$. Now in the error of the best polynomial approximation of degree n, $e_n(x)$ is also composed of Chebyshev polynomials $\sum\limits_{r=n+1}^{\infty} a_r T_r(x)$, and its integral contains terms of order n^{-1}. Unless $p_1(x)$ is very small, therefore, it will ultimately dominate, even to the extent that $e_n(x) = p_1^{-1}E_n(x)$ is a good approximation to the solution of the error equation. For this purpose, however, we would like to perturb the given condition so that any arbitrary constant introduced by the integration in (141) is as small as possible. This requires the perturbation of the given condition so that $e_{n+1}(x) = p_1^{-1}E_n(x)$ is satisfied by the new condition. We observe, in this context, the small constant term in (137) compared with that of (130), and the verification that the first approximation in (138) is very near the final correct result for $\bar{e}_2(x)$, and much more accurate in this connexion than that of (131).

In terms of the algebraic equations we have further confirmation of these remarks. The algebraic equations for the error are given by

$$\mathbf{Pe = b}; \qquad (142)$$

we are 'splitting' the matrix $\mathbf{P}$ in the form

$$\mathbf{P = Q + R}, \qquad (143)$$

and performing the iterative scheme

$$\mathbf{Qe}^{(r+1)} + \mathbf{Re}^{(r)} = \mathbf{b}. \qquad (144)$$

Here $\mathbf{Q}$ 'comes from' $p_1(x)$ in (140), and $\mathbf{R}$ from the integration term. In (30), for example, $\mathbf{Q}$ is the matrix corresponding to the constant coefficients and $\mathbf{R}$ corresponds to the coefficients with factor r^{-1} in that expression. Clearly $\mathbf{R}$ is negligible, compared with $\mathbf{Q}$, for sufficiently large r. The perturbation of the given condition corresponds to the fact that we want to suppress the contributions from the terms $a_{n+1}, a_{n+2}, \dots$ in the first row of equations like (31), the row which represents the initial condition. Otherwise these contributions, which are not reduced by the factor r^{-1}, may be embarrassingly large.

5.41 These considerations suggest that although the solution of successive subsets of the Chebyshev equations of type (31) for the integrated system will usually converge at a satisfactory rate to an acceptable approximation, and we can estimate the error at any stage by the methods outlined, we might get a still faster convergence rate by solving a perturbed problem. For (29) this is the integrated system

$$(1+x)p_n(x)+\int (1+x+x^2)p_n(x)\,dx$$
$$= x-\tfrac{1}{2}x^2+\tau_{n+1}T^*_{n+1}(x)+\tau_{n+2}T^*_{n+2}(x)+\tau_{n+3}T^*_{n+3}(x), \quad (145)$$

where the nature of the perturbing terms is arranged so that (145) has an exact solution $p(x)=\sum_{r=0}^{n}{}' a_r T^*_r(x)$. The perturbed condition is obtained from the approximation

$$(1+x)e_n(x) = \tau_{n+1}T^*_{n+1}(x)+\tau_{n+2}T^*_{n+2}(x)+\tau_{n+3}T^*_{n+3}(x), \quad (146)$$

and is given by

$$p_n(0)-\tfrac{3}{4}p_n(1) = 1+\{(-1)^{n+1}-\tfrac{3}{8}\}\tau_{n+1}+$$
$$+\{(-1)^{n+2}-\tfrac{3}{8}\}\tau_{n+2}+\{(-1)^{n+3}-\tfrac{3}{8}\}\tau_{n+3}. \quad (147)$$

For $n = 2$ the resulting equations of type (31) are

$$\left.\begin{aligned}
\tfrac{1}{8}a_0 \quad -\tfrac{7}{4}a_1 \quad +\tfrac{1}{4}a_2 &= 1-\tfrac{11}{8}\tau_3+\tfrac{5}{8}\tau_4-\tfrac{11}{8}\tau_5 \\
\tfrac{29}{64}a_0 +\tfrac{13}{8}a_1 +\tfrac{1}{16}a_2 &= \tfrac{1}{4} \\
\tfrac{1}{16}a_0 +\tfrac{23}{64}a_1 +\tfrac{3}{2}a_2 &= -\tfrac{1}{16} \\
\tfrac{1}{192}a_0 +\tfrac{1}{24}a_1+\tfrac{61}{192}a_2 &= \tau_3 \\
\tfrac{1}{256}a_1 +\tfrac{1}{32}a_2 &= \tau_4 \\
\tfrac{1}{320}a_2 &= \tau_5
\end{aligned}\right\}, \quad (148)$$

which apart from the first equation are of course precisely the relevant set drawn from (31). The fact that this first equation changes in successive approximations is a disadvantage for the method of forward elimination, which we have previously recommended in general. It has no particular disadvantage, however, for the backward recurrence process of **5.10**, nor for the rather analogous method used in **5.31** for the production of the form $\sum_{r=0}^{n} b_r x^r$ which, as we saw, was extremely convenient in this case.

5.42 All that we have discussed here applies also to the general second-order system of type (24), in the form of its doubly-integrated system (27). Indeed in the particular case in which $q_2 = 2q_1'$ in (24), so that the single integral vanishes in (27), we are even more attracted to the assumption that the error is dominated by $q_1^{-1}(x)E(x)$, where $E(x)$ is the perturbing term $\Sigma \tau_p T_p(x)$. Here the double integral contributes terms of order n^{-2}; and perturbation of *both* given conditions, so that $e(x) = q_1^{-1}(x)E(x)$ is satisfied by the new conditions, should give a very accurate solution indeed. We give various examples confirming these conjectures in **5.45–5.49** below.

Perturbation theory for the original system

5.43 For the treatment of the original system, say by a subset of equations (67) for the $\sum\limits_{r=0}^{2}{}' a_r^{(3)} T_r^*(x)$ approximation for (29), it is easy to see that we have solved exactly the perturbed differential equation

$$(1+x)p_2'(x)+(1+x+x^2)p_2(x)$$
$$= 1-x+\tau_2 T_2^*(x)+\tau_3 T_3^*(x)+\tau_4 T_4^*(x), \quad (149)$$

with the same given condition. The equation for the error is then

$$\left.\begin{aligned}(1+x)e_2'(x)+(1+x+x^2)e_2(x)\qquad\qquad\\= \tau_2 T_2^*(x)+\tau_3 T_3^*(x)+\tau_4 T_4^*(x)\\e_2(0) = \tfrac{3}{4} e_2(1)\qquad\qquad\qquad\qquad\end{aligned}\right\}. \quad (150)$$

With $e_2(x)$ of order $\tau_3 T_3^*(x)$, it is clear that the first term on the left of (150) is the dominant partner of the operator, and to find a good approximation to $e_2(x)$ we have to perform some process of integration. The integral of the right-hand side of (150), however, is not quite the 'best' perturbation for the integrated system, since it will contain a term in $T_1^*(x)$. For this reason the $p_n(x)$ obtained from the original system is in general a little inferior to that obtained from the integrated system. Moreover we have no easy way of assessing the good 'general' perturbation of the given conditions analogous to that of **5.41** for the integrated system.

In only one case does the treatment of the original system have any virtue. This applies when, in the general error equation

$$p_1(x)e_n'(x)+p_2(x)e_n(x) = E_n(x), \quad (151)$$

10

corresponding to (23), the term $p_2(x)$ is dominant. This could happen, for example, when $p_1(x)$ vanishes at some point of the range, typified by $p_1(x) = x$ in the range $0 \leq x \leq 1$. In this case, moreover, we cannot estimate the proper form of the perturbation for the given conditions.

Both these points are exemplified by the system

$$xy' - y = x, \qquad y(1) = 0, \tag{152}$$

with the integrated form

$$xy - \int 2y \, dx = \tfrac{1}{2}x^2 + A. \tag{153}$$

The form (153) has no advantage over (152), at least for small-order approximations, and we cannot from the error equation deduce a good approximation for $e_n(x)$ by neglecting the integral in (153). We might be able to do this, however, if the factor x can be cancelled in the error equation, which we discussed briefly in relation to the determination of the solution in the form $\sum\limits_{r=0}^{n} b_r x^r$, and we give examples of this in **5.47–5.49** below.

For (152) the 'unintegrated' treatment gives the error equation

$$x e_n'(x) - e_n(x) = \tau_n T_n^*(x), \qquad e_n(1) = 0, \tag{154}$$

only one 'τ term' being needed as we can easily deduce by recording the relevant algebraic equations. Now the error $e_n(x)$ is a maximum at one of the points $x = 0$, $x = 1$ or a point at which $e_n'(x) = 0$. Immediately this gives, from (154), the result $\max |e_n(x)| = |\tau_n|$, so that at least we have here the satisfaction of a rigorous error analysis.

Summary

5.44 We can now summarize our findings, and illustrate them with some examples.

(i) For the first-order system (23), we can integrate to produce (25). To find the Chebyshev series $\sum\limits_{r=0}^{\infty}{}' a_r T_r(x)$ we have an infinite set of algebraic equations, of which the solutions of successive leading sets give results which converge to the Chebyshev series.

(ii) For the subset of order $n+1$ in (i) the resulting solution is a polynomial $p_n(x) = \sum\limits_{r=0}^{n}{}' a_r^{(n+1)} T_r(x)$, which is the exact solution of a perturbed system. The error of this solution can usually be found by an iterative process, the first approximation to which is $(p_1(x))^{-1}E_n(x)$, where $E_n(x)$ is the perturbing term of the form $\Sigma \tau_p T_p(x)$, where the number and nature of the τ terms are determinable from the relevant algebraic equations.

(iii) This first approximation for the error is usually very accurate if the given condition is perturbed so that $e_n(x) = (p_1(x))^{-1}E_n(x)$ everywhere. The resulting polynomial is then a better approximation of order n to the best polynomial of this order obtained by truncating the Chebyshev series. We can then also set up a perturbed problem whose successive solutions converge rather faster to the Chebyshev series.

(iv) This perturbed problem can be solved in the form $p_n(x) = \sum_{r=0}^{n} b_r x^r$. The algebraic equations are 'easier' and the corresponding matrix sparser, and solution by a process of back-substitution, similar to backward recurrence for the Chebyshev series, is very attractive. We can also easily cancel common powers of x, which gives more power in all relevant cases to the statements in (ii) and (iii).

(v) The corresponding treatment of the original unintegrated system has little to recommend it, either for simplicity of computation or for the accuracy of successive approximations, except possibly for approximations at a stage in which the Chebyshev series is converging very slowly. For all practical purposes it can be discarded.

Example 1

5.45 We have already obtained some results for the first-order system

$$(1+x)y'+(1+x+x^2)y = 1-x, \qquad y(0)-\tfrac{3}{4}y(1) = 1, \quad 0 \le x \le 1. \tag{155}$$

The perturbation on the right needed to produce a solution $p_n(x)$ is

$$E_n(x) = \tau_n T_n^*(x)+\tau_{n+1} T_{n+1}^*(x)+\tau_{n+2} T_{n+2}^*(x). \tag{156}$$

The integrated form is

$$(1+x)y+ \int (x+x^2)y \, dx = x-\tfrac{1}{2}x^2, \tag{157}$$

and the perturbation on the right needed to produce a solution $p_n(x)$ is

$$E_n(x) = \tau_{n+1} T_{n+1}^*(x)+\tau_{n+2} T_{n+2}^*(x)+\tau_{n+3} T_{n+3}^*(x). \tag{158}$$

The corresponding perturbation to be introduced in the given condition, the second of (155), is then given by (147).

The Chebyshev series, and the respective quadratic polynomials obtained from (155) and (157) with the original condition, and from (157) with the perturbed condition (147), together with their maximum errors, are given to five decimal places by

$$
\left.
\begin{aligned}
y(x) &= 1{\cdot}058\ 31T_0^* - 0{\cdot}434\ 54T_1^* - 0{\cdot}026\ 80T_2^* + \\
&\quad + 0{\cdot}010\ 45T_3^* - 0{\cdot}000\ 40T_4^* - 0{\cdot}000\ 04T_5^* - \ldots \\
p_2(x) &= 1{\cdot}082\ 55T_0^* - 0{\cdot}420\ 74T_1^* - 0{\cdot}027\ 73T_2^* \\
&\qquad\qquad \max |e_2(x)| = 0{\cdot}042 \\
p_2(x) &= 1{\cdot}042\ 12T_0^* - 0{\cdot}426\ 32T_1^* - 0{\cdot}026\ 37T_2^* \\
&\qquad\qquad \max |e_2(x)| = 0{\cdot}032 \\
p_2(x) &= 1{\cdot}058\ 82T_0^* - 0{\cdot}435\ 67T_1^* - 0{\cdot}025\ 52T_2^* \\
&\qquad\qquad \max |e_2(x)| = 0{\cdot}014
\end{aligned}
\right\}. \quad (159)
$$

Example 2

5.46 We have also given some computation for the second-order system

$$
\left.
\begin{aligned}
y'' + xy' + xy &= 1 + x + x^2, \quad -1 \le x \le 1 \\
y(0) &= 1, \qquad y'(0) + 2y(1) - y(-1) = -1
\end{aligned}
\right\}. \quad (160)
$$

The perturbation in the differential equation needed to produce a solution $p_n(x)$ again has the form (156), with T^* replaced by T.

The integrated system is

$$
y + \int xy\,dx + \iint (xy - y)\,dxdx = \tfrac{1}{2}x^2 + \tfrac{1}{6}x^3 + \tfrac{1}{12}x^4, \quad (161)
$$

and the perturbation on the right needed to produce a solution $p_n(x)$ again has the form (158), with T^* replaced by T.

The corresponding perturbations to be introduced in the given conditions are easily found to be

$$
\left.
\begin{aligned}
p_n(0) &= 1 + (-1)^m \tau_{2m} \\
p_n'(0) + 2p_n(1) - p_n(-1) \\
&= -1 + \{3 + (-1)^{m-1}(2m-1)\}\tau_{2m-1} + \tau_{2m} + \\
&\qquad + \{3 - (-1)^{m-1}(2m+1)\}\tau_{2m+1}
\end{aligned}
\right\}, \quad (162)
$$

for $n+2 = 2m$, and

$$p_n(0) = 1+(-1)^m(\tau_{2m}-\tau_{2m+2})$$
$$p'_n(0)+2p_n(1)-p_n(-1)$$
$$= -1+\tau_{2m}+\{3+(-1)^m(2m+1)\}\tau_{2m+1}+\tau_{2m+2}$$

$\left.\right\}$, (163)

for $n+1 = 2m$.

Corresponding to (159) we find the results

$$y(x) = 1\cdot268\ 58T_0-0\cdot632\ 42T_1+0\cdot274\ 31T_2+$$
$$+0\cdot016\ 84T_3+0\cdot005\ 46T_4-0\cdot002\ 27T_5-$$
$$-0\cdot000\ 26T_6+0\cdot000\ 05T_7$$
$$p_4(x) = 1\cdot269\ 92T_0-0\cdot637\ 33T_1+0\cdot274\ 66T_2+$$
$$+0\cdot007\ 67T_3+0\cdot004\ 74T_4, \quad \max|e_4(x)| = 0\cdot013\ 0$$
$$p_4(x) = 1\cdot268\ 93T_0-0\cdot637\ 23T_1+0\cdot274\ 47T_2+$$
$$+0\cdot017\ 24T_3+0\cdot005\ 54T_4, \quad \max|e_4(x)| = 0\cdot006\ 5$$
$$p_4(x) = 1\cdot268\ 53T_0-0\cdot632\ 40T_1+0\cdot274\ 28T_2+$$
$$+0\cdot017\ 07T_3+0\cdot005\ 50T_4, \quad \max|e_4(x)| = 0\cdot002\ 8$$

$\left.\right\}$. (164)

In both (159) and (164) the last solution is almost the best possible approximation of relevant degree. In the fourth of (159) the error has four alternate maxima and minima with size varying between about 0·010 and 0·014, and in the fourth of (164) the six alternate maxima and minima vary between about 0·002 1 and 0·002 8.

Example 3

5.47 The system

$$xy''+y'+16xy = 0, \qquad y(0) = 1, \qquad y'(0) = 0, \quad -1 \leq x \leq 1,$$

(165)

obviously has an even solution. A quartic polynomial approximation $\sum_{r=0}^{2} a_{2r}\ T_{2r}(x)$ is the exact solution of

$$x\ p''_4\ (x)+p'_4(x)+16x\ p_4(x) = \tau_5\ T_5(x),$$

(166)

only one τ term being necessary. The solution which satisfies the given conditions is

$$p_4(x) = \tfrac{1}{7}\{T_0(x) - 5T_2(x) + T_4(x)\}, \tag{167}$$

and its maximum error, compared with $y(x) = J_0(4x)$, is about $0\cdot220$ near $x = 0\cdot6$.

The twice-integrated system, with a perturbation which can produce a quartic polynomial approximation, is

$$xp_4(x) - \int p_4(x)\,dx + \int\int 16xp_4(x)\,dx\,dx = \tau_7\,T_7(x), \tag{168}$$

and the solution which satisfies the given conditions is

$$p_4(x) = \tfrac{1}{14}\{T_0(x) - 10T_2(x) + 3T_4(x)\}. \tag{169}$$

Its maximum error is less than half that of (167), with a distribution

x	$0\cdot0$	$\cdot1$	$\cdot2$	$\cdot3$	$\cdot4$	$\cdot5$	$\cdot6$	$\cdot7$	$\cdot8$	$\cdot9$	$1\cdot0$
$e_4(x)$	0	$\cdot009$	$\cdot031$	$\cdot060$	$\cdot086$	$\cdot097$	$\cdot088$	$\cdot057$	$\cdot011$	$-\cdot029$	$-\cdot032$

$$\tag{170}$$

We cannot, however, say from (168) how we should perturb the given conditions. On the other hand if we divide (168) by x before applying the perturbation, we can write

$$p_4(x) - \frac{1}{x}\int p_4(x)\,dx + \frac{1}{x}\int\int 16x\,p_4(x)\,dx\,dx = \tau_6\,T_6(x), \tag{171}$$

and we can find the *polynomial* form $p_4(x) = \sum_{r=0}^{2} b_{2r}\,x^{2r}$ which satisfies this. Moreover it indicates that the error is nearly $\tau_6\,T_6(x)$, so that we take as perturbed condition

$$p_4(0) = 1 - \tau_6. \tag{172}$$

The solution of (171) and (172) is

$$p_4(x) = \tfrac{1}{175}(171 - 576x^2 + 336x^4), \tag{173}$$

and its error distribution is

x	$0\cdot0$	$\cdot1$	$\cdot2$	$\cdot3$	$\cdot4$	$\cdot5$	$\cdot6$	$\cdot7$	$\cdot8$	$\cdot9$	$1\cdot0$
$e_4(x)$	$-\cdot023$	$-\cdot016$	$\cdot003$	$\cdot025$	$\cdot045$	$\cdot050$	$\cdot038$	$\cdot010$	$-\cdot023$	$-\cdot037$	$\cdot003$

$$\tag{174}$$

Again we have nearly halved the maximum error of the previous result, and the number of alternate maxima and minima, though not quite their size, is that of the minimax solution.

We can do even a little better by cancelling x *before* the second integration, which ensures that the derivative $p_4'(x)$, and not just

$x\,p_4'(x)$, is zero at the origin. The first integration gives

$$x\,p_4'+\int 16x\,p_4\,dx = 0, \tag{175}$$

and division by x followed by another integration produces

$$p_4(x)+\int x^{-1}\left(\int 16x\,p_4(x)\,dx\right)dx = \tau_6\,T_6(x),\quad p_4(0)=1-\tau_6. \tag{176}$$

The solution is

$$p_4(x) = \tfrac{1}{71}(69-240x^2+144x^4), \tag{177}$$

with a rather smaller maximum error, a satisfactory error distribution, and a comparison with $\tau_6\,T_6(x)$ given by

x	0·0	·1	·2	·3	·4	·5	·6	·7	·8	·9	1·0
$e_4(x)$	−·028	−·022	−·006	·013	·028	·030	·015	−·013	−·041	−·044	·017
$\tau_6 T_6(x)$	−·028	−·023	−·010	·007	·022	·028	·021	·002	−·021	−·026	·028

$$\tag{178}$$

5.48 It is also interesting to apply the mixed method of **5.20–5.24**. The basic equation for the coefficients of the Chebyshev series $\sum\limits_{r=0}^{\infty}{}' a_{2r}\,T_{2r}(x)$ and its derivatives is

$$\tfrac{1}{2}(a_{r+1}^{(2)}+a_{r-1}^{(2)})+a_r^{(1)}+8(a_{r+1}+a_{r-1}) = 0. \tag{179}$$

If we eliminate the $a_r^{(2)}$ coefficients, which is equivalent to a *single* integration, we obtain

$$r(a_{r+1}^{(1)}+a_{r-1}^{(1)})+8(a_{r-2}-a_{r+2}) = 0. \tag{180}$$

This can be used, with backward recurrence in conjunction with the integrating equation

$$a_{r-1}^{(1)}-a_{r+1}^{(1)} = 2ra_r, \tag{181}$$

to build up the solution without further adjustment. A simple multiplying factor can then be applied to satisfy the remaining equation

$$\tfrac{1}{2}a_0-a_2+a_4-\ldots = 1, \tag{182}$$

the unperturbed given condition. With

$$a_6 = a_8 = \ldots = 0,\quad a_4 = 1;\qquad a_5^{(1)} = a_7^{(1)} = \ldots = 0, \tag{183}$$

we find

$$\left.\begin{array}{ccccccc} r & 0 & 1 & 2 & 3 & 4 \\ a_r & 1 & 0 & -4 & 0 & 1 \\ a_r^{(1)} & 0 & -8 & 0 & 8 & 0 \end{array}\right\}, \tag{184}$$

and the multiplier $2/11$ gives the required solution

$$p_4(x) = \tfrac{1}{11}(T_0 - 8T_2 + 2T_4). \tag{185}$$

Its maximum error is about $0 \cdot 140$, somewhere between that of the result for the original system and that for the doubly-integrated system, both with unperturbed conditions. This result, of course, could have been predicted from our previous general analysis, and confirms our expectations.

Example 4

5.49 We also have some success with cancellation in the more 'difficult' problem

$$xy' - y = x, \qquad y(1) = 0, \quad 0 \le x \le 1, \quad y = x \log x. \tag{186}$$

For the direct solution of the perturbed differential equation, with the original condition, we find

$$p_2(x) = \tfrac{1}{8}(-1 - 7x + 8x^2), \tag{187}$$

with a maximum error of $\tfrac{1}{8}$ at the origin. The corresponding solution of the perturbed integrated system

$$xy - \int 2y \, dx = \tfrac{1}{2}x^2 + \tau_3 T_3^*(x), \tag{188}$$

with the unperturbed condition, is

$$p_2(x) = \tfrac{1}{48}(-9 - 39x + 48x^2). \tag{189}$$

The error has a larger maximum of $\tfrac{3}{16}$ at the origin, but rather smaller values elsewhere.

Again we cannot decide how to perturb the given condition, but the differential equation implies that y is also zero at the origin, and the assumption

$$p_2(x) = b_1 x + b_2 x^2 \tag{190}$$

allows us to solve the perturbed integrated system

$$p_2(x) - x^{-1} \int 2p_2(x) \, dx = \tfrac{1}{2}x + \tau_2 T_2^*(x), \qquad p_2(1) = \tau_2. \tag{191}$$

The solution is

$$p_2(x) = \tfrac{1}{16}(-23x + 24x^2), \tag{192}$$

with a smaller maximum error of about $0 \cdot 10$ near $x = 0 \cdot 1$.

In *most* cases, we conclude, the integrated system gives better answers than the original system, and in *all* our examples integration, together with perturbation of the associated conditions and possibly with cancellation of a common power of x, has improved the accuracy still further.

The general linear differential equation

5.50 We turn briefly to the general linear differential equations of type (23) and (24), where the coefficients are no longer polynomials. The basic idea is simple. We propose to find the Chebyshev series by taking the polynomial approximation $p_n(x) = \sum_{r=0}^{n} {}' a_r T_r(x)$, satisfying the given conditions, and satisfying the differential equations exactly at certain selected points. For a differential equation of order m there will usually be m given conditions, so that we need $n-m+1$ other equations for the determination of the $n+1$ coefficients a_r. We then select the matching points at the zeros of the Chebyshev polynomial T_{n-m+1}, and solve the resulting $n+1$ linear equations for the a_r. As $n \to \infty$ we expect our $p_n(x)$ to tend to the Chebyshev series. We need not, of course, concentrate on the Chebyshev form. With $p_n(x) = \sum_{r=0}^{n} b_r x^r$ we shall obtain the same result, perhaps more easily.

As a simple example we consider the system

$$\left. \begin{array}{ll} y'' + y \sin x = e^x, & 0 \le x \le 1 \\ y(0) = 1, & y(1) = 0 \end{array} \right\}, \qquad (193)$$

and seek an approximation $p_n(x) = \sum_{r=0}^{n} b_r x^r$. The given conditions provide two equations, and we therefore satisfy the differential equation at the zeros of $T_{n-1}^*(x)$. With $n = 2, 3, 4$ we find successive polynomial approximations

$$\left. \begin{aligned} p_2(x) &= 1 - 1 \cdot 749x + 0 \cdot 749x^2 \\ &= 0 \cdot 406 T_0^*(x) - 0 \cdot 500 T_1^*(x) + 0 \cdot 094 T_2^*(x) \\ p_3(x) &= 1 - 1 \cdot 693x + 0 \cdot 391x^2 + 0 \cdot 302x^3 \\ &= 0 \cdot 395 T_0^*(x) - 0 \cdot 509 T_1^*(x) + 0 \cdot 105 T_2^*(x) + \\ &\qquad\qquad\qquad\qquad + 0 \cdot 009 T_3^*(x) \\ p_4(x) &= 1 - 1 \cdot 664x + 0 \cdot 491x^2 + 0 \cdot 054x^3 + 0 \cdot 121x^4 \\ &= 0 \cdot 402 T_0^*(x) - 0 \cdot 509 T_1^*(x) + 0 \cdot 098 T_2^*(x) + \\ &\qquad\qquad\qquad + 0 \cdot 009 T_3^*(x) + 0 \cdot 001 T_4^*(x) \end{aligned} \right\}, \qquad (194)$$

with some evidence of convergence.

Inspection is usually our only guide, since we shall rarely be able to perform any significant error analysis. The labour of computation is also significant, since at each stage we have to form the equations separately and to solve them separately, without compensating economies.

5.51 The basis of this method, and its connexion with the corresponding process for equations with polynomial coefficients, are fairly obvious. For suppose that our polynomial $p_n(x)$ is a reasonable approximation, so that, very nearly,

$$y - p_n(x) = a_{n+1} T_{n+1}(x). \tag{195}$$

Then the differential equation gives

$$q_1(x) p_n''(x) + q_2(x) p_n'(x) + q_3(x) p_n(x)$$
$$= q_4(x) - a_{n+1}\{q_1(x) T_{n+1}''(x) + q_2(x) T_{n+1}'(x) + q_3(x) T_n(x)\}, \tag{196}$$

and it is easy to see that the perturbation on the right-hand side is dominated by a multiple of $a_{n+1} q_1(x) T_{n-1}(x)$. The matching at the zeros of $T_{n-1}(x)$ is then a sound procedure. In the corresponding τ method of our earlier work the perturbation on the right of (196) is in fact a linear combination $\Sigma \tau_p T_p(x)$, with τ_{n-1} usually the largest of the τ_p. If the other τ_p are zero, or negligible, the two methods are virtually identical for the case of polynomial coefficients.

This suggests that the corresponding integrated treatment would also have advantages here. It is rarely convenient, however, because the relevant indefinite integrations can rarely be performed. In the present example we can form the doubly integrated equation

$$y + \iint y \sin x \, dx dx = e^x + Ax + B, \tag{197}$$

where A and B are arbitrary constants and we assume a polynomial form $\sum_{r=0}^{n} b_r x^r$ for y. We can then satisfy (197) at the zeros of $T_{n+1}^*(x)$, obtaining $n+3$ equations (two coming from the given conditions) for the $n+1$ coefficients b_r and the constants A and B.

For $n = 2$, (197) gives

$$b_0(1 - \sin x) + b_1(x - 2\cos x - x\sin x) +$$
$$+ b_2(x^2 - x^2 \sin x - 4x\cos x + 6\sin x) = e^x + Ax + b, \tag{198}$$

and the satisfaction of this at the zeros of $T_3^*(x)$, together with the satisfaction of the initial conditions, gives a result

$$p_2(x) = 1 - 1 \cdot 773x + 0 \cdot 773x^2 = 0 \cdot 403T_0^* - 0 \cdot 500T_1^* + 0 \cdot 097T_2^*, \quad (199)$$

which is clearly a little better than the $p_2(x)$ of (194).

We have little hope of further improvement by perturbing the given conditions. Our previous success with this process depended on a precise knowledge of the perturbing terms in the integrated system, but here we cannot in general find them in closed form. We may conclude, for the general linear differential system, that our method cannot claim the same advantages over other numerical methods which the corresponding approach for the special system clearly enjoys.

Non-linear differential equations

5.52 Finally, we mention some recent work on the Chebyshev solution of non-linear differential systems. We can apply the 'method of selected points', but the algebraic equations for the coefficients are now also non-linear, and we must use iterative methods for their solution. One alternative method is to use some form of iteration with respect to the differential equation, finding by linear processes successive solutions which increase steadily in accuracy as a result of a convergent process. A second is to apply a form of Newton's process for solving non-linear equations, which at each stage requires the solution of linear equations.

The first alternative (Wright 1964, Clenshaw and Norton 1963) solves the first-order differential equation

$$y' = f(x, y), \quad (200)$$

with some given initial condition, by means of the Picard iteration

$$y'_{r+1} = f(x, y_r), \quad (201)$$

whose integrated form is given by

$$y_{r+1} = \alpha + \int_0^x f(x, y_r) \, dx. \quad (202)$$

If at some stage we have an approximation

$$y_r = \sum_{s=0}^{n} {}' a_s^{(r)} T_s(x), \quad (203)$$

we can find the corresponding approximation

$$f_r = f(x, y_r) \sim \sum_{s=0}^{n}{}' b_s^{(r)} T_s(x),\tag{204}$$

by one of the processes discussed in Chapter 2. In analogy with the method of selected points we might use the interpolation formula (equation (52) of Chapter 2), which gives

$$b_s^{(r)} = \frac{2}{n+1} \sum_{k=0}^{n} f_r(x_k)\, T_s(x_k), \qquad x_k = \cos\!\left(\frac{2k+1}{n+1}\cdot\frac{\pi}{2}\right),\tag{205}$$

and f_r agrees exactly with its approximation at the zeros of $T_{n+1}(x)$. Collocation at the points $x_k = \cos(k\pi/n)$ (equation (51) of Chapter 2) is a second possibility with perhaps some slight computational advantages.

The known formulae for integrating a finite Chebyshev series then give from (202) an approximation

$$y_{r+1} = \sum_{s=0}^{n}{}' a_s^{(r+1)} T_s(x),\tag{206}$$

for use at the next step. We can keep n constant in the early stages and allow it to increase as the earlier coefficients settle down to constant values which, for large enough n, will tend to the coefficients of the Chebyshev series for $y(x)$.

For the second-order system

$$y'' = f(x, y, y'),\tag{207}$$

with initial conditions specifying $y(0)$ and $y'(0)$, we can proceed in a similar manner, iterating in the form

$$y''_{r+1} = f(x, y_r, y'_r).\tag{208}$$

With assumed Chebyshev approximations for y_r and y'_r we can compute the right of (208) in Chebyshev form, and hence find Chebyshev approximations for y'_{r+1} and y_{r+1} by successive integrations, satisfying the initial conditions in the process.

5.53 Success clearly depends on a guarantee of convergence of the Picard iteration. For the system (200) it is known that the method converges if $f(x, y)$ and $\dfrac{\partial}{\partial y} f(x, y)$ are bounded, and $f(x, y)$ is absolutely integrable in a rectangular region containing all relevant

(x, y). Similar conditions apply to a system of first-order equations of initial-value type.

There seem to be no comparable theorems for boundary-value problems, or problems with mixed conditions, and in such circumstances we may prefer a modification of Newton's general process for solving non-linear equations. For the system (200) a small change δy in y gives formally

$$(y+\delta y)' = f(x, y+\delta y) = f(x, y)+\delta y\frac{\partial}{\partial y}f(x, y)+O(\delta y^2), \quad (209)$$

suggesting the iterative process

$$y'_{r+1} = f(x, y_r)+(y_{r+1}-y_r)\frac{\partial}{\partial y}f(x, y_r). \quad (210)$$

Though we know of no guarantee of convergence (some sufficient conditions are given by Kalaba, 1959), we might expect the method to succeed for a starting approximation sufficiently near to the true solution, and that the nature of the associated conditions, of initial-value or boundary-value type for higher-order or simultaneous systems, would have little effect on at least the existence of convergence.

For the equation (207) the corresponding Newtonian iteration is given by

$$y''_{r+1} = f(x, y_r, y'_r)+(y_{r+1}-y_r)\frac{\partial}{\partial y}f(x, y_r, y'_r)+$$

$$+(y'_{r+1}-y'_r)\frac{\partial}{\partial y}f(x, y_r, y'_r). \quad (211)$$

In all cases we have to solve linear differential equations at each stage of the iteration, satisfying the initial or boundary conditions at each stage. Any of the methods discussed for linear systems can obviously be used, preferably with approximations represented by Chebyshev series rather than powers of x. The selected points method will also have computational advantages when the coefficients of the equation have Chebyshev approximations of large order. For this reason, in particular, Norton (1964) recommends the use of only the more dominant terms in the expansion of $\partial f/\partial y$ in (209) and $\partial f/\partial y$ and $\partial f/\partial y'$ in (211), and finds that the saving at each stage compensates for the slightly slower rate of convergence.

In the papers quoted in this section several examples indicate the general superiority of the Newton method in respect of the number of iterations needed for convergence, but more numerical evidence is required before we can give an authoritative evaluation in comparison with other standard methods.

Additional notes on Chapter 5

The use of Chebyshev polynomials for solving differential equations was first introduced by Lanczos (1938), who generally concentrated on finding polynomial approximations, in the form $p_n(x) = \sum\limits_{r=0}^{n} b_r x^r$, to the original differential system. This process we illustrated in **5.32**. Though we have generally preferred the integrated system, with the approximation $p_n(x) = \sum\limits_{r=0}^{n}{}' a_r T_r(x)$, the original method has some interesting implications, both theoretical and practical, which we now discuss briefly.

For the system

$$(1+x)y'+y = 0, \qquad y(0) = 1,$$

our polynomial $p_n(x)$ satisfies exactly the system

$$(1+x)p_n'(x)+p_n(x) = \tau_n T_n^*(x), \qquad p_n(0) = 1,$$

and the corresponding algebraic equations are

$$\left.\begin{aligned}
b_0 \qquad\qquad\qquad &= 1 \\
b_0+b_1 \qquad\qquad &= \tau_n\, c_n^{(0)} \\
2b_1+2b_2 \qquad &= \tau_n\, c_n^{(1)} \\
\cdot\qquad\qquad \cdot\qquad & \\
(n+1)b_n &= \tau_n\, c_n^{(n)}
\end{aligned}\right\},$$

where $c_n^{(r)}$ is the coefficient of x^r in $T_n^*(x)$. Ignoring the first equation, the rest form an upper triangular set $\mathbf{Ub} = \mathbf{c}$, where the rth element of $\mathbf{c}$ is $\tau_n\, c_n^{(r)}$. We can easily invert $\mathbf{U}$, by a process of back-substitution, and can do this column by column without specifying at any particular stage the value of n. We have

$$\mathbf{U}^{-1} = \begin{bmatrix}
u_{11} & u_{12} & u_{13} & \cdot & \cdot \\
 & u_{22} & u_{23} & \cdot & \cdot \\
 & & u_{33} & \cdot & \cdot \\
 & & & \cdot & \cdot & \cdot
\end{bmatrix},$$

where the rth column of $\mathbf{U}^{-1}$ is the solution of the first r rows and columns of $\mathbf{U}$ with the rth column of the unit matrix on the right-hand side.

We can then express the solution of the differential equation for $p_n(x)$ in the form

$$p_n(x) = \sum_{r=0}^{n} c_r Q_r(x),$$

where the $Q_r(x)$ are the *canonical polynomials*

$$Q_0(x) = u_{11}, \qquad Q_1(x) = u_{22}\,x + u_{12},$$

$$Q_2(x) = u_{33}\,x^2 + u_{23}\,x + u_{13}, \ldots.$$

This can be regarded as the general solution corresponding to the differential operator involved. In our example $c_r = \tau_n\, c_n^{(r)}$, and for a selected n we now compute τ_n from the condition $p_n(0) = 1$, obtaining the formal particular solution

$$p_n(x) = \frac{\displaystyle\sum_{r=0}^{n} c_n^{(r)} Q_r(x)}{\displaystyle\sum_{r=0}^{n} c_n^{(r)} Q_r(0)}.$$

Here $Q_0(x) = 1$, $Q_1(x) = \frac{1}{2}(x-1)$, $Q_2(x) = \frac{1}{3}(x^2 - x + 1), \ldots$, and it is interesting to note that $Q_r(x)$ is proportional to the partial sum

$$S_r(x) = 1 - x + x^2 - x^3 + \ldots + (-1)^r x^r$$

of the Taylor's series

$$y(x) = 1 - x + x^2 - x^3 + \ldots.$$

Our solution is a weighted average of these partial sums, and the weights turn the slowly-convergent Taylor's series into a rapidly convergent expansion in terms of the canonical polynomials.

For the problem of equation (59) the canonical polynomials can be written in the form

$$Q_r(z) = \frac{(-1)^r}{(r+1)!}\{1 - (1!)z + (2!)z^2 - \ldots + (-1)^r (r!)z^r\}, \quad r = 0, 1, \ldots,$$

and the weighting now turns the *divergent* asymptotic series,

$$y(z) = 1 - (1!)z + (2!)z^2 - \ldots + (-1)^r (r!)z^r + \ldots,$$

into a rapidly convergent expansion in the canonical polynomials.

In general the differential system will not be homogeneous, and we may need more than one τ term. For (29), for example, we must solve the perturbed equation

$$
\begin{aligned}
(1+x)p_n'(x) &+ (1+x+x^2)p_n(x) \\
&= 1-x+\tau_{n+2}\,T_{n+2}^*(x)+\tau_{n+1}\,T_{n+1}^*(x)+\tau_n\,T_n^*(x) \\
&= \sum_{r=0}^{n+2} c_r x^r,
\end{aligned}
$$

and the algebraic equations are

$$
\left.\begin{aligned}
b_0 + b_1 \qquad\qquad\qquad &= c_0 \\
b_0 + 2b_1 + 2b_2 \qquad\qquad &= c_1 \\
b_0 + b_1 + 3b_2 + 3b_3 \quad\; &= c_2 \\
b_1 + b_2 + 4b_3 + 4b_4 &= c_3 \\
\cdot \quad\;\; \cdot \quad\;\; \cdot \quad\;\; \cdot \quad\;\; \cdot&
\end{aligned}\right\}.
$$

The canonical polynomials, formed by inverting the upper triangular part of these equations, are

$$
Q_0(x) = 1, \qquad Q_1(x) = x-1, \qquad Q_2(x) = x^2-x-2,\dots,
$$

and the general solution is $p_n(x) = \sum_{r=0}^{n} c_{r+2}\,Q_r(x)$. The unknown τ_r are contained in the c_r, and are computed from the first pair of the algebraic equations and the extra equation given by the associated condition.

Two useful by-products follow. First, the solution can be obtained in a more general finite range $0 \le x \le a$ without the need for a preliminary change of variable. We merely alter a relevant term of the perturbation from $T^*(x)$ to $T^*(x/a)$, so that the argument of the Chebyshev polynomial has the correct range. The coefficient $c_n^{(r)}$ then becomes $c_n^{(r)}/a^r$, and the formal solution is otherwise unchanged.

Second, we can take for a the complex number z, solve the differential equation, and then put $x = z$. This gives a rational function for the solution, valid at any point z for which the line from the origin to this point does not pass through a singularity of $y(z)$. For the function $(1+z)^{-1}$, for example, this method gives the rational approximation

$$p_2(z) = \frac{\sum_{r=0}^{2} c_n^{(r)} z^{-r} Q_r(z)}{\sum_{r=0}^{2} c_n^{(r)} z^{-r} Q_r(0)} = \frac{8+4z-z^2}{8+12z+3z^2}.$$

These extensions, of course, are very similar to those suggested in Exercises 19 and 20 of Chapter 4 for the approximation of rational functions.

The canonical polynomials can be used in connexion with the integrated systems, and also in connexion with the approximation form $p_n(x) = \sum_{r=0}^{n}{}' a_r T_r(x)$, but the general approach is obvious and we suppress the details.

EXERCISES 5

1. Find the solutions of the leading 4×4 subset of equations (11), first by the method of matrix decomposition, with interchanges where necessary, and then by the method of backward recurrence.

2. The result of Exercise 1 gives a cubic approximation to the function $(1+x+x^2)^{-1}$ in $-1 \le x \le 1$. Find the maximum error of this approximation, without computing $(1+x+x^2)^{-1}$. Find also a more accurate cubic approximation and determine its maximum error.

3. From the results of equations (121), deduce two cubic approximations to $\log(1+x)$, and determine their maximum errors.

4. Find a cubic approximation $p_3(x) = \sum_{r=0}^{n}{}' a_r T_r(x)$ to the solution of the system

$$(3+2x)y'-y = 0, \qquad -1 \le x \le 1, \qquad y(0) = 1,$$

using (i) the original system, (ii) the mixed system, (iii) the integrated system and (iv) the integrated system with perturbation of the given condition. Estimate the maximum errors of the results (iii) and (iv) by the methods of **5.38** and **5.39**, and verify them by solving analytically the given differential system.

5. Find the corresponding solutions for (i), (iii) and (iv) of Exercise 4 in the form $p_3(x) = \sum_{r=0}^{3} b_r x^r$. Estimate the maximum error of the result of (i).

11

6. Repeat Exercises 4 and 5 for the system

$$y'' - 2(1+2x^2)y = 0, \qquad y(0) = 1, \qquad y'(0) = 0,$$

for a quartic approximation. (The analytical solution is $y = e^{x^2}$.)

7. Find an approximate eigenvalue and eigenfunction $\sum\limits_{r=0}^{2} b_r x^r$ for the problem $y'' + \lambda y = 0$, $y(0) = 0$, $y(1) = 0$, by
   (i) solving the original system with the same boundary conditions,
   (ii) solving the twice-integrated system with the same boundary conditions,
   (iii) solving the twice-integrated system with perturbed boundary conditions.

Show that the resulting approximations to the smallest eigenvalue are respectively 16, 9·6 and 9·907, compared with $\lambda = \pi^2 \sim 9\cdot870$, and discuss the error distribution of the corresponding computed eigenfunctions.

8. Find the first four approximations to the solution of equation (59) by the methods of **5.17, 5.18**, and **5.20**, and determine rigorously their maximum errors.

9. Repeat Exercise 8 with the methods of **5.30** and **5.32**. Compute the errors of these solutions, compared with the correct three-decimal values

y	0·0	0·1	0·2	0·3	0·4	0·5	0·6	0·7	0·8	0·9	1·0
z	1·000	0·916	0·852	0·801	0·759	0·723	0·691	0·664	0·639	0·617	0·596

Can we gain any advantage from the method of **5.33**?

10. Complete the computation of **5.23**, obtaining a quartic approximation to the Chebyshev series solution of equation (35).

11. Estimate, by the method of **5.38**, the maximum error of the quartic approximation (39) to the solution of the system (35).

Find the approximate perturbation of the given conditions, and estimate the error distribution of the resulting quartic approximation.

12. Find, by the method of **5.38**, the error distribution of the approximation (177) as a solution of (160).

13. We remarked in **5.43** that, for the production of a polynomial approximation, the differential system generally gives a 'poor' perturbation. We can get a 'better' perturbation as follows. If $p_n(x) = y + \tau_{n+1} T_{n+1}(x)$ (or $T_{n+1}^*(x)$ where relevant, and with additional terms where necessary), substitution in the differential

equation gives a 'good' perturbation. To this we can fit the best polynomial of relevant degree (so that $p_n(x)$ can satisfy exactly the relevant differential equation), and use this as the 'best' perturbation. The perturbation of the given condition comes from the original assumption for $p_n(x)$. Try this for the system

$$(1+x)y'+y = 0, \qquad y(0) = 1, \qquad y = (1+x)^{-1},$$

finding the quadratic approximation

$$p_2(x) = 0{\cdot}705\ 9T_0^*(x)-0{\cdot}242\ 7T_1^*(x)+0{\cdot}044\ 1T_2^*(x).$$

Find the corresponding result

$$p_2(x) = 0{\cdot}695\ 7T_0^*(x)-0{\cdot}260\ 9T_1^*(x)+0{\cdot}043\ 5T_2^*(x)$$

for the perturbation $\tau_2 T_2^*(x)$ of the differential equation with original given condition, and verify that the maximum error of the former is only about one-third of the latter.

14. Try the method of Exercise 13 for the problems of Exercises 4 and 6 and that of **5.8**.

15. Discuss the application of Exercise 13 for the integrated system. Illustrate the method on the problems of Exercises 4 and 13.

16. Discuss the solution, by the various methods of this chapter, of two simultaneous first-order equations. Illustrate with the solution of Exercise 6, writing $y' = z$, $z' = 2(1+2x^2)y$, $y(0) = 1$, $z(0) = 0$.

17. In **5.12** we solved the relevant linear equations by the Gauss-Seidel iterative method. This is certain to converge if in every row of the matrix the modulus of the diagonal term is greater than the sum of the moduli of the other terms. This is clearly likely to happen for the equations derived from the integrated system, in all rows except those representing the given conditions. By preliminary elimination of the first unknown a_0, and possibly the second a_1, we may produce a diagonally dominant set, easily soluble by iteration. We thereby produce the Chebyshev series to any degree of accuracy required. Try this for equations (31). (This method is discussed by Scraton (1965).)

18. The method of Exercise 17 may fail for the problem of **5.16**, or at least will produce slow convergence. Investigate this. Can we get faster convergence by using the form $\sum_{r=0}^{n} b_r x^r$, with cancellation of a common power of x in the differential equation? Investigate this with respect to the problems of **5.47** and **5.49**.

19. Find a rational approximation to e^z, valid at every point in the complex plane.

20. Discuss the use of canonical polynomials for the problems and methods of **5.8** and **5.11**.

21. Discuss the use of canonical polynomials for the problems and methods of **5.30** and **5.31**.

22. Discuss the treatment by canonical polynomials when the relevant upper triangular matrix is singular. Use the problem of **5.16** as illustration.

6

Linear Integral and Partial Differential Equations

Introduction

6.1 In previous chapters we have concentrated on finding Chebyshev series or corresponding polynomial approximations for functions of a single variable x in a finite range $a \leq x \leq b$. The minimax theory, the known theorems about convergence, and the fact of rapid convergence of the Chebyshev series gave these methods a firm theoretical and practical basis. There are few comparable theories for functions of two or more variables, and the methods of this chapter are mostly speculative, sometimes of practical value but generally lacking rigorous background.

The underlying theme of this chapter is the representation in Chebyshev series of functions of two independent variables. For partial differential equations the solutions are functions of these variables. For integral equations the solution involves only one independent variable, but the fact that the kernel involves two such variables makes this type of problem relevant to this chapter.

In the last section, maintaining the theme, we give a brief account of curve fitting in two dimensions, by methods which are just extensions of those of **4.16-4.18** for similar problems in one variable.

Fredholm integral equations of second kind

6.2 We discuss some methods for solving the equation

$$\int\limits_{-1}^{1} k(x, y)f(y) \, dy = f(x) + g(x), \tag{1}$$

in which $g(x)$ and the kernel $k(x, y)$ are given functions of their respective variables. The choice of the limits of integration is not particularly restrictive, since any finite range can be reduced to

$(-1, 1)$ by a linear transformation of y. The range $(0, 1)$ may be more appropriate in some contexts. Without considering existence theorems, we assume that $g(x), f(x)$, and $k(x, y)$ all have convergent Chebyshev expansions for all relevant x and y, and we look for the solution $f(x)$ in this form.

(i) *Degenerate kernel*

6.3 The solution is obtained without difficulty in one particular case, when the kernel has the degenerate form

$$k(x, y) = \sum_{r=1}^{p} X_r(x) Y_r(y), \tag{2}$$

for finite p. Writing

$$A_r = \int_{-1}^{1} Y_r(y) f(y) \, dy, \quad r = 1, 2, ..., p, \tag{3}$$

we determine $f(x)$ from (1) in the form

$$f(x) = \sum_{r=1}^{p} A_r X_r(x) - g(x), \tag{4}$$

and substitution in (3) then gives

$$A_r = \sum_{s=1}^{p} A_s \int_{-1}^{1} X_s(y) Y_r(y) \, dy - \int_{-1}^{1} g(y) Y_r(y) \, dy, \quad r = 1, 2, ..., p. \tag{5}$$

This is a set of linear algebraic equations for the constants A_r, with coefficients and right-hand sides involving the integrals of known functions.

As a simple example we consider the equation

$$\int_{-1}^{1} (x+y) f(y) \, dy = f(x) + x^2, \tag{6}$$

in which $X_1(x) = x$, $Y_1(y) = 1$, $X_2(x) = 1$, $Y_2(y) = y$. From (4) the solution is

$$f(x) = A_2 + A_1 x - x^2, \tag{7}$$

and (5) gives

$$A_1 = 2A_2 - \tfrac{2}{3}, \qquad A_2 = \tfrac{2}{3} A_1, \tag{8}$$

so that

$$f(x) = \tfrac{4}{3} + 2x - x^2. \tag{9}$$

Now if $X_r(x)$, $Y_r(x)$ and $g(x)$ are given in Chebyshev form

$$\left.\begin{array}{c} X_r(x) = \sum_{s=0}^{\infty}{}' \alpha_s^{(r)} T_s(x), \qquad Y_r(x) = \sum_{s=0}^{\infty}{}' \beta_s^{(r)} T_s(x) \\[2ex] g(x) = \sum_{s=0}^{\infty}{}' \gamma_s^{(r)} T_s(x) \end{array}\right\}, \qquad (10)$$

then the expressions for products and integrals of Chebyshev polynomials will enable us to compute the integrals in (5) in more complicated cases. Moreover if the series in (10) converge rapidly not many terms are involved and the computation is not prohibitive.

(ii) Non-degenerate kernel

6.4 If the kernel cannot be expressed as a finite series (2) the computation is considerably more involved. In theory we can find a Chebyshev-series solution if we write

$$f(x) = \sum_{r=0}^{\infty} a_r T_r(x), \qquad g(x) = \sum_{r=0}^{\infty} g_r T_r(x), \qquad (11)$$

substitute in (1), interchange the order of integration and summation in the first term, and produce the equation

$$\sum_{s=0}^{\infty} a_s \int_{-1}^{1} k(x, y) T_s(y)\, dy = \sum_{r=0}^{\infty} a_r T_r(x) + \sum_{r=0}^{\infty} g_r T_r(x). \qquad (12)$$

If we can now find the expansion

$$\int_{-1}^{1} k(x, y) T_s(y)\, dy = \sum_{r=0}^{\infty} b_{sr} T_r(x), \qquad (13)$$

we can equate corresponding coefficients of each $T_r(x)$ on both sides of (12), which is legitimate since the Chebyshev polynomials form a complete set of independent functions, to produce an infinite set of algebraic equations for the required coefficients a_r, given by

$$\sum_{s=0}^{\infty} a_s b_{sr} = a_r + g_r, \qquad r = 0, 1, \dots. \qquad (14)$$

The a_r will decrease rapidly for sufficiently large r, so that in a convenient method of solving (14) we select the first $n+1$ rows and columns, perform Gauss elimination and back-substitution for the last few coefficients a_n, a_{n-1}, a_{n-2}, say, decide by inspection whether convergence is sufficiently rapid for the required precision with this selected value of n, and if necessary add some extra rows and columns with only a small additional amount of work.

This method will succeed, for example, for an equation involving the kernel

$$k(x, y) = |x-y|, \tag{15}$$

which has a discontinuous derivative at $x = y$. Though the Chebyshev series for $k(x, y)$ consequently converges only slowly for any x in $(-1, 1)$, we can find the *finite* series

$$\left. \begin{aligned} I_s &= \int_{-1}^{1} |x-y|\, T_s(y)\, dy \\ &= -\frac{1+(-1)^s}{s^2-4} T_0(x) + \frac{1-(-1)^s}{s^2-1} T_1(x) + \\ &\qquad\qquad + \frac{T_{s+2}(x)}{2(s+1)(s+2)} - \frac{T_s(x)}{s^2-1} + \frac{T_{s-2}(x)}{2(s-1)(s-2)} \\ I_0 &= \tfrac{3}{2} T_0(x) + \tfrac{1}{2} T_2(x), \qquad I_1 = \tfrac{1}{12} T_3(x) - \tfrac{3}{4} T_1(x) \\ I_2 &= \tfrac{1}{24} T_4(x) - \tfrac{1}{3} T_2(x) - \tfrac{3}{8} T_0(x) \end{aligned} \right\} . \tag{16}$$

For the integral equation

$$\tfrac{1}{2} \int_{-1}^{1} |x-y|\, f(y)\, dy = f(x) + g(x), \tag{17}$$

for example, the resulting algebraic equations are then typified by

$$\frac{a_{r-2}}{4r(r-1)} - \left(1 + \frac{1}{2(r^2-1)}\right) a_r + \frac{a_{r+2}}{4r(r+1)} = g_r, \tag{18}$$

and there are two special equations relating to the coefficients of $T_0(x)$ and $T_1(x)$.

In addition to the method just outlined we could here use the τ method, of Chapter 5, to produce a finite polynomial approximation to $f(x)$ which is the exact solution of a slightly perturbed problem. For example with

$$f^*(x) = \sum_{r=0}^{m} a_r T_r(x), \qquad g^*(x) = \sum_{r=0}^{N} g_r T_r(x), \quad N \leq m, \tag{19}$$

we can here solve exactly the system

$$\tfrac{1}{2} \int\limits_{-1}^{1} |x-y|\, f^*(y)\, dy = f^*(x)+g^*(x)+\tau_{m+2}(x)T_{m+2}(x), \qquad (20)$$

with a computed value of τ_{m+2}.

6.5 In general we shall not be able to find exact formulae of type (16), and an alternative procedure is to use a degenerate kernel which approximates well to $k(x, y)$ at all relevant regions of the (x, y) plane. For example, we might take the approximation

$$k^*(x, y) = \sum_{r=0}^{n} T_r(x) \sum_{s=0}^{n} k_{rs}^* T_s(y), \qquad (21)$$

together with (19), and solve exactly the perturbed integral equation

$$\int\limits_{-1}^{1} k^*(x, y)f^*(y)\, dy = f^*(x)+g^*(x), \qquad (22)$$

either by the method of **6.3** or by equating corresponding coefficients of each $T_r(x)$.

In practice we shall usually find the coefficients k_{rs}^* in (21) in two stages. First, for a given x_i, we can find the approximate expansion

$$k^*(x_i, y) = \sum_{s=0}^{n} \alpha_s(x_i)T_s(y), \qquad (23)$$

by one of the interpolation formulae of **2.13**. Then for each value of s in (23) we fit the coefficients $\alpha_s(x_i)$ by the polynomial

$$\alpha_s(x) = \sum_{r=0}^{n} k_{rs}^* T_r(x), \qquad (24)$$

using the same interpolation formula, and so produce (21).

This form has some advantages in relation to the resulting linear equations for the required coefficients a_r. The equations are typified by

$$\sum_{s=0}^{m} a_s b_{sr} = a_r+g_r, \quad r = 0, 1,..., n, \qquad (25)$$

where

$$b_{sr} = \sum_{j=0}^{n} k_{rj} t_{sj}, \tag{26}$$

$$t_{sj} = \int_{-1}^{1} T_s(y)T_j(y)\,dy = \left.\begin{array}{l} -\left\{\dfrac{1}{(j+s)^2-1}+\dfrac{1}{(j-s)^2-1}\right\} \quad \text{for even } s+j \\[2mm] = 0 \qquad\qquad\qquad\qquad\qquad\qquad \text{for odd } s+j \end{array}\right) \tag{27}$$

From this we find, for an *even* kernel $k(x, y) = k(-x, -y)$, that equations (25) are reducible to two sets, one for the even coefficients and one for the odd coefficients, with obvious savings in the computation.

6.6 Though it is not easy in advance to specify satisfactory values of m in (19) and n in (21) to secure the required accuracy, we can determine an upper bound to the error induced by particular choices, by a formula of Kantorovich and Krylov (1958). If

$$\int_{a}^{b} |k(x, y)-k^*(x, y)|\,dy < h, \quad |g(x)-g^*(x)| < \eta, \quad |g(x)| < M,$$
$$\tag{28}$$

and

$$\int_{a}^{b} |\gamma(x, y)|\,dy < B, \tag{29}$$

where $\gamma(x, y)$ is the resolvent kernel for the approximate integral equation (22), then

$$|f(x)-f^*(x)| < \frac{Mh(1+B)^2}{1-h(1+B)} + \eta(1+B). \tag{30}$$

Now we can clearly estimate h and η, if only by direct computation, and the resolvent kernel is contained in the solution of (22) expressed in the form

$$f^*(x) = -g^*(x) + \int_{-1}^{1} \gamma(x, y)g^*(y)\,dy. \tag{31}$$

Close inspection of the method of **6.3** shows that $\gamma(x, y)$ is obtained in the course of the computation, and we can therefore estimate B. This result does not separate the effects of m and n, but generally we can estimate a satisfactory m from *a posteriori* inspection of coefficients a_r obtained from a particular m, and this gives an estimate of a suitable h and therefore of n in (21).

6.7 As an example we consider Love's equation

$$-\frac{1}{\pi}\int_{-1}^{1}\frac{f(y)}{1+(x-y)^2}\,dy = f(x)-1, \qquad (32)$$

treated by finite-difference methods by Fox and Goodwin (1953). For simplicity we take $n = 2$ in (23), and choosing x_i as the zeros of $T_3(x)$ we find, rounded to three decimals, the approximations

$$\left.\begin{array}{l}
-\pi k^*(x_0, y) = 0{\cdot}587T_0(y)+0{\cdot}380T_1(y)+ \\
\qquad\qquad\qquad +0{\cdot}016T_2(y), \quad x_0 = \cos(\pi/6) \\
-\pi k^*(x_1, y) = 0{\cdot}750T_0(y)- \\
\qquad\qquad\qquad -0{\cdot}250T_2(y), \quad x_1 = \cos(\pi/2) \\
-\pi k^*(x_2, y) = 0{\cdot}587T_0(y)-0{\cdot}380T_1(y)+ \\
\qquad\qquad\qquad +0{\cdot}016T_2(y), \quad x_2 = \cos(5\pi/6)
\end{array}\right\}, \quad (33)$$

using equation (51) of Chapter 2 with $y_k = \cos(k\pi/2)$, $k = 0, 1, 2$. We can then interpolate column-wise, using equation (52) of Chapter 2, to find

$$-\pi k^*(x, y) = T_0(x)\{0{\cdot}641T_0(y)-0{\cdot}073T_2(y)\}+T_1(x)\{0{\cdot}439T_1(y)\}+$$
$$+T_2(x)\{-0{\cdot}109T_0(y)+0{\cdot}177T_2(y)\}. \quad (34)$$

Substitution in (32), and use of (27), then give the identity

$$-\frac{1}{\pi}\{(1{\cdot}331a_0-0{\cdot}495a_2)T_0(x)+0{\cdot}293a_1\,T_1(x)+$$
$$+(-0{\cdot}336a_0+0{\cdot}238a_2)T_2(x)\}$$
$$= a_0\,T_0(x)+a_1\,T_1(x)+a_2\,T_2(x)-T_0(x). \quad (35)$$

We easily verify that the equations obtained from successive coefficients of $T_r(x)$ split into two pairs, one for the even coefficients and one for the odd coefficients. Here we find $a_1 = 0$, corresponding to the known fact that the solution is even, and then

$$a_0 = 0.710, \qquad a_2 = 0.071. \tag{36}$$

To this precision the correct values are 0.708 and 0.049 respectively, and we leave as an exercise the determination of the error bound given by (30).

6.8 Alternatively, we can proceed directly from the approximation (23) to the kernel at the selected points x_i, and satisfy exactly the integral equation

$$\int_{-1}^{1} k^*(x_i, y) \sum_{r=0}^{m} a_r T_r(y) \, dy = \sum_{r=0}^{m} a_r T_r(x_i) + g(x_i) \tag{37}$$

at each x_i, $i = 0, 1, \ldots, m$. There is then no need to approximate to $g(x)$, and we have enough linear equations for the determination of the required a_r.

If we choose the same points x_i as in **6.7** the result is clearly identical with that already obtained, though the linear equations are no longer separable into even and odd sets, and we have less confidence about error estimation. Elliott (1963) used this method, and tried to estimate the necessary number of terms in both the approximation to $k(x_i, y)$ and that to $f(x)$, which is the number of collocation points. He based his estimate on the predicted size of the coefficient a_m of the last term in $f(x)$, but the results were hardly sufficiently sharp to be of practical value.

An idea of a useful set of collocation points can be obtained by methods similar to those used for differential equations. If we assume that our polynomial approximation closely satisfies the equation

$$f(x) = f_m(x) + \tau_{m+1} T_{m+1}(x), \tag{38}$$

for constant τ_{m+1}, then substitution in the integral equation gives

$$\int_{-1}^{1} k(x, y) T_{m+1}(y) \, dy = T_{m+1}(x), \tag{39}$$

and we should choose the zeros of this equation as collocation points. For sufficiently large m they will be close to the zeros of $T_{m+1}(x)$, and this chioce was made in **6.7**.

Other Fredholm equations

6.9 The methods outlined will clearly find approximate solutions to the eigenvalue problem

$$\int_{-1}^{1} k(x, y)f(y)\,dy = \lambda f(x), \tag{40}$$

the integral equation (40) of the third kind being replaced by an approximating algebraic problem

$$(\mathbf{A} - \lambda \mathbf{I})\mathbf{f} = \mathbf{0}, \tag{41}$$

in obvious notation.

For the Fredholm equation of the first kind,

$$\int_{a}^{b} k(x, y)f(y)\,dy = g(x), \tag{42}$$

the formal solution is expressible in the form

$$f(x) = \sum_{r=1}^{\infty} \frac{\alpha_r}{\lambda_r} f_r(x), \qquad g(x) = \sum_{r=1}^{\infty} \alpha_r f_r(x), \tag{43}$$

where λ_r is an eigenvalue of (40) with eigenfunction $f_r(x)$. There are obvious difficulties (see, for example, Baker *et al.*, 1964) if there are only a finite number of non-zero eigenvalues, which is the case with a degenerate kernel, since there is no possible solution unless $g(x)$ is expressible exactly as a linear combination of the corresponding finite set of eigenfunctions.

More generally, the problem is ill-conditioned if any λ_r is very small, since small changes in the corresponding α_r in (43), corresponding to small changes in $g(x)$, make large changes in the solution $f(x)$. Now it is clear from (27) that the (r, s) element of the matrix $\mathbf{A}$ in (41) will in general be of order at most $1/(r+s)$, so that in the infinite matrix successive rows and columns have smaller and smaller elements. It follows that there may be a large number of small eigenvalues, tending to zero in the limit, and the problem is correspondingly very ill-conditioned.

Parabolic partial differential equations

6.10 We now consider the solution of partial differential equations of parabolic type in two independent variables x and y, in which the range of x is adjusted to the finite interval $-1 \leq x \leq 1$, and y effectively covers the semi-infinite range $0 \leq y \leq \infty$.

The simplest parabolic equation is given by

$$\frac{\partial f}{\partial y} = \frac{\partial^2 f}{\partial x^2}, \tag{44}$$

and has the associated initial condition

$$f(x, 0) = g(x), \quad -1 \leq x \leq 1, \tag{45}$$

and boundary conditions

$$\left. \begin{aligned} h_1(y)f(1, y) + k_1(y)\frac{\partial}{\partial x}f(1, y) &= l_1(y), \quad x = +1 \\[2ex] h_{-1}(y)f(-1, y) + k_{-1}(y)\frac{\partial}{\partial x}f(-1, y) &= l_{-1}(y), \quad x = -1 \end{aligned} \right\} . \tag{46}$$

Our methods will apply to more complicated equations of type (44), and this will become obvious in the sequel.

This problem is commonly solved by finite-difference methods. In particular we might use the Crank-Nicolson formula, which replaces (44) by the approximation

$$f(x, y_r + \delta y) - f(x, y_r) = \tfrac{1}{2}\,\delta y\left\{\frac{\partial^2}{\partial x^2}f(x, y_r + \delta y) + \frac{\partial^2}{\partial x^2}f(x, y_r)\right\}. \tag{47}$$

If the function $f(x, y_r)$ is known, (47) can be solved as an ordinary differential equation for $f(x, y_r + \delta y)$. It is a two-point boundary problem with conditions given by (46) evaluated at $y = y_r + \delta y$. We therefore have a step-by-step process in y, the initial conditions being used at the very first step.

Each successive boundary-value problem can obviously be solved quite conveniently by any of the methods of Chapter 5, and has been treated in this way by Elliott (1961). The method of canonical polynomials is particularly valuable if the differential equation has coefficients independent of y, since these polynomials are the same at every step.

Analogue of the τ method

6.11 The finite-difference approach effectively computes the solution only at successive discrete values of y. It has also the disadvantage that (47) involves a truncation error in the y direction, the effect of which is not easy to assess. With a view to eliminating this error we can seek directly a solution in one of the forms

$$f(x, y) = \sum_{r=0}^{\infty}{}' a_r(y)T_r(x), \qquad f(x, y) = \sum_{r=0}^{n}{}' a_r(y)T_r(x), \qquad (48)$$

continuous in both x and y. For simplicity of notation we write

$$\frac{d}{dy} a_r(y) = \dot{a}_r . \qquad (49)$$

Borrowing an idea from Chapter 5, we assume solutions

$$f(x, y) = \sum_{r=0}^{\infty}{}' a_r(y)T_r(x), \qquad \frac{\partial^2 f}{\partial x^2}(x, y) = \sum_{r=0}^{\infty}{}' a_r^{(2)}(y)T_r(x), \qquad (50)$$

substitute in the differential equation and equate corresponding coefficients of $T_r(x)$, obtaining the infinite set of ordinary differential equations

$$\dot{a}_r = a_r^{(2)}, \quad r = 0, 1,.... \qquad (51)$$

We have some additional relations from (**5.18**), given by

$$a_r^{(2)} = 4 \sum_{s=1}^{\infty} s(r+s)(r+2s)a_{r+2s}, \qquad (52)$$

and the initial and boundary conditions (45) and (46).

If $g(x)$ is expressible in the form

$$g(x) = \sum_{r=0}^{\infty}{}' g_r T_r(x), \qquad (53)$$

the initial conditions merely provide the starting values

$$a_r(0) = g_r, \quad r = 0, 1,.... \qquad (54)$$

For the boundary conditions we have

$$f(\pm 1, y) = \sum_{r=0}^{\infty}{}' (\pm 1)^r a_r(y), \qquad \frac{\partial}{\partial x} f(\pm 1, y) = \sum_{r=1}^{\infty} (\pm 1)^{r+1} r^2 a_r(y), \qquad (55)$$

(see Exercise 13 of Chapter 3), and then

$$h_{\pm 1}(y) \sum_{r=0}^{\infty}{}' (\pm 1)^r a_r(y) + k_{\pm 1}(y) \sum_{r=1}^{\infty} (\pm 1)^{r+1} r^2 a_r(y) = l_{\pm 1}(y). \qquad (56)$$

Equations (51), (52), (54), and (56) serve to determine uniquely the required functions $a_r(y)$.

6.12 To see the effect of the necessary truncation of the expansions (50), we consider the differential equation (44) with initial condition

$$f(x, 0) = 1-x^2 = \tfrac{1}{2}\{T_0(x) - T_2(x)\}, \tag{57}$$

and boundary conditions

$$f(1, y) = f(-1, y) = y. \tag{58}$$

We assume the *finite* approximation

$$f(x, y) = \sum_{r=0}^{4}{}' a_r(y) T_r(x), \quad \frac{\partial^2}{\partial x^2} f(x, y) = \sum_{r=0}^{2}{}' a_r^{(2)}(y) T_r(x), \tag{59}$$

and equations (51) and (52) become

$$\dot{a}_0 = 8a_2 + 64a_4, \quad \dot{a}_1 = 24a_3, \quad \dot{a}_2 = 48a_4, \tag{60}$$

together with $\qquad \dot{a}_3 = 0, \quad \dot{a}_4 = 0. \tag{61}$

Though these equations apparently have a solution which satisfies the initial conditions we have no possibility of satisfying the boundary conditions. The problem is similar to that resulting from the assumption of a polynomial solution for ordinary differential equations, and we resolve it by a technique analogous to the τ method. With this assumption we can solve exactly the perturbed problem

$$\frac{\partial f}{\partial y} = \frac{\partial^2 f}{\partial x^2} + \dot{a}_3 T_3(x) + \dot{a}_4 T_4(x), \tag{62}$$

the equations corresponding to (61) becoming identities. There are five unknown functions in the three equations (60), but we can eliminate two of them, say a_3 and a_4, by means of the boundary conditions which here give the two equations

$$\tfrac{1}{2}a_0 \pm a_1 + a_2 \pm a_3 + a_4 = y. \tag{63}$$

The resulting equations for a_1, and its initial condition, show that $a_1(y)$ and $a_3(y)$ are identically zero, corresponding to the fact that the analytical solution is obviously even in x. For a_0 and a_2 we find the ordinary differential systems

$$\left. \begin{array}{ll} \dot{a}_0 + 32a_0 + 56a_2 = 64y, & a_0(0) = 1 \\ \dot{a}_2 + 24a_0 + 48a_2 = 48y, & a_2(0) = -\tfrac{1}{2} \end{array} \right\}, \tag{64}$$

which can be solved analytically. The other required function a_4 then follows from (63). We find

$$\left.\begin{aligned}
a_0 &= 2y - \tfrac{1}{2} + 1\cdot469\ 65e^{\lambda_1 y} + 0\cdot030\ 45e^{\lambda_2 y} \\
a_2 &= \qquad \tfrac{1}{4} - 0\cdot774\ 33e^{\lambda_1 y} + 0\cdot024\ 33e^{\lambda_2 y} \\
a_4 &= \qquad\qquad 0\cdot039\ 98e^{\lambda_1 y} - 0\cdot039\ 98e^{\lambda_2 y} \\
\lambda_1 &= -2\cdot476\ 7, \qquad \lambda_2 = -77\cdot52
\end{aligned}\right\}. \tag{65}$$

The true solution of the problem is given by

$$f(x, y) = -\tfrac{1}{2} + y + \tfrac{1}{2}x^2 + \sum_{r=0}^{\infty} A_r\, e^{-(r+\frac{1}{2})^2 \pi^2 y} \cos(r+\tfrac{1}{2})\pi x, \tag{66}$$

where the coefficients A_r depend on the initial function $g(x)$. The exponents for $r = 0$ and 1 are respectively about $-2\cdot467\ 4$ and $-22\cdot206\ 6$. We have approximated very well to the first, very badly to the second, and neglected the rest.

Prior integration

6.13 With the same number of terms we can often improve the accuracy by the method of *prior integration*, discussed in Chapter 5 for ordinary differential equations. Integrating (44) twice we obtain

$$\left.\begin{aligned}
\frac{\partial f}{\partial x} &= \int^x \frac{\partial f}{\partial y}\, dx + A(y) = \phi(x) + A(y) \\
f &= \int^x \phi(x)\, dx + x\, A(y) + B(y)
\end{aligned}\right\}, \tag{67}$$

where $A(y)$ and $B(y)$ are arbitrary functions of y. With the assumed solution (59) we find

$$\phi(x) = \sum_{r=0}^{4}{}' \tfrac{1}{2}\dot{a}_r \left\{\frac{T_{r+1}(x)}{r+1} - \frac{T_{r-1}(x)}{r-1}\right\}, \tag{68}$$

and

$$\int^x \phi(x)\, dx = \sum_{r=0}^{4}{}' \tfrac{1}{4}\dot{a}_r \left\{\frac{1}{(r+1)(r+2)}T_{r+2}(x) - \frac{2}{r^2-1}T_r(x) + \right.$$

$$\left. + \frac{1}{(r-1)(r-2)}T_{r-2}(x)\right\}. \tag{69}$$

Substituting in the second of (67), perturbed to read

$$f(x, y) = \int^x \phi(x)\,dx + x\,A(y) + B(y) - \tfrac{1}{80}\dot{a}_3\,T_5(x) - \tfrac{1}{120}\dot{a}_4\,T_6(x), \quad (70)$$

we find that we can equate corresponding coefficients of $T_2(x)$, $T_3(x)$ and $T_4(x)$ to produce the equations

$$\left.\begin{aligned}
a_2 &= \tfrac{1}{8}\dot{d}_0 \;-\tfrac{1}{6}\dot{d}_2 + \tfrac{1}{24}\dot{d}_4 \\
a_3 &= \tfrac{1}{24}\dot{d}_1 - \tfrac{1}{16}\dot{d}_3 \\
a_4 &= \tfrac{1}{48}\dot{d}_2 - \tfrac{1}{30}\dot{d}_4
\end{aligned}\right\}. \quad (71)$$

The coefficients of $T_5(x)$ and $T_6(x)$ vanish identically, and we need not consider the coefficients of $T_0(x)$ and $T_1(x)$ which include the functions $A(y)$ and $B(y)$. Instead we use the two equations given by the boundary conditions (63). These and (71) serve to determine all the required functions $a_r(y)$, and $A(y)$ and $B(y)$ can subsequently be evaluated if necessary.

We find that a_1 and a_3 are identically zero, and a_0 and a_2 are obtained from the system

$$\left.\begin{aligned}
\tfrac{5}{48}\dot{d}_0 - \tfrac{5}{24}\dot{d}_2 - a_2 &= -\tfrac{1}{24}, & a_0(0) &= 1 \\
\tfrac{1}{60}\dot{d}_0 + \tfrac{13}{240}\dot{d}_2 + \tfrac{1}{2}a_0 + a_2 &= y + \tfrac{1}{30}, & a_2(0) &= -\tfrac{1}{2}
\end{aligned}\right\}, \quad (72)$$

the function a_4 finally coming from the boundary conditions (63). We find

$$\left.\begin{aligned}
a_0 &= 2y - \tfrac{1}{2} + 1\cdot461\,85e^{\lambda_1 y} + 0\cdot038\,15e^{\lambda_2 y} \\
a_2 &= \tfrac{1}{4} - 0\cdot774\,33e^{\lambda_1 y} + 0\cdot024\,33e^{\lambda_2 y} \\
a_4 &= \phantom{2y-\tfrac{1}{4}-}0\cdot043\,40e^{\lambda_1 y} - 0\cdot043\,40e^{\lambda_2 y} \\
\lambda_1 &= -2\cdot469\,2, \qquad \lambda_2 = -22\cdot216\,5
\end{aligned}\right\}. \quad (73)$$

We have improved slightly on the previous approximation to the first exponent, and also obtained a very good approximation to the second.

Special cases

6.14 In general the coefficients h and k in the boundary conditions (46) will be functions of y, so that the coefficients in the ordinary differential equations of types (64) and (72) are also functions of y. These equations may then have to be solved by numerical methods.

If h and k are constants, however, the systems (64) and (72) are of the general form

$$\mathbf{M\dot{a}} = \mathbf{Na} + \mathbf{b}(y), \qquad \mathbf{a}(0) = \mathbf{g}, \tag{74}$$

where $\mathbf{M}$ and $\mathbf{N}$ are constant matrices, say of order n, $\mathbf{a}$ the vector with components a_r, $\mathbf{b}(y)$ a vector of functions of y, and $\mathbf{g}$ the vector of coefficients in the suitably truncated expansion (53).

If $\mathbf{M}$ is not singular we can write (74) in the form

$$\mathbf{\dot{a}} = \mathbf{Pa} + \mathbf{c}(y), \qquad \mathbf{a}(0) = \mathbf{g}. \tag{75}$$

We can solve (75) analytically, in the form

$$\mathbf{a} = \sum_{i=1}^{n} (\alpha_i e^{\lambda_i y} + \beta_i) \mathbf{u}_i, \tag{76}$$

where $\mathbf{u}_i$ are the eigenvectors of the matrix $\mathbf{P}$ with eigenvalues λ_i, assumed distinct, $\mathbf{v}_i$ are the eigenvectors of the transposed matrix $\mathbf{P}'$, and

$$\alpha_i = \frac{\mathbf{v}_i' \, \mathbf{a}(0)}{\mathbf{v}_i' \, \mathbf{u}_i}, \qquad \beta_i = \frac{\mathbf{v}_i' \, t_i}{\mathbf{v}_i' \, \mathbf{u}_i}, \tag{77}$$

$$t_i = \int_0^y e^{\lambda_i(y-t)} \mathbf{c}(t) \, dt. \tag{78}$$

The computation is not very difficult, and changes in the initial conditions, giving the vector $\mathbf{a}(0)$, are easily incorporated.

6.15 The exponents λ_i are usually negative, so that as $y \to \infty$ we here find the steady-state solution

$$\mathbf{a} = \sum_{i=1}^{n} \beta_i \mathbf{u}_i, \tag{79}$$

which is independent of the initial state $\mathbf{a}(0) = \mathbf{g}$. The latter remark is not always true, and depends on the boundary conditions. Consider, for example, the problem of **6.12**, with initial condition like (57) but with the new boundary conditions

$$\frac{\partial}{\partial x} f(1, y) = \frac{\partial}{\partial x} f(-1, y) = 0. \tag{80}$$

The relations (63) are then replaced by

$$a_1 \pm 4a_2 + 9a_3 \pm 16a_4 = 0, \tag{81}$$

so that $4a_2+16a_4 = 0$, $a_1+9a_3 = 0$. The odd functions again vanish identically, and for the even functions we replace (64) by

$$\dot{a}_0 = -8a_2, \qquad \dot{a}_2 = -12a_2, \tag{82}$$

with solutions

$$a_2 = a_2(0)e^{-12y}, \qquad a_0 = a_0(0)-\tfrac{2}{3}a_2(0)+\tfrac{2}{3}a_2(0)e^{-12y}. \tag{83}$$

The prior integration method produces a solution of similar type,

$$a_2 = a_2(0)e^{-(60/7)y}, \qquad a_0 = a_0(0)-\tfrac{29}{60}a_2(0)+\tfrac{29}{60}a_2(0)e^{-(60/7)y}, \tag{84}$$

and in both cases the steady state depends on the initial state.

6.16 It is interesting to compare the Chebyshev method with other known methods, and to consider some matters arising. Our basic method, of course, is very similar to the classical method of separating variables and using Fourier series. For analytical solutions like (66), obtained with the Fourier method, and in which the effect of the initial state disappears with increasing y, we may need a large number of Fourier terms to get good results for small y, whereas for large y many fewer terms are required. The Chebyshev solution will have similar aspects, though in virtue of the more rapid convergence of the Chebyshev series we would expect to need fewer terms in all cases. When the initial state persists, the accuracy of the resulting steady state certainly depends more closely on the number of Chebyshev terms, and this corresponds to the fact that in each case the steady-state solution of finite-difference methods depends on the selected intervals and the corresponding truncation errors. This is indicated by the results of (83) and (84), which have rather different steady states, whereas those of **6.12** and **6.13** have the same steady states agreeing exactly with the true solution.

Discontinuities at the 'corner' points $(1, 0)$ and $(-1, 0)$ lead to difficulties with all methods. The analytical solution based on a Fourier expansion has a very poor rate of convergence for small y, and we need to use, instead, a series of error functions. The finite-difference method also produces poor results, with any intervals, for small y. Our present method has similar problems, though these have been passed over in the discussion.

We remarked in **6.12** and **6.13** that the eliminated functions a_r could be recovered from the boundary conditions. Our solution then satisfies the boundary conditions and the perturbed differential equation, but *not necessarily* the initial condition. In this respect the first example was satisfactory because the conditions on the lines $x = \pm 1$ were compatible with those on the line $y = 0$ at the corner points. In the second example we lost this compatibility, and a more drastic discontinuity is presented by the conditions

$$f(\pm 1, y) = 0, \qquad f(x, 0) = 1. \tag{85}$$

In these cases some of the computed functions a_r will not satisfy their initial conditions, and then many terms will be needed to give good accuracy for small y.

Elliptic partial differential equations

6.17 The parabolic problem is of *initial-value* type, whereas for the elliptic problem we shall generally have a region contained within a closed boundary, at each point of which one or more *boundary* conditions is specified. Here we concentrate on linear second-order elliptic differential equations, with a closed boundary of finite length on which one condition is given at every point. The boundary condition may specify the function value (the Dirichlet problem), or its normal derivative (the Neumann problem), or a linear combination of these quantities, and its nature may be different in different parts of the boundary. The general case is difficult to analyse, and we concentrate here on the Dirichlet problem, in which the required function $f(x, y) = u(x, y)$, a given function, on the boundary $g(x, y) = 0$. We shall also assume that $u(x, y)$ is twice differentiable at every boundary point.

6.18 Since the region is bounded in both coordinate directions, we can make a simple transformation of the independent variable to ensure that the region is circumscribed by the square with vertices at $(\pm 1, \pm 1)$, as shown in Fig. 2.

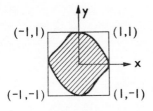

Fig. 2

We might then assume a solution in the form

$$f(x, y) = g(x, y) \sum_{r=0}^{m} \sum_{s=0}^{n} a_{rs} T_r(x) T_s(y) + u(x, y), \qquad (86)$$

which at least satisfies the Dirichlet boundary condition.

Before considering the determination of the coefficients a_{rs}, we examine the double Chebyshev expansion and its partial sums

$$\left. \begin{aligned} f(x, y) &= \sum_{r=0}^{\infty} \sum_{s=0}^{\infty} a_{rs} T_r(x) T_s(y) \\ f_{p,q}(x, y) &= \sum_{r=0}^{p} \sum_{s=0}^{q} a_{rs} T_r(x) T_s(y) \end{aligned} \right\}. \qquad (87)$$

Although we know of no theorems in two dimensions comparable to those relating to the convergence of Chebyshev series in one variable, it is not unreasonable to expect that a suitably well-behaved $f(x, y)$ would have a uniformly convergent expansion of this kind, and that the rate of decrease of its coefficients would be at least as satisfactory as that of any other expansion. We shall assume such a convergent expansion, so that

$$f(x, y) = \lim_{p \to \infty} f_{p,p} = \lim_{p \to \infty} \lim_{q \to \infty} f_{p,q} = \lim_{q \to \infty} \lim_{p \to \infty} f_{p,q}. \qquad (88)$$

Then

$$f_{p+1,q+1} - f_{p,q} = T_{p+1}(x) \sum_{s=0}^{q} a_{p+1,s} T_s(y) + T_{q+1}(y) \sum_{r=0}^{p+1} a_{r,q+1} T_r(x), \qquad (89)$$

which vanishes at all points (x_i, y_j) for which

$$T_{p+1}(x_i) = 0 = T_{q+1}(y_j). \qquad (90)$$

A reasonable interpolation process, for a given function $f(x, y)$, therefore computes $f_{p,q}(x, y)$, in which there are $(p+1)(q+1)$ coefficients, by equating $f_{p,q}$ with $f(x, y)$ at the $(p+1)(q+1)$ combinations of zeros of $T_{p+1}(x)$ and $T_{q+1}(y)$. This is a natural extension of the corresponding method of interpolation in one variable, though again we have no strongly comparable theorems about the minimax properties of the right-hand side of (89).

The method of selected points

6.19 In the case of ordinary differential equations we agreed, with some justification, to satisfy the differential equation exactly at certain points, which we normally took to be the zeros of a relevant Chebyshev polynomial. Here we make the same decision, and again with less justification. The process will certainly provide some sort of approximation; we can compute afterwards the perturbed problem which we have solved exactly, and *a posteriori* inspection, perhaps for different orders of approximation, may give some grounds for confidence in the approximate solutions.

We consider the elastic torsion problem for a square section, which requires the solution of the system

$$\nabla^2 f = \frac{\partial^2 f}{\partial x^2} + \frac{\partial^2 f}{\partial y^2} = -2, \quad f(\pm 1, \pm 1) = 0. \tag{91}$$

The solution is obviously even in x and y, so that we can take even polynomials in (86) and match at the positive zeros of the relevant Chebyshev polynomials. It is also more convenient, though not essential, to work with the polynomial form

$$f_{2m,2n}(x, y) = (1-x^2)(1-y^2) \sum_{r=0}^{m} \sum_{s=0}^{n} b_{2r,2s} x^{2r} y^{2s}. \tag{92}$$

We obtain the coefficients from linear algebraic equations, each one of which represents the satisfaction of the first of (91), for $f_{2m,2n}(x, y)$, at one combination of positive zeros of $T_{2m+2}(x)$, $T_{2n+2}(y)$.

It is clearly desirable to take $m = n$, and for $m = n = 0$ we have the simple solution

$$f_{0,0}(x, y) = (1-x^2)(1-y^2), \qquad \nabla^2 f_{0,0} = -2 + T_2(x) + T_2(y), \tag{93}$$

in which the differential equation is satisfied at the single point $(1/\sqrt{2}, 1/\sqrt{2})$. With $m = n = 1$ we have four coefficients and four selected points

$$(x, y) = ((\tfrac{1}{2} \pm \tfrac{1}{4}\sqrt{2})^{\frac{1}{2}}, (\tfrac{1}{2} \pm \tfrac{1}{4}\sqrt{2})^{\frac{1}{2}}). \tag{94}$$

We obtain

$$\left. \begin{aligned} f_{2,2}(x, y) &= (1-x^2)(1-y^2)(0\cdot6 + 0\cdot8 x^2 y^2) \\ \nabla^2 f_{2,2} &= -2 + (1\cdot2 y^2 - 0\cdot2)T_4(x) + (1\cdot2 x^2 - 0\cdot2)T_4(y) \end{aligned} \right\}. \tag{95}$$

In Table 1 we give the analytical solution (upper figure, multiplied by 1 000) and the corresponding figures derived from (95), for equally-spaced points at interval $\tfrac{1}{4}$ in the relevant part of the square. The accuracy is quite good for such a low-order approximation.

TABLE 1

x	$y = 0$	$\frac{1}{4}$	$\frac{1}{2}$	$\frac{3}{4}$
0	589			
	600			
$\frac{1}{4}$	558	529		
	562	530		
$\frac{1}{2}$	459	435	363	
	450	431	366	
$\frac{3}{4}$	280	266	226	145
	262	258	234	163

The Chebyshev forms of the two solutions are

$$
\left.\begin{aligned}
f_{0,0} &= T_0(x)\{\tfrac{1}{4}T_0(y)-\tfrac{1}{4}T_2(y)\}+T_2(x)\{-\tfrac{1}{4}T_0(y)+\tfrac{1}{4}T_2(y)\} \\
f_{2,2} &= \tfrac{1}{8}[T_0(x)\{1\cdot3T_0(y)-1\cdot2T_2(y)-0\cdot1T_4(y)\}+ \\
&\quad +T_2(x)\{-1\cdot2T_0(y)+1\cdot2T_2(y)+0\cdot0T_4(y)\}+ \\
&\quad +T_4(x)\{-0\cdot1T_0(y)+0\cdot0T_4(y)+0\cdot1T_4(y)\}]
\end{aligned}\right\}, \quad (96)
$$

and we note a reasonably rapid decrease in the size of the later coefficients.

6.20 The ideas and methods of **6.18-6.19** are taken from Mason (1965). For suitable problems they are attractively simple, and might give good results with a Chebyshev approximation of low order. It is clear, however, that much more work, both theoretical and practical, is needed to give them a firm basis. Even the choice of the Chebyshev zeros as selected points may be far from the optimum. In the example treated we can certainly say that we have solved exactly a perturbed differential equation of the form

$$\nabla^2 f_{2m,2n} = -2+\tau_m(x,y)T_{2m+2}(x)+\tau_n(x,y)T_{2n+2}(y), \quad (97)$$

with correct boundary conditions. But we cannot claim either that the perturbation is as small as possible, or that the corresponding difference $f(x,y)-f_{2m,2n}(x,y)$ is minimized.

Indeed, if in the last example, with the same assumed approximation, we satisfy the differential equation at the more symmetrically disposed points

$$(x,y) = (\tfrac{1}{3},\tfrac{1}{3}), \quad (\tfrac{1}{3},\tfrac{2}{3}), \quad (\tfrac{2}{3},\tfrac{1}{3}), \quad (\tfrac{2}{3},\tfrac{2}{3}), \quad (98)$$

we obtain a result whose maximum error, at the points contained in Table 1, is only three units in the last figure and with constant sign.

The selection may also need closer attention in cases like that of Fig. 2, in which some of the Chebyshev points may lie between the boundary of the region and the circumscribing square. Whether this matters must depend on the nature of the solution, for example in the possibility of its analytical continuation into the unshaded parts of Fig. 2.

The eigenvalue problem

6.21 Within its theoretical limitations, however, the method is also useful for the eigenvalue problem typified by

$$\nabla^2 f + \lambda f = 0, \quad f = 0 \text{ on } g(x, y) = 0. \tag{99}$$

The satisfaction of (99) at the selected points, with the assumption (86) with $u(x, y) = 0$, gives rise to a matrix eigenvalue problem of the form

$$(\mathbf{A} + \lambda \mathbf{B})\mathbf{a} = \mathbf{0}, \tag{100}$$

where $\mathbf{A}$ and $\mathbf{B}$ are matrices and $\mathbf{a}$ is the vector of coefficients a_{rs}. The 'size' of this problem will often be much less than that of other methods, and is relatively trivial for modern computers.

For the square boundary with vertices at $(\pm 1, \pm 1)$, we have for $m = n = 0$ the easy solution $\lambda = 8$, and for $m = n = 1$ we find the approximate value 4·95 for the smallest eigenvalue, its correct result being $\pi^2/2 \sim 4\cdot93$. With the matching points (98) we find the approximate value 4·97, which here has a slightly larger error than that of the Chebyshev matching points.

Mason has used this method on a more formidable problem, the determination of one or two of the eigenvalues of the L-shaped membrane comprising three unit squares as shown in Fig. 3.

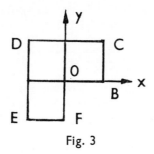

Fig. 3

The eigenfunction corresponding to the smallest eigenvalue has a violent discontinuity at the point O, and its Chebyshev series would converge very slowly indeed. It is preferable to 'remove' the singularity, and this is done by means of the conformal transformation

$$w = z^{\frac{3}{2}}. \tag{101}$$

With an ambiguity of notation which should not be troublesome, the problem is transformed to the solution of

$$\nabla^2 f + \tfrac{9}{4}(x^2 + y^2)^{\frac{1}{3}}\lambda f = 0, \tag{102}$$

where f vanishes on the boundary

$$g(x, y) = y\{y^2(3x^2 - y^2)^2 - 4(x^2 + y^2)^{\frac{3}{2}} + 4\} = 0, \tag{103}$$

shown pictorially in Fig. 4.

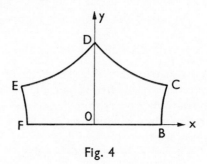

Fig. 4

The region is circumscribed within the rectangle

$$x = \pm a, \quad y = 0, b; \qquad a = 2^{-\frac{8}{3}}3^{\frac{1}{2}}, \quad b = 2^{\frac{1}{3}}, \tag{104}$$

and we have the situation of Fig. 2. We can transform the rectangle into a square or, more easily, use expansions in terms of $T_r(x/a)$ and $T_s^*(y/b)$. The first eigenfunction is even in x, so that we use only the even $T_{2r}(x/a)$ and the assumed solution

$$f_{2m,n} = g(x, y) \sum_{r=0}^{m} \sum_{s=0}^{n} a_{2r,s} T_{2r}(x/a) T_s^*(y/b). \tag{105}$$

With $m = n = 6$ Mason obtained results correct to about one part in 3×10^4 for the smallest eigenvalue $\lambda \sim 9.64$, with an amount of work considerably less than that of finite-difference methods, say, used in the transformed problem by Reid and Walsh (1965).

Curve fitting in two dimensions

6.22 Finally we mention some possibilities of using Chebyshev polynomials for problems of curve fitting in two dimensions. We know of no valuable process for the general problem, in which the data are specified at arbitrary points in a region of the (x, y) plane. Treatment is possible, however, for two easier problems in which the given region is contained in the square with vertices $(\pm 1, \pm 1)$.

In the first problem the data points are the mesh points of a rectangular grid. We have already illustrated in **6.5** an appropriate method for a continuous function $k(x, y)$, with specially selected values of x and y. In the more general problem we make no assumption about the mesh lengths, or the numbers of points in either direction, other than that the points (x_r, y_s) lie on a rectangular grid, with $r = 0, 1, ..., m$, and $s = 0, 1, ..., n$.

For each value y_s of y we can generate a set of orthogonal polynomials by the method of **4.16** and **4.17**. Since the x_r are the same for each y_s, a single set of polynomials suffices for all y_s provided that the weights are the same for each y_s. With this assumption we can find the approximation

$$\left.\begin{aligned} f(x, y_s) &= \sum_{j=0}^{p} c_j(y_s)\psi_j(x) \\ c_j(y_s) &= \frac{\displaystyle\sum_{r=0}^{m} w(x_r)f(x_r, y_s)\psi_j(x_r)}{\displaystyle\sum_{r=0}^{m} w(x_r)\psi_j^2(x_r)} \end{aligned}\right\}. \tag{106}$$

For each value of j, from 0 to p, we can then find similar approximations to the coefficients of the orthogonal polynomials, in the form

$$c_j(y) = \sum_{k=0}^{q} b_{jk}\,\phi_k(y), \qquad b_{jk} = \frac{\displaystyle\sum_{s=0}^{n} w(y_s)c_j(y_s)\phi_k(y_s)}{\displaystyle\sum_{s=0}^{n} w(y_s)\phi_k^2(y_s)}. \tag{107}$$

The fitted two-dimensional curve is then given by

$$f(x, y) = \sum_{j=0}^{p} \sum_{k=0}^{q} b_{jk}\,\psi_j(x)\phi_k(y). \tag{108}$$

It is easy to see that the result is the least-squares solution of the problem

$$S = \sum_{r=0}^{m} \sum_{s=0}^{n} \left\{ f(x_r, y_s) - \sum_{j=0}^{p} \sum_{k=0}^{q} b_{jk} \, \psi_j(x_r)\phi_k(y_s) \right\}^2$$
$$= \text{minimum}, \tag{109}$$

and it follows that the order in which we take the separate x and y fittings is immaterial.

The results (106)–(108) can obviously be converted into finite Chebyshev form, or we can find these forms directly, by the method of **4.18**, to compute the final result

$$f(x, y) = \sum_{j=0}^{p} \sum_{k=0}^{q} a_{jk} T_j(x) T_k(y). \tag{110}$$

6.23 This process has one important feature, simplifying the computation, that only one set of orthogonal polynomials has to be produced in each direction. In the second of our problems we can proceed in a similar way, but the amount of work is greater and we do not produce the exact least-squares solution.

We assume that the data points lie on the lines $y = y_s$, $s = 0, 1, ..., n$, but the number and position of the x coordinates also depend on s, and on the line $y = y_s$ we take data points at x_r, $r = 0, 1, ..., m(s)$. For each y_s we can as before compute the approximation

$$\left. \begin{aligned} f(x, y_s) &= \sum_{j=0}^{p} c_j(y_s)\psi_{j(s)}(x) \\ c_j(y_s) &= \frac{\displaystyle\sum_{r=0}^{m(s)} w(x_r, y_s) f(x_r, y_s)\psi_{j(s)}(x_r)}{\displaystyle\sum_{r=0}^{m(s)} w(x_r, y_s)\psi_{j(s)}^2(x_r)} \end{aligned} \right\}. \tag{111}$$

We cannot, however, proceed to fit polynomials in the y direction to the terms $c_j(y_s)$ because, as indicated in the notation of (111), the $\psi_{j(s)}(x)$ polynomials vary with s. This difficulty is overcome quite neatly by Clenshaw and Hayes (1965), by expressing each of (111) in terms of the same orthogonal polynomial. The obvious standard choice is the $T_k(x)$ polynomials, for which we already know how to compute the relevant approximations. By the method of **4.18** we first find

$$f(x, y_s) = \sum_{j=0}^{p} c_j(y_s)T_j(x), \tag{112}$$

and can then use the same method to obtain

$$c_j(y) = \sum_{k=0}^{q} a_{jk} T_k(y), \tag{113}$$

to give the final double Chebyshev series of form (110).

This of course, is not the result of minimizing the quantity

$$S = \sum_{r=0}^{m(s)} \sum_{s=0}^{n} \left[f(x_r, y_s) - \sum_{j=0}^{p} \sum_{k=0}^{q} a_{jk} T_j(x_{r(s)})T_k(y_s) \right]^2, \tag{114}$$

and can be regarded only as a 'reasonable' fit for sufficiently large p and q. In practice, of course, this is all that is necessary.

Clenshaw and Hayes (1965) consider various other points, for example a more general form of our second problem in which the mesh lines in the x direction terminate on curved boundaries. They also treat curve fitting with constraints, such as specified values of the function or its derivatives at certain points.

Additional notes on Chapter 6

In both the τ method of **6.11–6.12** and the method of prior integration in **6.13** we effectively satisfied the boundary conditions accurately, but relied on compatibility of the boundary conditions and the initial conditions for the complete satisfaction of the latter. This we discussed briefly in **6.16**, with particular reference to the 'persistence' of the initial state in the steady-state solution.

The method of prior integration can be varied so that the initial conditions are satisfied exactly, and the incompatibility is transferred to the boundary conditions. This we do, for example in the process of **6.13**, by deferring the truncation of (50) to the finite approximation (59). In equation (69) this merely involves the replacement of $\sum\limits_{r=0}^{4}{}'$ by $\sum\limits_{r=0}^{\infty}{}'$. Equating coefficients of $T_2(x)$, $T_4(x)$, $T_6(x)$,... (ignoring the odd terms which vanish identically in this example), we replace (71) by the equations

$$a_2 = \tfrac{1}{8}\dot{a}_0 - \tfrac{1}{6}\dot{a}_2 + \tfrac{1}{24}\dot{a}_4,$$
$$a_4 = \tfrac{1}{48}\dot{a}_2 - \tfrac{1}{30}\dot{a}_4 + \tfrac{1}{80}\dot{a}_6,$$
$$a_6 = \tfrac{1}{120}\dot{a}_4 - \tfrac{1}{70}\dot{a}_6 + \tfrac{1}{168}\dot{a}_8,$$

. . . .

If we now assume $\dot{a}_6 = a_8 = \dot{a}_8 = 0$, but not yet that $a_6 = 0$, and substitute for a_6 in the boundary condition corresponding to (63), which now reads

$$\tfrac{1}{2}a_0 + a_2 + a_4 + a_6 = y,$$

we produce the *three* independent *differential* equations

$$\tfrac{1}{2}a_0 + a_2 + a_4 + \tfrac{1}{120}\dot{a}_4 = y,$$
$$a_2 - \tfrac{1}{8}\dot{a}_0 + \tfrac{1}{6}\dot{a}_2 - \tfrac{1}{24}\dot{a}_4 = 0,$$
$$a_4 - \tfrac{1}{48}\dot{a}_2 + \tfrac{1}{30}\dot{a}_4 = 0.$$

To solve these uniquely we must make use of three starting values, here given by

$$a_0(0) = 1, \qquad a_2(0) = -\tfrac{1}{2}, \qquad a_4(0) = 0,$$

so that we represent accurately the initial condition (57). The solution is

$$a_0 = 2y - \tfrac{1}{2} + 1 \cdot 461\ 39e^{\lambda_1 y} + 0 \cdot 034\ 62e^{\lambda_2 y} + 0 \cdot 00400e^{\lambda_3 y},$$

$$a_2 = \quad \tfrac{1}{4} - 0 \cdot 773\ 11e^{\lambda_1 y} + 0 \cdot 019\ 43e^{\lambda_2 y} + 0 \cdot 003\ 67e^{\lambda_3 y},$$

$$a_4 = \quad\quad 0 \cdot 043\ 30e^{\lambda_1 y} - 0 \cdot 045\ 79e^{\lambda_2 y} + 0 \cdot 002\ 48e^{\lambda_3 y},$$

$$\lambda_1 = -2 \cdot 467\ 4, \qquad \lambda_2 = -23 \cdot 711, \qquad \lambda_3 = -393 \cdot 8,$$

which may be compared with (65) and (73) obtained by the other methods. The exponent λ_1 is here identical to five figures with that of the true solution, and λ_2 is still very accurate.

The neglect of a_6 now gives, for the boundary condition at $x = \pm 1$, the result

$$\tfrac{1}{2}a_0 + a_2 + a_4 = y + 0 \cdot 000\ 89e^{\lambda_1 y} - 0 \cdot 009\ 05e^{\lambda_2 y} + 0 \cdot 008\ 16e^{\lambda_3 y},$$

which is not exactly y except at $y = 0$, where $a_6 = 0$, and at $y = \infty$. Normally we should have to neglect a_6, if we want to satisfy exactly an initial condition representable exactly by $\sum\limits_{r=0}^{4}{}' a_r(0)T_r(x)$, because $a_6 = \dot{a}_4/120$ will not necessarily be zero at $y = 0$.

For the problem of **6.15**, where the initial and boundary conditions are 'very incompatible' at $x = \pm 1$, $y = 0$, the same approach gives the equations

$$a_2 = \tfrac{1}{8}\dot{a}_0 - \tfrac{1}{6}\dot{a}_2 + \tfrac{1}{24}\dot{a}_4,$$

$$a_4 = \tfrac{1}{48}\dot{a}_2 - \tfrac{1}{30}\dot{a}_4,$$

$$a_6 = \tfrac{1}{120}\dot{a}_4,$$

and we have corresponding to (81) the boundary condition expressed as

$$4a_2 + 16a_4 + 36a_6 = 0.$$

Elimination of a_6 produces, after a little manipulation, the solutions

$$a_0(y) = a_0(0) - \tfrac{2}{3}a_2(0) - \tfrac{2}{15}a_4(0) + \tfrac{2}{3}a_2(y) + \tfrac{2}{15}a_4(y),$$

$$a_2(y) = \left(\frac{1}{2} + \frac{3}{\sqrt{106}}\right) Ae^{\lambda_1 y} + \left(\frac{1}{2} - \frac{3}{\sqrt{106}}\right) Be^{\lambda_2 y},$$

$$a_4(y) = -\frac{5}{2\sqrt{106}} Ae^{\lambda_1 y} + \frac{5}{2\sqrt{106}} Be^{\lambda_2 y},$$

$$\lambda_1 = \frac{-112 + 8\sqrt{106}}{3} \sim 9\cdot877, \qquad \lambda_2 = \frac{-112 - 8\sqrt{106}}{3} \sim 64\cdot789,$$

where A and B are constants determinable from the given $a_2(0)$, $a_4(0)$.

The steady-state solution is now

$$f(x, y) = \text{constant} = a_0(0) - \tfrac{2}{3}a_2(0) - \tfrac{2}{15}a_4(0),$$

while the correct result is

$$f(x, y) = \text{constant} = \int_{-1}^{1} g(x)\, dx.$$

If $g(x) = \tfrac{1}{2}a_0 T_0(x) + a_2 T_2(x) + a_4 T_4(x)$, we deduce that this method of prior integration has produced exactly the correct steady-state solution. The effect of this method is that the inaccuracies in the boundary conditions (the neglect of high-order 'harmonics') disappear for large enough y.

For solutions near $y = 0$, of course, we still need many terms in the Chebyshev expansion, and convergence is slow.

EXERCISES 6

1. Use the method indicated at the end of **6.3** to solve the problem of equation (6) in Chebyshev series form.

2. Show that the coefficients of the matrix of equations (17) are precisely those obtained by the method of integration (**5.11**) applied to a differential equation with left-hand side $d^2f(x)/dx^2-f(x)$, and explain this result.

3. Solve by the method of **6.3** the integral equation

$$\int_{-1}^{1} (1+e^{x-y})f(y)\, dy = 2f(x)+2 \sinh 1.$$

4. Solve the problem of Exercise 3 by each of the methods of **6.5** and **6.8**.

5. Solve the problem of **6.7** by the method of **6.8**.

6. With the notation of **6.3**, write

$$b_{rs} = \int_{-1}^{1} Y_r(y)\, X_s(y)\, dy, \qquad g_r = \int_{-1}^{1} g(y)Y_r(y)\, dy.$$

Then if $\boldsymbol{\eta}$ is the vector of functions Y_r, $\boldsymbol{\xi}'$ the transpose of the vector of functions $X_r(x)$, and the coefficients of b_{rs} form the matrix $\mathbf{B}$, show that the resolvent kernel of the integral equation is

$$\gamma(x, y) = \boldsymbol{\xi}'(\mathbf{I}-\mathbf{B})^{-1}\boldsymbol{\eta}.$$

7. Find the resolvent kernel for the solution $f^*(x)$ in **6.7**, and estimate the maximum error of the approximation (36).

8. Complete the solution of the example of **6.12**, and find upper bounds for the perturbations.

9. Repeat Exercise 8 with the method of **6.13**.

10. Perform the analysis of the 'analogous τ method' for the differential equation

$$\frac{\partial f}{\partial y} = \frac{\partial^2 f}{\partial x^2} + \frac{1}{x}\frac{\partial f}{\partial x}$$

with appropriate initial and boundary conditions.

11. Repeat Exercise 10 with the method of 'prior integration'.

12. Find the solution $f(x, y) = \sum_{r=0}^{4}{}' a_r(y)T_r(x)$ for the system

$$\frac{\partial f}{\partial y} = \frac{\partial^2 f}{\partial x^2}, \quad f(\pm 1, y) = 0, \quad f(x, 0) = 1,$$

and compare it with the analytical solution.

13. Discuss the solution of non-linear parabolic systems by a method of 'selected points'.

14. Verify that, in the example of **6.15**, the conditions

$$\frac{\partial f}{\partial x} = -2x, \quad (x = 1, -1)$$

in place of (80) will not produce a discontinuity in the initial values of the coefficients a_r.

15. Find some low-order approximations for the solution of

$$\nabla^2 f = -2, \quad f(\pm 1, \pm 2) = 0,$$

experimenting with various choices of selected points and with m not necessarily equal to n.

16. The coefficients in (96) form a 3×3 matrix. Explain why the matrix is symmetric, how this fact could be used to simplify the computation, and why each row and column has zero sum.

17. Find the smallest eigenvalue of the square membrane with vertices $(\pm 1, \pm 1)$, by collocating at the points (98).

18. Verify the statements of equations (101)–(104).

19. Discuss a method of selected points for the solution of the problem

$$\frac{\partial^2 f}{\partial x^2} + \frac{\partial^2 f}{\partial y^2} + \frac{1}{y}\frac{\partial f}{\partial y} = 1,$$

$$f = 0 \text{ on } x = \pm 1, y = 1; \quad \frac{\partial f}{\partial y} = 0 \text{ on } y = 0.$$

20. For equation (91), with assumption (92) and collocation at the points (98), find the approximate solution

$$f_{2,2}(x, y) = (1-x^2)(1-y^2)\{0.587\,8 + 0.082\,7(x^2+y^2) + 0.186\,0x^2y^2\},$$
$$\nabla^2 f_{2,2}(x, y) = -2 + (x^2-\tfrac{1}{9})(x^2-\tfrac{4}{9})(2.232y^2 - 0.207) +$$
$$+ (y^2-\tfrac{1}{9})(y^2-\tfrac{4}{9})(2.232x^2 - 0.207).$$

Express this $f_{2,2}(x, y)$ in Chebyshev form, and compare with (96).

Show that, with any selection of points, $\nabla^2 f_{2,2}(x, y) = 0$ at the corners $(x, y) = (\pm 1, \pm 1)$. (If the differential equation had to be satisfied at the boundary, the worst discrepancy would be at the corner points. Perhaps the solution (95) is inferior to that of this exercise because one of the Chebyshev zeros is close to the corner point $(+1, +1)$.)

7

Problems in Linear Algebra

Introduction

7.1 Chebyshev polynomials have considerable application in certain algebraic problems. The most important of these is in the acceleration of the rate of convergence of iterative processes for solving certain classes of linear algebraic equations. Here we give a brief introduction, and refer the reader to the work of Varga (1962) for a more extensive and thorough treatment. Our second illustration, which has had less application in practical computation, refers to a device of Lanczos for finding eigenvalues of matrices.

Iterative methods for linear equations

7.2 We consider the linear equations

$$\mathbf{Ay} = \mathbf{b}, \tag{1}$$

where $\mathbf{A}$ is a real square non-singular matrix of order n. For a general matrix we would normally use some direct method of solution, such as Gauss elimination with 'pivoting'. Unless the matrix is too large for the computing machine this direct process will produce a solution in finite time, and the accuracy of the computed answers will depend mainly on the degree of ill-conditioning of the problem.

For very large matrices, however, particularly of the special sparse type which arise, for example, in the finite-difference solution of elliptic partial differential equations, we may well prefer to use an iterative method. The general *stationary* iterative method for the solution of (1) is defined by

$$\mathbf{y}^{(r)} = \mathbf{Cy}^{(r-1)} + \mathbf{d}, \tag{2}$$

where $\mathbf{C}$, the *iteration matrix*, and $\mathbf{d}$, a vector, depend on $\mathbf{A}$ and $\mathbf{b}$.

The relation comes from the fact that if (2) converges to the solution of (1) then

$$(\mathbf{I}-\mathbf{C})\mathbf{A}^{-1}\mathbf{b} = \mathbf{d}. \tag{3}$$

To study the question of convergence we observe that the required solution satisfies

$$\mathbf{y} = \mathbf{C}\mathbf{y}+\mathbf{d}, \tag{4}$$

so that the error vector $\boldsymbol{\varepsilon}^{(r)} = \mathbf{y}-\mathbf{y}^{(r)}$ satisfies

$$\boldsymbol{\varepsilon}^{(r)} = \mathbf{C}\boldsymbol{\varepsilon}^{(r-1)} = \dots = \mathbf{C}^r\boldsymbol{\varepsilon}^{(0)}. \tag{5}$$

We get convergence, for arbitrary $\mathbf{y}^{(0)}$ giving arbitrary $\boldsymbol{\varepsilon}^{(0)}$, if and only if all the eigenvalues λ_s of $\mathbf{C}$, $s = 1, 2,\dots, n$, are less than unity in absolute value.

This is easily proved in the common case when $\mathbf{C}$ has a full set of normalized independent eigenvectors $\mathbf{x}^{(s)}$, with $\mathbf{x}^{(s)\prime}\mathbf{x}^{(s)} = 1$, say, for we can then write

$$\boldsymbol{\varepsilon}^{(0)} = \sum_{s=1}^{n} \alpha_s \mathbf{x}^{(s)}, \qquad \mathbf{C}^r\boldsymbol{\varepsilon}^{(0)} = \sum_{s=1}^{n} \alpha_s \lambda_s^r \mathbf{x}^{(s)}. \tag{6}$$

For arbitrary α_s we have $\mathbf{C}^r\boldsymbol{\varepsilon}^{(0)} \to \mathbf{0}$, the null vector, if and only if $|\lambda_s| < 1$ for all s. If the eigenvalues are distinct, with $|\lambda_1| > |\lambda_2| > \dots > |\lambda_n|$, then for sufficiently large r the dominant term in $\mathbf{C}^r\boldsymbol{\varepsilon}^{(0)}$ is $\alpha_1 \lambda_1^r \mathbf{x}^{(1)}$, and the *rate* of convergence ultimately depends on the size of $|\lambda_1|$, the *spectral radius*.

Chebyshev acceleration

7.3 Each component $\alpha_s \mathbf{x}^{(s)}$ of the error vector is decreased after r steps by the quantity λ_s^r, the value at λ_s of the simple polynomial λ^r of degree r. The 'smaller' eigenvectors are diminished rapidly, but the 'larger' persist for values of r depending on λ_s and the precision required. It is clear that we may obtain a faster rate of convergence by weighting the components of the error vector by a different polynomial in λ. This is effected by the introduction of the vector

$$\mathbf{z}^{(r)} = \sum_{t=0}^{r} \beta_{t,r}\, \mathbf{y}^{(t)}, \tag{7}$$

a linear combination of $\mathbf{y}^{(0)}, \mathbf{y}^{(1)},\dots, \mathbf{y}^{(r)}$. There is an obvious restriction on the coefficients $\beta_{t,r}$, for if $\mathbf{y}^{(0)} = \mathbf{y}$ so that the first 'guess' is correct, then $\mathbf{y}^{(1)} = \mathbf{y}^{(2)} = \ldots = \mathbf{y}$, and since we want $\mathbf{z}^{(r)}$ to converge to $\mathbf{y}$ we must have

$$\sum_{t=0}^{r} \beta_{t,r} = 1. \tag{8}$$

If the error in $\mathbf{z}^{(r)}$ is $\boldsymbol{\eta}^{(r)} = \mathbf{y} - \mathbf{z}^{(r)}$, we have

$$\boldsymbol{\eta}^{(r)} = \mathbf{y} - \sum_{t=0}^{r} \beta_{t,r} \, \mathbf{y}^{(t)} = \sum_{t=0}^{r} \beta_{t,r} (\mathbf{y} - \mathbf{y}^{(t)})$$

$$= \sum_{t=0}^{r} \beta_{t,r} \, \boldsymbol{\varepsilon}^{(t)} = \sum_{t=0}^{r} \beta_{t,r} \, \mathbf{C}^{t} \boldsymbol{\varepsilon}^{(0)}, \tag{9}$$

in virtue of (8) and (5), so that

$$\boldsymbol{\eta}^{(r)} = \sum_{t=0}^{r} \beta_{t,r} \sum_{s=1}^{n} \alpha_s \lambda_s^t \mathbf{x}^{(s)} = \sum_{s=1}^{n} p_r(\lambda_s) \alpha_s \mathbf{x}^{(s)}, \tag{10}$$

where $\qquad p_r(\lambda) = \beta_{0,r} + \beta_{1,r} \lambda + \ldots + \beta_{r,r} \lambda^r. \tag{11}$

We have succeeded in weighting the components $\mathbf{x}^{(s)}$ of the error vector with the polynomial $p_r(\lambda)$ at the values $\lambda_1, \lambda_2, \ldots, \lambda_n$.

For real λ the best polynomial, of course, is a multiple of a Chebyshev polynomial. If we know the range of λ to be $-1 < a \leq \lambda \leq b < 1$, that is if we know the locations of the extreme eigenvalues of $\mathbf{C}$, we can take

$$p_r(\lambda) = \frac{T_r\left(\dfrac{2\lambda - (b+a)}{b-a}\right)}{T_r\left(\dfrac{2 - (b+a)}{b-a}\right)}. \tag{12}$$

Of all polynomials of degree r which have the value unity at $\lambda = 1$, the polynomial (12) has the smallest deviation from zero in $a \leq \lambda \leq b$ (see Exercise 2, Chapter 1). In this range, moreover, $p_r(\lambda) \to 0$ as $r \to \infty$, since the numerator cannot exceed unity in absolute value and the denominator increases exponentially with r.

7.4 An interesting and important point is that we need not form both the $\mathbf{y}^{(r)}$ from (2) and the $\mathbf{z}^{(r)}$ from (7). By virtue of the recurrence relations satisfied by the Chebyshev polynomials we can generate the $\mathbf{z}^{(r)}$ directly. Consider, for example, the case in which we know the spectral radius $\rho = |\lambda_1|$ of $\mathbf{C}$, and take

$$-a = \rho = b. \tag{13}$$

Then

$$p_r(\lambda) = \frac{T_r(\lambda\rho^{-1})}{T_r(\rho^{-1})}, \tag{14}$$

and successive polynomials satisfy the recurrence relation

$$T_{r+1}(\rho^{-1})p_{r+1}(\lambda) = 2\lambda\rho^{-1}T_r(\rho^{-1})p_r(\lambda) - T_{r-1}(\rho^{-1})p_{r-1}(\lambda), \tag{15}$$

with $p_0(\lambda) = 1$, $p_1(\lambda) = \lambda$.

Recalling the relation between the eigenvalues of a matrix and its characteristic equation, we can from (15) write

$$T_{r+1}(\rho^{-1})p_{r+1}(\mathbf{C}) = 2\rho^{-1}T_r(\rho^{-1})\mathbf{C}p_r(\mathbf{C}) - T_{r-1}(\rho^{-1})p_{r-1}(\mathbf{C}). \tag{16}$$

Postmultiplying throughout by $\boldsymbol{\varepsilon}^{(0)}$, and using (9) and (10), we obtain

$$T_{r+1}(\rho^{-1})\boldsymbol{\eta}^{(r+1)} = 2\rho^{-1}T_r(\rho^{-1})\mathbf{C}\boldsymbol{\eta}^{(r)} - T_{r-1}(\rho^{-1})\boldsymbol{\eta}^{(r-1)}. \tag{17}$$

From (4) and the first of (9) we then obtain the required recurrence relation

$$\mathbf{z}^{(r+1)} = 2\rho^{-1}\frac{T_r(\rho^{-1})}{T_{r+1}(\rho^{-1})}(\mathbf{C}\mathbf{z}^{(r)}+\mathbf{d}) - \frac{T_{r-1}(\rho^{-1})}{T_{r+1}(\rho^{-1})}\mathbf{z}^{(r-1)}, \tag{18}$$

with $\mathbf{z}^{(0)} = \mathbf{y}^{(0)}$, $\mathbf{z}^{(1)} = \mathbf{y}^{(1)}$. This is of a similar form to the original (2), but involves two earlier vectors instead of one. It is a *nonstationary* iterative formula.

7.5 As a simple example we consider the system

$$\left.\begin{array}{rcl} 4y_1+2y_2 \;-y_3 &=& 5 \\ 3y_1+5y_2 \qquad &=& 8 \\ -y_1 \qquad +2y_3 &=& 1 \end{array}\right\}, \tag{19}$$

with solution $y_1 = y_2 = y_3 = 1$. The simplest iterative process is that of Jacobi. With the notation

$$\mathbf{A} = \mathbf{L}+\mathbf{D}+\mathbf{U}, \tag{20}$$

where $\mathbf{L}$ and $\mathbf{U}$ are respectively strictly lower and upper triangular matrices and $\mathbf{D}$ is a diagonal, the Jacobi iteration

$$\mathbf{y}^{(r)} = -\mathbf{D}^{-1}(\mathbf{L}+\mathbf{U})\mathbf{y}^{(r-1)}+\mathbf{D}^{-1}\mathbf{b} \tag{21}$$

here becomes

$$\mathbf{y}^{(r)} = \begin{bmatrix} 0 & -0\cdot5 & 0\cdot25 \\ -0\cdot6 & 0 & 0 \\ 0\cdot5 & 0 & 0 \end{bmatrix} \mathbf{y}^{(r-1)} + \begin{bmatrix} 1\cdot25 \\ 1\cdot60 \\ 0\cdot50 \end{bmatrix}. \tag{22}$$

The eigenvalues of the iteration matrix are $\lambda_1 = (0\cdot425)^{\frac{1}{2}}$, $\lambda_2 = 0$, $\lambda_3 = -(0\cdot425)^{\frac{1}{2}}$, so that the spectral radius ρ is approximately $0\cdot651\ 9$. Some successive iterates from (22) and from the corresponding Chebyshev method (18) are shown in Table 1, and we

TABLE 1

r	$\mathbf{y}^{(r)}$			$(\mathbf{\epsilon}^{(r)\prime}\mathbf{\epsilon}^{(r)})^{\frac{1}{2}}$	$\mathbf{z}^{(r)}$			$(\mathbf{\eta}^{(r)\prime}\mathbf{\eta}^{(r)})^{\frac{1}{2}}$
0	0	0	0	1·732 1	0	0	0	1·732 1
1	1·25	1·6	0·5	0·820 1	1·25	1·6	0·5	0·820 1
2	0·575	0·850	1·125	0·467 7	0·730 1	1·079 3	1·428 5	0·512 6
3	1·106 2	1·255 0	0·787 5	0·348 5	1·039 0	1·093 6	0·921 9	0·127 9
4	0·819 4	0·936 3	1·053 1	0·198 7	0·962 2	0·962 2	0·962 2	0·065 5
5	1·045 1	1·108 4	0·909 7	0·148 1	1·005 3	1·012 9	0·989 3	0·017 6
6	0·923 2	0·972 9	1·022 5	0·084 5	0·994 8	1·001 6	1·008 3	0·009 9
7	1·019 2	1·046 1	0·961 6	0·063 0	1·000 7	1·001 8	0·998 5	0·002 4
8	0·967 4	0·988 5	1·009 6	0·035 9	0·999 2	0·999 3	0·999 3	0·001 3

observe the improvement in convergence with the Chebyshev method. The 'sizes' of the error at each stage, measured by the quantities $(\mathbf{\epsilon}^{(r)\prime}\mathbf{\epsilon}^{(r)})^{\frac{1}{2}}$ and $(\mathbf{\eta}^{(r)\prime}\mathbf{\eta}^{(r)})^{\frac{1}{2}}$, are also shown in the table.

Asymptotic convergence

7.6 The error in $\mathbf{y}^{(r)}$ is, of course, ultimately decreased at each stage by the factor $\rho = 0\cdot651\ 9$. The ultimate behaviour of the error in $\mathbf{z}^{(r)}$ needs a little more consideration. From the definition of the Chebyshev polynomials, for argument exceeding unity, we can write (18) in the form

$$\left.\begin{aligned} \mathbf{z}^{(r+1)} &= 2\cosh\theta\frac{\cosh r\theta}{\cosh(r+1)\theta}(\mathbf{C}\mathbf{z}^{(r)}+\mathbf{d}) - \frac{\cosh(r-1)\theta}{\cosh(r+1)\theta}\mathbf{z}^{(r-1)} \\ \rho^{-1} &= \cosh\theta \end{aligned}\right\}, \tag{23}$$

and this is ultimately equivalent to the *stationary* iterative process

$$\mathbf{z}^{(r+1)} = (1+e^{-2\theta})(\mathbf{C}\mathbf{z}^{(r)}+\mathbf{d}) - e^{-2\theta}\mathbf{z}^{(r-1)}. \tag{24}$$

The error vector then satisfies the iteration

$$\mathbf{\eta}^{(r+1)} = (1+e^{-2\theta})\mathbf{C}\mathbf{\eta}^{(r)} - e^{-2\theta}\mathbf{\eta}^{(r-1)}. \tag{25}$$

To analyse this three-term recurrence we write it in the form

$$\begin{bmatrix} \boldsymbol{\eta}^{(r+1)} \\ \boldsymbol{\eta}^{(r)} \end{bmatrix} = \begin{bmatrix} (1+e^{-2\theta})\mathbf{C} & -e^{-2\theta}\mathbf{I} \\ \mathbf{I} & \mathbf{O} \end{bmatrix} \begin{bmatrix} \boldsymbol{\eta}^{(r)} \\ \boldsymbol{\eta}^{(r-1)} \end{bmatrix}, \tag{26}$$

so that the ultimate convergence depends on the spectral radius of the matrix on the right of (26). It is easy to see that the eigenvalues μ of this matrix satisfy the equation

$$\mu^2 - \mu(1+\alpha)\lambda + \alpha = 0, \quad \alpha = e^{-2\theta}, \tag{27}$$

where λ is an eigenvalue of $\mathbf{C}$. The largest $|\mu|$ corresponds to the largest $|\lambda| = \rho$, and after some manipulation we find

$$|\mu|_{\max} = \rho^{-1}\{1-(1-\rho^2)^{\frac{1}{2}}\}. \tag{28}$$

In our example this quantity is approximately 0·37, so that our device has improved very significantly the asymptotic rate of convergence.

It is worth remarking, finally, that (18) can be written as

$$\mathbf{z}^{(r+1)} = \bar{\mathbf{z}}^{(r+1)} + \frac{T_{r-1}(\rho^{-1})}{T_{r+1}(\rho^{-1})}(\bar{\mathbf{z}}^{(r+1)} - \mathbf{z}^{(r-1)}), \tag{29}$$

where $\bar{\mathbf{z}}^{(r+1)}$ is the result of applying one step of the original process (2) to the current 'best' vector $\mathbf{z}^{(r)}$. Equation (29) effectively makes a small correction to the vector $\bar{\mathbf{z}}^{(r+1)}$.

Spectroscopic eigenvalue analysis

7.7 Our final application relates to a method of Lanczos (1957) for finding the eigensolutions of a matrix $\mathbf{A}$ with real eigenvalues. It is a variant of a classical iterative method. There are two main iterative methods, in the first of which, the *direct* iterative method, we compute the sequence of vectors

$$\mathbf{y}^{(r)} = \mathbf{A}\mathbf{y}^{(r-1)}, \quad \mathbf{y}^{(0)} \text{ arbitrary.} \tag{30}$$

If the eigenvalues are real, with different moduli and with $\lambda_1 > \lambda_2 > \dots > \lambda_n$, then the vector $\mathbf{y}^{(r)}$ will converge, as $r \to \infty$, to the eigenvector corresponding to the larger of $|\lambda_1|$ and $|\lambda_n|$, and the eigenvalue is the ultimate ratio of corresponding elements of $\mathbf{y}^{(r+1)}$ and $\mathbf{y}^{(r)}$.

For if the eigenvalues are distinct the corresponding vectors are independent and span the space of real vectors with n components, and we can find the expansion

$$\mathbf{y}^{(0)} = \sum_{s=1}^{n} \alpha_s \mathbf{x}^{(s)}, \qquad \mathbf{A}\mathbf{x}^{(s)} = \lambda_s \mathbf{x}^{(s)}. \tag{31}$$

Then

$$\mathbf{y}^{(r)} = \mathbf{A}^r \mathbf{y}^{(0)} = \sum_{s=1}^{n} \alpha_s \lambda_s^r \mathbf{x}^{(s)}, \tag{32}$$

and the right-hand side is ultimately dominated by one of the terms $\alpha_1 \lambda_1^r \mathbf{x}^{(1)}$ or $\alpha_n \lambda_n^r \mathbf{x}^{(n)}$. A variant of the method uses the direct iteration

$$\mathbf{y}^{(r)} = (\mathbf{A} - p\mathbf{I})\mathbf{y}^{(r-1)}, \tag{33}$$

and with suitable choice of p we can obtain either of the extreme eigensolutions. No intermediate solution is obtainable with this process.

Any solution, however, can be obtained with the *inverse* iterative method, in which we compute the vector sequence $\mathbf{y}^{(0)}, \mathbf{y}^{(1)}, \ldots$, from the iteration

$$(\mathbf{A} - p\mathbf{I})\mathbf{y}^{(r)} = \mathbf{y}^{(r-1)}. \tag{34}$$

We now converge to the eigensolution for which $|\lambda - p|$ has the smallest value, that is for which λ is nearest to the selected p. Any solution can be obtained, though the amount of work involved in computing the full eigensystem by this process is clearly not trivial.

7.8 Lanczos (1957) uses a variant of the direct iterative method, the modification ensuring that all the spectral components in an equation corresponding to (32) enter and persist with more or less equal force. As usual this is arranged by replacing λ_s^r in (32) by an appropriate Chebyshev polynomial.

We assume that all eigenvalues of $\mathbf{A}$ lie in the range $-1 \leq \lambda \leq 1$ (for a given matrix $\mathbf{B}$ we need only take $\mathbf{A} = \rho^{-1}\mathbf{B}$, where ρ is the spectral radius of $\mathbf{B}$). Then in place of the $\mathbf{y}^{(r)}$ of (32) we seek vectors $\mathbf{z}^{(r)}$ given by

$$\mathbf{z}^{(r)} = \sum_{s=1}^{n} \alpha_s T_r(\lambda_s)\mathbf{x}^{(s)}, \tag{35}$$

where $T_r(\lambda)$ is the standard Chebyshev polynomial. These could be found, as in **7.3**, by forming appropriate linear combinations of the vectors $\mathbf{y}^{(r)}$, but preferably we generate the $\mathbf{z}^{(r)}$ directly, as in **7.4**,

14

from the recurrence

$$\mathbf{z}^{(r+1)} = 2\mathbf{A}\mathbf{z}^{(r)} - \mathbf{z}^{(r-1)}, \qquad \mathbf{z}^{(1)} = \mathbf{A}\mathbf{z}^{(0)}, \quad \mathbf{z}^{(0)} \text{ arbitrary.} \quad (36)$$

If all the eigenvalues are known to be positive we use the T_r^* polynomials and replace (36) by

$$\left.\begin{array}{l} \mathbf{z}^{(r+1)} = 2(2\mathbf{A}-\mathbf{I})\mathbf{z}^{(r)} - \mathbf{z}^{(r-1)} \\[2mm] \mathbf{z}^{(1)} = (2\mathbf{A}-\mathbf{I})\mathbf{z}^{(0)}, \quad \mathbf{z}^{(0)} \text{ arbitrary} \end{array}\right\}. \quad (37)$$

7.9 With (36), and with $\lambda_s = \cos\theta_s$, our vector $\mathbf{z}^{(r)}$ can be written in the form

$$\mathbf{z}^{(r)} = (\alpha_1 \cos r\theta_1)\mathbf{x}^{(1)} + (\alpha_2 \cos r\theta_2)\mathbf{x}^{(2)} + \ldots + (\alpha_n \cos r\theta_n)\mathbf{x}^{(n)}. \quad (38)$$

For $r = 0, 1, \ldots, N$, say, we have values of a vector function which is composed of sums of terms with periods $2\pi/\theta_s$ and unknown amplitudes, and we have the classical problem of the 'search for hidden periodicities'.

Following Lanczos (1957), we introduce the function $\mathbf{Z}(p)$, analogous to the Fourier transform, defined by

$$\mathbf{Z}(p) = \tfrac{1}{2}\mathbf{z}^{(0)} + \mathbf{z}^{(1)}\cos\frac{\pi}{N}p + \ldots +$$

$$+ \mathbf{z}^{(N-1)}\cos(N-1)\frac{\pi}{N}p + \tfrac{1}{2}\mathbf{z}^{(N)}\cos N\frac{\pi}{N}p. \quad (39)$$

With the use of a simple trigonometric identity we deduce the result

$$\mathbf{Z}(p) = \frac{1}{4}\sum_{s=1}^{n}\alpha_s\mathbf{x}^{(s)}\left\{\sin N\left(\theta_s - \frac{\pi p}{N}\right)\cot\frac{1}{2}\left(\theta_s - \frac{\pi p}{N}\right) + \right.$$

$$\left. + \sin N\left(\theta_s + \frac{\pi p}{N}\right)\cot\frac{1}{2}\left(\theta_s + \frac{\pi p}{N}\right)\right\}. \quad (40)$$

In the neighbourhood of $p = N\theta_s/\pi$ this function is dominated by its first term, and has a 'peak' at $p = N\theta_s/\pi$. We propose to deduce the θ_s, and hence the λ_s, by inspecting the computed values of $\mathbf{Z}(p)$ for a range of p in $(0, N)$. In particular it is convenient to take integer values $0, 1, \ldots, N$ of p, and we then find

$$\mathbf{Z}(p) = \frac{(-1)^p}{4}\sum_{s=1}^{n}\alpha_s\mathbf{x}^{(s)}\sin N\theta_s\left\{\cot\frac{1}{2}\left(\theta_s - \frac{\pi p}{N}\right) + \cot\frac{1}{2}\left(\theta_s + \frac{\pi p}{N}\right)\right.$$

$$(41)$$

If $\qquad\qquad \theta_1 = \frac{\pi}{N}(k+\varepsilon), \qquad 0 \leq \varepsilon \leq 1, \qquad\qquad (42)$

we see that for large enough N the values of $\mathbf{Z}(p)$, for $p = k-1, k,$ $k+1, k+2$ are dominated by the contribution from $\alpha_1 \mathbf{x}^{(1)}$, and in the ith component have values approximately proportional to

$$Z_i^{(1)}(k-1), \ Z_i^{(1)}(k), \ Z_i^{(1)}(k+1), \ Z_i^{(1)}(k+2)$$
$$= \frac{(-1)^{k-1}}{2} \frac{N}{\pi} \sin N\theta_1 \left\{ \frac{1}{1+\varepsilon}, \frac{-1}{\varepsilon}, \frac{-1}{1-\varepsilon}, \frac{1}{2-\varepsilon} \right\}. \quad (43)$$

The sequence of alternating signs due to the term $(-1)^p$ is broken by the occurrence of two like signs at $p = k$ and $p = k+1$.

At the same points we find, with a little manipulation which assumes that θ_s, $s \neq 1$, is sufficiently remote from θ_1, that the contributions from the term in $\alpha_s \mathbf{x}^{(s)}$ at these points are approximately proportional to

$$\left. \begin{array}{l} Z_i^{(s)}(p) = (-1)^p \dfrac{\sin N\theta_s \sin \theta_s}{\cos \theta_1 - \cos \theta_s} \left\{ 1 + \dfrac{\pi}{2N} \alpha_p \sin \theta_1 \right\} \\[2ex] \alpha_{k-1} = 1+\varepsilon, \quad \alpha_k = \varepsilon, \quad \alpha_{k+1} = \varepsilon-1, \quad \alpha_{k+2} = \varepsilon-2 \end{array} \right\}. \quad (44)$$

We almost eliminate these contributions if we consider instead of $\mathbf{Z}(p)$ the quantities

$$\mathbf{Y}(p) = \mathbf{Z}(p-1) + 2\mathbf{Z}(p) + \mathbf{Z}(p+1), \quad p = k, k+1, \quad (45)$$

and this device makes even smaller the second contribution, so far neglected, from the second term in $\alpha_1 \mathbf{x}^{(1)}$.

The major contributions to $\mathbf{Y}(p)$ at the points $p = k$, $p = k+1$, are then proportional to

$$Y_i(k), \ Y_i(k+1)$$
$$= \frac{(-1)^{k-1}}{2} \cdot \frac{N}{\pi} \sin N\theta_1 \left\{ \frac{-2}{\varepsilon(1-\varepsilon)(1+\varepsilon)}, \frac{-2}{\varepsilon(1-\varepsilon)(2-\varepsilon)} \right\}, \quad (46)$$

so that
$$\frac{Y_i(k)}{Y_i(k+1)} = \frac{(2-\varepsilon)}{(1+\varepsilon)}, \quad (47)$$

and the required ε comes from

$$\varepsilon = \frac{2 - Y_i(k)/Y_i(k+1)}{1 + Y_i(k)/Y_i(k+1)}. \quad (48)$$

We then find θ_1 from (42), and $\lambda_1 = \cos \theta_1$.

Example

7.10 As an example we consider the matrix

$$\mathbf{A} = \tfrac{1}{7}\begin{bmatrix} 1 & 1 & 3 \\ 1 & -2 & 1 \\ 3 & 1 & 3 \end{bmatrix}, \tag{49}$$

whose roots are real, in virtue of its symmetry, but not necessarily positive. A theorem of Gershgorin states that the modulus of the eigenvalues cannot exceed the maximum row sum of absolute values, and the factor $\tfrac{1}{7}$ is chosen so that this maximum is unity.

The computation is summarized in Table 2. We have taken $N = 12$ and give the vectors $\mathbf{z}^{(r)}$ for $r = 0, 1, \ldots, 12$. The corresponding values of $\mathbf{Z}(p)$ show that we expect to locate an eigenvalue corresponding to $k = 2$ in (42). The formation of $\mathbf{Y}(p)$ in this region gives the three possible results

$$\cos \theta_1 = \lambda_1 = 0.773\ 6,\ 0.775\ 6,\ 0.774\ 5, \tag{50}$$

the correct value being $0.775\ 0$ to four figures.

The other two roots, which are obviously in the neighbourhood of $p = 6$, 7 and 8, are somewhat too close together to give good results. The table suggests that the second vector component might give some useful result, with $k = 7$, and from the computed $\mathbf{Y}(p)$ we find

$$\cos \theta_2 = \lambda_2 = -0.319\ 0, \tag{51}$$

TABLE 2

r, p	$10^4\mathbf{z}^{(r)}$			$10^3\mathbf{Z}(p)$			$10^3\mathbf{Y}(p)$		
0	10 000	10 000	10 000	+1 345	+228	+1 549			
1	7 143	0	10 000	−1 561	−292	−1 838			
2	612	−5 102	4 694	+3 115	+770	+3 936	8404	2699	11 535
3	−4 402	4 431	−6 910	+3 735	+1 451	+5 501	9881	3123	13 467
4	−6 526	−662	−13 124	−704	−549	−1 471			
5	−8 893	−9 667	−10 123	+111	+495	+931			
6	−7 449	751	−5 944	+632	−638	−1 064			−1 960
7	1 889	5 410	−1 148	+621	+3 738	−763		8067	−2 637
8	8 550	−3 630	8 126	−952	+1 229	−47		5683	
9	6 477	1 431	14 410	+579	−513	+89			
10	6 051	8 782	10 191	−459	+346	−99			
11	6 487	−1 808	2 025	+409	−285	+101			
12	−2 986	−5 316	−3 408	−395	+268	−101			

the correct value being $-0.329\,4$. Similarly the third component would appear to be the best choice for the third solution, with $k = 6$, and we find

$$\cos\theta_3 = \lambda_3 = -0.187\,7, \tag{52}$$

a less satisfactory result compared with the true value $-0.159\,9$.

To obtain good answers to λ_2 and λ_3 we would need a larger value of N, but even with $N = 12$ we have a good knowledge of the useful regions to investigate for larger N. Lanczos remarks that a separation in the peaks of about four 'units' is necessary for good results.

Though in theory we need work with only one component of $\mathbf{Z}(p)$, it may happen that the corresponding component of the eigenvector is very small, or perhaps a particular α_s in the expansion of the arbitrary $\mathbf{z}^{(0)}$ is small, giving a lack of precision in the results. In this example the true eigensystem is approximately

$$\left.\begin{array}{ll}
\lambda_1 = 0.775\,0, & \mathbf{x}^{(1)} = (0.731, 0.233, 1) \\[4pt]
\lambda_2 = -0.329\,4, & \mathbf{x}^{(2)} = (-0.270, 1, -0.036) \\[4pt]
\lambda_3 = -0.159\,9, & \mathbf{x}^{(3)} = (1, 0.242, -0.787)
\end{array}\right\}, \tag{53}$$

and $\alpha_1 = 1.236$, $\alpha_2 = 0.646$, $\alpha_3 = 0.271$. This verifies that the first and third components are best for λ_1, the second for λ_2, and the first and third for λ_3, though in the latter we might find serious contamination from $\mathbf{x}^{(1)}$.

7.11 The computation of the eigenvectors presents little difficulty. They are, of course, proportional to the values of $\mathbf{Y}(p)$ at the value of p nearest to the critical point. For the first solution we find

$$\mathbf{Y}(3) = (0.734, 0.232, 1), \tag{54}$$

which is very close to the truth. The other roots, however, are not sufficiently well separated to give any reliable information about their eigenvectors.

This method has not, to our knowledge, received extensive numerical investigation. It is unlikely to compare favourably with the powerful methods based on similarity transforms which are now available (see, for example, Wilkinson 1965), but it is an interesting process which might have useful applications in other contexts.

EXERCISES 7

1. Prove the formulae of equations (18) and (28).

2. It is interesting to note, in Table 1, that the elements of $z^{(4)}$ all have the same value. Show that the exact value is $8(1-\rho^2)/(8-8\rho^2+\rho^4)$. (Hint: show that $C^3 = \rho^2 C$, where $C = -D^{-1}(L+U)$, and that $(I-C)^{-1}d = A^{-1}b = (1, 1, 1)$ in this example.) Show also that, for any right-hand sides in equations (19), a knowledge of ρ and the vector $z^{(4)}$ enables us to write down the correct answers immediately.

3. With the notation of equation (20) the *Gauss-Seidel* iterative scheme is given by

$$y^{(r)} = -(L+D)^{-1}Uy^{(r-1)}+(L+D)^{-1}b.$$

Show that for the example of **7.5** the spectral radius of the Gauss-Seidel iteration matrix is $\rho = 0.425$ (the square of that for the Jacobi iteration), and that for the limiting Chebyshev iteration the spectral radius is about 0.223.

4. If the eigenvalues of the iteration matrix are real, in the range $-1 < a \leq \lambda \leq b < 1$, show that the recurrence relation corresponding to (18) is given by

$$z^{(r+1)} = \frac{2}{b-a}\cdot\frac{T_r(s)}{T_{r+1}(s)}[\{2C-(b+a)I\}z^{(r)}+2d]-\frac{T_{r-1}(s)}{T_{r+1}(s)}z^{(r-1)},$$

where $s = \{2-(b+a)\}/(b-a)$. If $b = \rho$ and $a = 0$, show that this can be expressed as

$$z^{(r+1)} = 2\rho^{-1}\frac{T_r^*(\rho^{-1})}{T_{r+1}^*(\rho^{-1})}[(2C-\rho I)z^{(r)}+2d]-\frac{T_{r-1}^*(\rho^{-1})}{T_{r+1}^*(\rho^{-1})}z^{(r-1)}.$$

Show also that the limiting spectral radius of this iteration is $e^{-\theta}$, where $\rho^{-1} = \cosh^2\frac{1}{2}\theta$.

5. It is known that the Gauss-Seidel method, but not necessarily the Jacobi method, will converge if the matrix A is symmetric and positive definite. The eigenvalues of the iteration matrix, however, may not be real so that Chebyshev acceleration may not be applicable.

On the other hand the Aitken *double-sweep* method converges, and its iteration matrix has real eigenvalues. It is defined by

$$\mathbf{y}^{(r+\frac{1}{2})} = -(\mathbf{D}+\mathbf{L})^{-1}\mathbf{U}\mathbf{y}^{(r)}+(\mathbf{D}+\mathbf{L})^{-1}\mathbf{b},$$

$$\mathbf{y}^{(r+1)} = -(\mathbf{D}+\mathbf{U})^{-1}\mathbf{L}\mathbf{y}^{(r+\frac{1}{2})}+(\mathbf{D}+\mathbf{U})^{-1}\mathbf{b},$$

where the symmetry requires $\mathbf{U} = \mathbf{L}'$, the transpose of $\mathbf{L}$. The full step is embodied in the equation

$$\mathbf{y}^{(r+1)} = (\mathbf{D}+\mathbf{L}')^{-1}\mathbf{L}(\mathbf{D}+\mathbf{L})^{-1}\mathbf{L}'\mathbf{y}^{(r)}+(\mathbf{D}+\mathbf{L}')^{-1}\{\mathbf{I}-\mathbf{L}(\mathbf{D}+\mathbf{L})^{-1}\}\mathbf{b},$$

and the rate of convergence can be accelerated with the Chebyshev method of **7.4**.

Consider the system

$$y_1+\tfrac{1}{2}y_2+\tfrac{1}{2}y_3 = 2,$$

$$\tfrac{1}{2}y_1 +y_2+\tfrac{1}{2}y_3 = 2,$$

$$\tfrac{1}{2}y_1+\tfrac{1}{2}y_2 +y_3 = 2.$$

Show that the Jacobi method diverges, and that the Gauss-Seidel method converges but with two complex eigenvalues in the iteration matrix. Show also that the spectral radius for the Gauss-Seidel method, the Aitken method, and the ultimate form of the Chebyshev acceleration of the latter given by equation (18), are respectively $1/(2\sqrt{2}) \sim 0.354$, $(9+\sqrt{17})/32 \sim 0.410$, and 0.214 approximately. Show finally that the Chebyshev method of Exercise 4 is applicable here, and that its ultimate spectral radius is approximately 0.13.

6. Prove the results of equations (40), (41), (43) and (44).

7. The matrix

$$\mathbf{B} = \begin{bmatrix} 5 & -1 & -2 \\ -1 & 3 & -2 \\ -2 & -2 & 5 \end{bmatrix}$$

is symmetric and positive definite. Investigate its eigenvalues and vectors by the method of spectroscopic analysis, using equation (37) for the generation of the vectors $\mathbf{z}^{(r)}$. (Note: the eigenvalues of $(1/9)\mathbf{B}$ are approximately 0.09, 0.56 and 0.80, and the corresponding values of θ are approximately 1.5, 1.0 and 0.6 radians, reasonably well separated with $N = 12$ in **7.9**.)

References

BAKER, C. T. H., FOX, L., MAYERS, D. F. and WRIGHT, K. (1964) Numerical solution of Fredholm integral equations of first kind, *Computer J.* **7**, 141–148.

BEASLEY, J. D. (1965) A note on the rearrangement of Chebyshev series, *Computer J.* **8**, 278–279.

BIRKHOFF, G. and MACLANE, S. (1956) *A survey of modern algebra*, New York, The Macmillan Company.

CLENSHAW, C. W. (1955) A note on the summation of Chebyshev series, *Math. Tab. Wash.* **9**, 118–120.

—— (1957) The numerical solution of linear differential equations in Chebyshev series, *Proc. Camb. Phil. Soc.* **53**, 134–149.

—— (1960) Curve fitting with a digital computer, *Computer J.* **2**, 170–173.

—— (1962) Chebyshev series for mathematical functions, *Math. Tab. Nat. Phys. Lab.* **5**, London, H.M. Stationery Office.

—— and CURTIS, A. R. (1960) A method for numerical integration on an automatic computer, *Numerische Math.* **2**, 197–205.

—— and HAYES, J. G. (1965) Curve and surface fitting, *J. Inst. Maths. Applics.* **1**, 164–183.

—— and NORTON, H. J. (1963) The solution of non-linear ordinary differential equations in Chebyshev series, *Computer J.* **6**, 88–92.

COMRIE, L. J. (1931) *British Association Mathematical Tables*, Vol. 1, Cambridge University Press.

DAVIS, P. J. (1963) *Interpolation and approximation*, New York, Blaisdell Publishing Company.

ELLIOTT, D. (1961) A method for the numerical integration of the one-dimensional heat equation using Chebyshev series. *Proc. Camb. Phil. Soc.* **57**, 823–832.

—— (1963) A Chebyshev series method for the numerical solution of Fredholm integral equations, *Computer J.* **6**, 102–111.

—— (1965) Truncation errors in two Chebyshev series approximations, *Math. Comp.* **19**, 234–248.

FORSYTHE, G. E. (1957) Generation and use of orthogonal polynomials for data-fitting with a digital computer, *J. Soc. Indust. Appl. Math.* **5**, 74–88.

FOX, L. (1956) The use and construction of mathematical tables, *Math. Tab. Nat. Phys. Lab.* **1**, London, H.M. Stationery Office.

—— (1962) Chebyshev methods for ordinary differential equations, *Computer J.* **4**, 318–331.

—— (1965) The proper use of recurrence relations, *Math. Gazette* **49**, 371–387.

—— and GOODWIN, E. T. (1953) The numerical solution of non-singular linear integral equations, *Phil. Trans.* A, **245**, 501–534.

HASTINGS, C. (1957) *Approximations for digital computers*, 2nd ed., Princeton University Press.

HILDEBRAND, F. B. (1956) *Introduction to numerical analysis*, New York and London, McGraw-Hill.

KALABA, R. (1959) On non-linear differential equations, the maximum operator, and monotone convergence, *J. Math. Mech.* **8**, 519.

KANTOROVICH, L. V. and KRYLOV, V. I. (1958) *Approximate methods of higher analysis* (translated by C. D. Benster), The Netherlands, P. Noordhoff Ltd.

LANCZOS, C. (1938) Trigonometric interpolation of empirical and analytical functions, *J. Math Phys.* **17**, 123–199.

—— (1952) Tables of Chebyshev Polynomials, *Appl. Math. Ser.* U.S. Bur. Stand. **9**, Washington, Government Printing Office.

—— (1957) *Applied analysis*, New York, Prentice-Hall; London, Pitman.

MAKINOUCHI, S. (1965) Note on the recurrence techniques for the calculation of Bessel functions $I_r(x)$, *Osaka University Technology Reports* **15**, No. 659.

MASON, J. C. (1965) *Some new approximations for the solution of differential equations*, Oxford D.Phil. Thesis.

MILLER, J. C. P. (1946) *The Airy Integral*, British Association Mathematical Tables, Part-Volume B, Cambridge University Press.

—— (1952) Bessel functions, Part II, *Mathematical Tables* X, Cambridge University Press.

NORTON, H. J. (1964) The iterative solution of non-linear ordinary differential equations in Chebyshev series, *Computer J.* **7**, 76–85.

NOVODVORSKII, E. P. and PINSKER, I. S. (1951) The process of equating maxima, *Uspehi Mat. Nauk.* **6**, 174–181 (English translation by A. Shenitzer).

OLVER, F. W. J. (1964) Error analysis of Miller's recurrence algorithm, *Math. Comp.* **18**, 65–74.

REID, J. K. and WALSH, J. E. (1965) An elliptic eigenvalue problem for a re-entrant region, *J. Soc. Indust. Appl. Math.* **13**, 837–850.

SCRATON, R. E. (1965) The solution of linear differential equations in Chebyshev series, *Computer J.* **8**, 57–61.

STEFFENSEN, J. F. (1950) *Interpolation*, 2nd ed. (1st English ed. 1927), New York, Chelsea.

TODD, J. (1962) *Survey of numerical analysis*, New York and London, McGraw-Hill.

VARGA, R. S. (1962) *Matrix iterative analysis*, New Jersey, Prentice-Hall, Inc.

WILKINSON, J. H. (1965) *The algebraic eigenvalue problem*, Oxford University Press.

WRIGHT, K. (1964) Chebyshev collocation methods for ordinary differential equations, *Computer J.* **6**, 358–363.

Index